H
u
hurting

MARY HATHAWAY
ILLUSTRATIONS BY JOHN HAYSOM

A LION BOOK
Oxford · Batavia · Sydney

Text copyright © 1987 Mary Hathaway
This edition copyright © 1990 Lion Publishing

Published by
Lion Publishing plc
Sandy Lane West, Littlemore, Oxford, England
ISBN 0 7459 1646 5
Albatross Books Pty Ltd
PO Box 320, Sutherland, NSW 2232, Australia
ISBN 0 7324 0132 1

This material originally appeared in two books
published in 1987, under the titles *Peace Be Still*
and *Towards the Dawn*
This combined edition 1990

Acknowledgments
Bible quotations from *Good News Bible*,
copyright © 1966, 1971 and 1976 American
Bible Society, published by Bible Societies/Collins

British Library Cataloguing in Publication Data
Hathaway, Mary
Hope for when I'm hurting.
1. Christian life — Devotional works
I. Title   II. Series
242
ISBN 0 7459 1646 5

Printed and bound in Spain

Introduction

In the space of a year in my early twenties, I underwent surgery for a thyroid complaint, suffered a broken engagement and had a nervous breakdown. It seemed as if I would never lead a normal life again. Being ill can be a lonely and depressing experience, especially if the illness is prolonged. But eventually, with specialist help, the healing process began.

Knowing from the inside the misery of illness and depression, I have put together some pieces of my own writing and some verses from the Bible which helped me during that time, in the hope that others who suffer may perhaps find in them stepping stones to help them through their own darkness.

For I do believe it is possible to come through. Although I still get depressed at times, I can see that one of the verses from the Bible I found very precious is beginning to come true for me.

'The winter is over,
the rains have stopped;
in the countryside
the flowers are in bloom,
this is the time for singing.'

Mary Hathaway

Where are you, God?

Where are you, God?
How can I know you?
If I try to pray my words
bounce back off the ceiling
and I feel embarrassed
at talking to myself.
Eternal things are unreal
and few believe in you
in that mad rush of people
that is the world.
I am trying to talk to you —
are they mad or am I?

Sometimes I do not want to find you —
it's too disturbing.
But God, you would rather
I brought the turmoil of my thoughts
to you than use them as an excuse
not to pray.

Whether I want you or not,
I must find you,
for without you life has no meaning
and I cannot rest until I reach you.
Help me to know you God,
teach me to pray.
Where are you,
who are you
God, my God?

CIRCLE OF THORNS

God of the storm and rain,
God of the wild sea raging,
hear me, hear my crying.
God of the uncontrollable,
God of the mind of man,
hear me, hear my crying.
God of the circle of thorns,
God dead and living again,
bring me through this dying
to find you real again.

God of the circle of thorns,
hear me — in your mercy.

Lord, you have examined me
and you know me.
You know everything I do;
from far away you understand
all my thoughts.
You see me, whether I am working or resting;
you know all my actions.
Even before I speak,
you already know what I will say.
You are all round me on every side;
you protect me with your power.
Your knowledge of me is too deep;
it is beyond my understanding.

From Psalm 139, verses 1-6

THE PAIN MACHINE

Let me out.
Let me out
of this slow grinding pain machine
manufacturing grey living,
which clouds each waking
and frets sleep into jagged edges.
Not a pain I will die of,
not a pain I can succumb to
but an extra burden
while I carry on
with all my living.

It is the fighting of it
which is so wearisome,
draining the emotions,
exhausting the strength
and dulling the mind,
wearing life thin —
so anger flames
where there was love
and sharp words
where there was gentleness
and even joy goes grey.

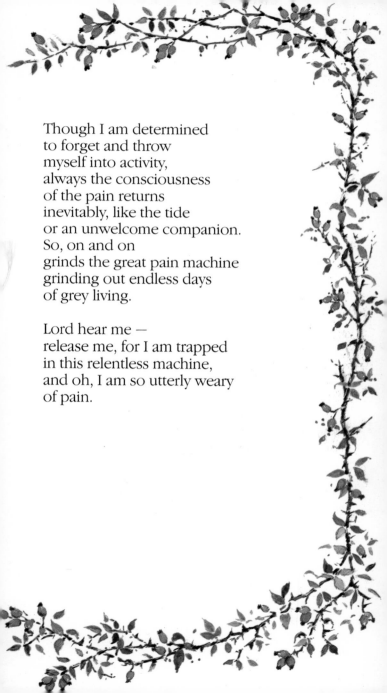

Though I am determined
to forget and throw
myself into activity,
always the consciousness
of the pain returns
inevitably, like the tide
or an unwelcome companion.
So, on and on
grinds the great pain machine
grinding out endless days
of grey living.

Lord hear me —
release me, for I am trapped
in this relentless machine,
and oh, I am so utterly weary
of pain.

Come to me, all of you who are tired
from carrying heavy loads,
and I will give you rest.
Take my yoke and put it on you,
and learn from me,
because I am gentle and humble in spirit,
and you will find rest.

From Matthew's Gospel, chapter 11, verses 28-30

Let the Storm Break

Let the storm break.
Don't push it to the back of your mind
or pretend it isn't there.
Storms that are hidden
become savage things.
It is better to let the storm come and weep
than to let it stay hidden
and turn the heart sour and bitter.
Tears are a cleansing stream.

Let the storm break —
all the pent up sorrow, pain and despair —
bow your head and let it flow over you.
And then, though your spirit feels crushed
and utterly broken,
after a little while the impossible will happen
and you will raise your head again.
Life will creep back into your numbed spirit.
But, best of all,
the storm will have blown itself out
and once again your whole being will be free,
free and cleansed and able to love.

So I Shall Feel the Waves

'When you go through deep waters
and great trouble,
I will be with you.
When you go through rivers
of difficulty,
you will not drown.
When you walk through the fire
of oppression,
you will not be burned up,
the flames will not consume you.'

Isaiah 43, verse 2

So I shall feel the waves
and hear the storm,
the waters will sometimes cover me,
the currents will pull at my feet,
I shall be afraid for my life,

but —
I shall not drown.

So I shall feel the heat,
I shall be scorched,
I shall be burned,
and despair of my life,

but —
the flames will not consume me.

You do not promise a life
full of frothy joy,
you promise *life* —
in all its fullness,
with its pain and suffering
as well as its love and joy.

You are real, Lord,
you are true, Lord,
and I rest in your word
in my despair and confusion
in the sure knowledge
that I *shall* come through.

Fear

This morning I saw someone else afraid
and I was sad to see so much fear.
For I know fear well —
he has been my constant companion.
Fear is more terrible than pain.

It is good not to be afraid.
But to know fear
and go back and conquer it
is a greater victory.
For all mankind knows fear
and lives with it
but few break out of its prison.

To conquer fear
is to step out into sunlight
from the shadow.
It is to have the freedom of the skies
after living in a cage.
It is to look life in the face,
the past, the present and the future
and to know they are but servants,
not domineering masters,
enslaving, crippling,
stunting every good potential.

So Lord, in your mercy,
help me win this battle
because no one could have been
more afraid than I.
That is why it is imperative
that I should win —

so Lord, in your mercy,
help me to win!

I waited patiently for the Lord's help;
then he listened to me and heard my cry.
He pulled me out of a dangerous pit,
out of the deadly quicksand.
He set me safely on a rock
and made me secure.
He taught me to sing a new song,
a song of praise to our God.

From Psalm 40, verses 1-3

Two Pierced Hands

I had a sorrow so deep
that human love could not penetrate
its deepest recesses.
I stumbled through the valley
of suffering in my mind,
down, down into the depths of the darkness.
And there in the tearless pain beyond pain
I saw two hands outstretched.
Two pierced hands —
that was all I could see —
two pierced hands held out to me.

I knew that my sorrow was shared
to the uttermost,
that I did not stand alone in the darkness,
that every part of my pain was understood.
Two loving hands —
that was all I could see —
two loving hands held out to me.

I felt no lessening of pain.
The stark reality of sorrow was still there,
to be faced and lived with.
But I was not alone.
In healing silence
two pierced hands had held mine
in the depths of that darkness.
Two sharing hands —
that was all I had seen —
two sharing hands held out to me.

THE CURTAIN

The foundations of my life
are in eternity.
But sometimes
a barrier comes between
eternity and now
and I am lost, confused
and often afraid.

But I am so glad
when, after a while,
I reach out my hand
and touch eternity again.
My life steadies,
things come into focus,
I know where I am going.

And I realize
that what seemed
an impenetrable wall
was only a fragile curtain
yielding easily
to the touch
of an outstretched hand.

YOU WERE LONELY JESUS

You were lonely Jesus.
It seemed wrong
even to put it into words
because you are God,
all sufficient,
all knowing,
all powerful.
How could you
ever suffer loneliness?
And yet
while you were a man
you were lonely.

Help me to accept
my times of loneliness
and to remember
that we are called
to share your suffering
so that we may also
share your glory.
Help me
not to take it out on other people
because they cannot always understand,
and especially help me
not to expect too much
from those who love me most.

Let me not be afraid to stand alone,
for if only I will turn from other people
and look for you,
you are always there.
I can share my loneliness with you —
if I choose to let you in.

For I am certain that nothing
can separate us from his love;
neither death nor life,
neither angels
nor other heavenly rulers or powers,
neither the present nor the future,
neither the world above
nor the world below —
there is nothing in all creation
that will be able to separate us
from the love of God which is ours
through Christ Jesus our Lord.

Paul's letter to the Romans, chapter 8, verse 38

30

THE HARVEST

The plough
cuts deep
into the ground,
laying open
the earth
to the wind,
the rain
and the sun,
making her naked
and vulnerable,
preparing her womb
for the sowing
of the seed
and the mystery
of birth.

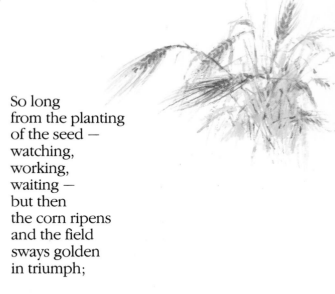

So long
from the planting
of the seed —
watching,
working,
waiting —
but then
the corn ripens
and the field
sways golden
in triumph;

the pain forgotten
in the joy of harvest.

I *am telling you the truth,*
a grain of wheat remains no more
than a single grain unless it is dropped
into the ground and dies.
If it does die, then it produces many grains.

John's Gospel, chapter 12, verse 24

CARVE GOD OUT OF THE DARK

Carve God
out of the dark
with faith,
as a miner
hews coal
out of a mine.

Carve him out
with faith,
the only tool left
in the darkness
that dwells
under the earth,
at the very bottom
of the pit.

Once you have
found God there,
you need not fear.
For you know then
that he *can* be found —
anywhere.

CANDLE AT DUSK

As darkness falls,
so your flame
grows ever brighter.
The night crowds in,
shadows rushing down
on every side —
but they do not put you out.
And the flame that seemed
so small, so insignificant
against the sun,
comes into its own
with the deepening of the night.

As a hen shelters
her chickens under her wings
from danger,
so the newborn shadows
of the gathering dusk
fly to you —
darkness sheltering
under the wings
of light.

So burn in me
candle of God.

Let your love
draw all my shadows
swiftly to yourself.
So when night comes
and fears and doubts
and every kind of sin
bear down upon my spirit,
let me bring them
to your light knowing
that it shines best
against the blackest darkness.

As a hen shelters
her chickens under her wings
from danger,
so I fly to you
that I may dwell in safety —

for in my darkness
I also need the shelter
of your wings
of light.

FRAGMENT

This is not the finish of the song,
only a pause in the singing.
I do not know the music,
that is all.

This is not the ending of the way,
only the beginning.
I do not know where to go,
that is all.

How this desert can become
a watered garden,
I do not know,
that is all —

but God is still God.

The Lord is the everlasting God;
he created all the world . . .
He strengthens those who are weak and
tired.
Even those who are young grow weak;
young men can fall exhausted.
But those who trust in the Lord for help
will find their strength renewed.
They will rise on wings like eagles;
they will run and not get weary;
they will walk and not grow weak.

Isaiah, chapter 40, verses 29-31

Made Anew with Love

I have watched
the ruin of my life
and seen no hope
of resurrection.

Yet I know
I too shall live
and see a purpose
in my pain
and harvest light
out of my darkness.
For I shall stand,
not broken down and desolate
before my God,
but tall and beautiful
and made anew with love.

THE FUTURE

I was afraid of the future,
for it was in darkness
and I saw no possible way
that I could go.

The future is still in darkness.
I can see no more of it
than I did before,
but now I see
a little more of my God.

So I walk forward,
not into darkness,
though the future is still unknown to me,
but into the sun
in the company of my God.

Lesley Ash not only used to read Jackie, she used to appear on the cover! See the back pages and cover from 1977!

"Girls don't realise it, but most fourteen-year-old boys read Jackie. I used to read Cathy and Claire every week." — Rik Mayall.

"I used to buy Jackie when I was younger — and I loved it!" — Hazell Dean.

"I read Jackie . . ." and so say all of us! Kim Wilde, Bananarama, Limahl, Paula Yates, Shirley Holliman, Wham!, Clare Grogan, Joan Armatrading, Tracey Ullman, Billy McKenzie, Dee C Lee, Nick Heyward, Janice Long, Cheryl Baker . . . we could go on, but we don't like to boast!

. . . AND take a wander down Memory Lane! Turn to the back pages for the continuing saga of 'Jackie through the ages' . . .

YOU SAID IT!
YOU SAID IT!
YOU SAID IT!
YOU SAID IT!
YOU SAID IT!
YOU SAID

Paul Weller has done his fair share of talking in the past few years. Not noted for being one of the least outspoken people around, here're a few of the controversial and not so controversial things he's said in his time . . .

Paul Weller on himself:
"I've got on well with everyone I've met."

"I don't eat meat or fish."

"I don't see myself as British any more."

"I don't care any more; I'm just going to do what I want to do and say what I want to say. I don't care if people think I've cracked or changed or whatever. I'm an angry young man."

"I'm a bit like Oscar Wilde."

Paul Weller on The Jam:
"It wasn't really a hard decision to split because I realised that The Jam was getting limited and it would become meaningless to carry on with it."

Paul Weller on The Style Council:
"It sums up something more than just music — it refers to culture more widely."

"This Europe thing is us trying to broaden our horizons and look further than our own lifestyles."

"We're a bit of a culture club, quite honestly."

Paul Weller on politics:
"The problem with England is that it's so tied up with America."

"The women at Greenham Common are the real patriots, the people who really care about England, and yet they are being slagged off."

Paul Weller on music:
"I really like Culture Club, George has got a brilliant voice."

"The British music scene is absolute rubbish. There are all these guitar-based bands churning out the same stuff, and it's meaningless, it doesn't do anything, it doesn't achieve anything, and it's just boring."

"Record companies call records 'product,' and sales 'units.' They might just as well be selling baked beans or dog food!"

Paul Weller on Nick Heyward's lyrics:
"Where's your head, Nick?"

and on the most fanciable human being . . .
"Mick Talbot."

Jackie

ACKNOWLEDGEMENTS

The Publishers would like to thank the team at DC Thomson & Co. Ltd for
all their help in compiling this book, particularly Martin Lindsay.

THIS IS A PRION BOOK

This edition first published in the UK in 2008 by Prion
An imprint of the Carlton Publishing Group
20 Mortimer Street
London W1T 3JW

Previously published as *The Best of Jackie Annual* (2006) and *More of The Best of Jackie Annual*
(2007)

ISBN: 978-1-85375-667-2

Edited and compiled by Rod Green

The Biggest
Jackie
Annual
Ever!

CONTENTS

TV AND POP

8   Jackie Christmas Show

24   Wanted Men!

27   Your Special Jackie Pop-a-Cross!

38   Star Spot

52   Watch This Space!

62   Face Up to Them!

86   Something Old… Something New

88   Something Borrowed… Something Blue

98   The Other Dallas Stars

108   Who do You View?

131   You Said It: Boy George

145   The Sound of Soul

146   Three Thrilling Days with David Cassidy

148   Slade Exclusive

161   Elton Talking Colourfully

152   Mick's Star Trek

154   Secrets of the Top Pop Show

166   An Osmond Day

174   Happy Birthday! Pop Stars Remember their Best Ever

176   Do You Believe In Ghosts? Jackie asks the stars

188   Headliners: A Jackie Special on the idols who have hit the headlines

200   Down on the Farm with the Bay City Rollers

202   Christmas Party Time: Who would you invite?

211   They've Got Style: Designers to the Stars

220   Our Super Day Out in Paris with David Essex

226   Wanted: Super Cops – TV's top detective

231   Watch Out: Our 'Annual' Look at TV Favourites

248   Take Two Guys: We talk to Bob Geldof and Billy Idol

260   Russian to the Top: Jackie exclusive on Nadia Comaneci and Olga Korbut

264   Take Two Girls: Tatum O'Neal and Jodie Foster

268   Our Favourite Bad Guys OK!

272   Girls at the Top

278   Photo Finish: All our favourite stars

Living

16   Do You Know When to Stop?

18   I Really Thought I Loved Him

26   Can You Make Friends?

28   I Had to Get Even

48   This Thing Called Love…

66   A–Z of How to Make the Most of Yourself

68   Your Jackie Guide to… Kissing!

75   Things That Scare Boys

84   ABC of Life, Love and You!

96   The Boy Facts!

99   How to Handle Him

100   Who's a Pretty Boy, Then?

104   The Jackie Guide to First Date Pitfalls

BEAUTY

17   How Sweet Are You?

19   Take a Good Look

117   Hair's Health

127   Curls, Curls, Curls!

177   Cover Girl Looks for You

209   Eye Openers

257   Be Right on Top: Try Out these super hairstyles

FEATURES

10	Boy Calendar 1980
14	Catch the Party Fever
15	Thumbs Up!
36	The Way to his Heart!
37	How's Your Dream Life?
42	Patchwork
44	A Happy New You!
49	Are You Charming Enough?
57	Something in the Way He Looks
59	Something in the Way You Look!
61	Face the Facts!
70	How to Put Him Off You!
74	What Line is He Handing You?
76	Are You a Write Give-Away?
79	Do You Know When to Take a Hint?
80	Clothes for all Reasons!
118	Warning! These Boys are Dangerous!
120	Don't Look Now – It's Superyawn!
126	How to Cope When he Says Goodbye
139	Body Talk!
156	Join the Magic Circle
190	Your Life Is In Your Hands: A Jackie Guide to palmistry
216	But What's He Really Like? A Jackie Guide to reading his thoughts by the way he sits down
222	Face Up To Him: The ancient art of face-reading
234	Will He Be Your Prince Charming? A panto guide to boys
236	Write for the Present: What your boyfriend's signature reveals about him
237	Jackie Survival Guide to Parties
238	It's Your Life – Enjoy It: Jackie careers advice
	Getting Him Into Shape:
244	What your fella's shape reveals about you
245	How to Have the Last Laugh
253	Flattery Gets You Everywhere
258	Who Wants Them? A Jackie Guide to unwanted boys and how to avoid them
259	How to Disguise That You Love Him
262	Do You Have Problem Parents?
275	21 Ways To Make Him Notice You

186, 252	Special Ideas to Brighten Your Life

FUN

35	How to Make Him Warm to You in Winter!
39	Penny for the Guy!
43	A Time for Love!
50	Catch Him if You Can!
51	Have You Got Bad Table Manners?
56	Are You a Dating Disaster?
60	Madge and Beryl
78	Spot the Grot
83	Don't Monkey Around With the Wrong Boy!
101	Getting Fruity
105	Boy Talk
106	Horrorscopes!
125	What Did He Mean by That?
132	Room Mates!
270	The Jungle Game

Cathy and Claire Specials

170	Confidence and How to Get it
192	Are You a Real Charmer?

QUIZZES

40   Could You Light His Fire?

54   Do You Have Animal Magic?

64   Are You Nice or Nasty?

72   How Moody Are You?

122   What do Boys Think of You?

138   How Liberated Are You?

140   Giant Pop Trivia Quiz

151   Where Do You Fit In?

158   Test Your Character with Our Superquiz
        'Love' or 'In Love':

168   How can you tell the difference?

182   Are You On The Right Track?

198   What's Your Nature?

204   Have You Got What it Takes?

206   How Dreamy Are You?

218   Do You Mean What You Say?

224   Are You Scared to Death?

230   Are You A Human Dustbin?

232   Are You A Space-Age Star?

240   Tree of Love

246   Will You Live Happily Ever After?

250   Which is the Season for You?

276   How Do You Picture Yourself?

READERS' TRUE EXPERIENCES

172   I Let My Parents Ruin Everything

228   I Was So Sure I Had Landed a Dream Job

242   I Knew He Was Married But I Didn't Care

FICTION

102   I Saw Him First

110   Leonard J. Watkins

Fashion

58   Madge and Beryl Knitting Pattern
90   Ears to It!
92   New Looks
124   Knit Wits!
128   Winter Wardrobe!
134   Fifty Ways to Look Fantastic!
144   Star Styles: Kim Wilde
165   Wool Done
194   Clever Clothes, Clever You
210   Party Pieces
212   Fashion Do's and Don'ts
254   Back to Basics

On-the-Spot Interviews

149   Do You Remember Your First Kiss?
187   What's Your Remedy for a Broken Heart?
266,140   What's The Worst Christmas Present You've Ever Had?

JACKIE KNIT-A-BIT PATTERNS

208   All Out in Stripes: Super stripey leg warmers, scarf and bag

256   Try a Fry-Up: Sausage, egg and chips beret and bag

274   Shrug it Off: A really useful shrug for winter

FOREWORD

Hello!

Welcome to this bumper compilation from the Jackie Annuals of the 1970s and 1980s. If you're like me, it's going to bring a lot of memories flooding back. Christmas just wouldn't have been the same if you didn't have Jackie there, that hard square wrapped in reindeers or snowdrops or something more sparkly. "I wonder what that could be," I'd say to my mum and maybe leave it for a few minutes, attacking the softer, more cushiony packages, tearing off the gift-wrapping to find—Wow! Brilliant!—a new pair of legwarmers, or fingerless gloves, or even a snood!

We knew what we wanted because every week Jackie magazine would let us in on what was hot and what was out. That worked with fashion accessories like big flashy earrings and how you wore your makeup, but not with your first love. Try it now: Donny or David? Do you still feel your heart skip a beat?

We never fell out of love with them—they just seemed to slip away and were replaced by other bands we could fall in love with. You can forget Take That! We had the original boy bands, the Osmonds, Kenny,

Pilot and (the ultimate) the Bay City Rollers! They gave way to Adam Ant, Duran Duran and Spandau Ballet, and Jackie was where you'd find out about all the latest groups.

Boys were important to Jackie readers and in the Annuals you'd find all the usual features, including the priceless advice of Cathy and Claire on "Confidence and How to Get It!"; articles that answered the questions you were asking—"Do you really know when to stop?", "What's the remedy for a broken heart?"—or guides to the things that we girls really worried about—"The Jackie Guide to Kissing" or "The Jackie Guide to First Date Pitfalls".

And what about those real-life experiences that readers wrote for the Annual? Could one of the paper's readers really be struggling with the guilt that she was dating a married man, or have blackmailed her elder sister after discovering she was dating an unsuitable boy? But it wasn't all teenage worries— Jackie could also cheer us up with fun features like "The ABC of Life, Love and You!" which surely covered everything you needed, from appearance to zest.

Meanwhile, looking back over the celebrity gossip of yester-year is a real nostalgia trip—does Elton John still own 300 shirts and 50 pairs of shoes, or has his collection grown over the years? What was Jodie Foster like when she was 15? You'll find some of the answers in the pages that follow.

The Annual first appeared in 1975 and former Jackie editor Sandy Monks has said: "We weren't sure what the response would be, but when you wrote to tell us how much you all loved it and how much you were looking forward to the next one, we breathed a sign of relief and knew that the first Annual had been worth waiting ten years for." It had been a whole decade because Jackie, the weekly magazine, first appeared in 1964. Copies of the magazine are hard to come by nowadays (even the later issues, because it ran for almost thirty years before coming to a close in 1993), but the annuals resurface occasionally. When you find them, they're usually slightly battered and a little worn through re-reading, while some of the pin-ups might have disappeared—to be hung on walls or mirrors. Seriously, a friend once told me

she pinned her pin-ups on a mirror so that when she looked at them she could imagine herself standing next to her idol!

We readers of Jackie have grown up now. Marriage and mortgages are the worries we face these days, rather than how to tell if a boy is right for you by the way he sits, or whether you dare ask your mum if you could get your hair curled into Farah Fawcett locks. There are a few things I look back on in the Jackie Annuals that make me cringe—check out those flares and platform shoes!—but there's so much more that will bring back all the glee that you felt when you saw it first time round: the quizzes, the articles about the stars, the problems pages… and some of those beauty tips and fashions wouldn't look so out of place today. The world has caught up with Jackie again and this is your chance to do the same.

Melissa Hyland

Diehard Jackie Fan!

BOY CALENDAR 1980

WHERE THEY'LL THEY'LL BE —AND HOW TO

SPRING

THE DAFFODILS are out, there's a spring in your step, the birds are pairing off and every boy's fancy is turning to love . . .

WHERE THEY'LL BE

Down by the riverbank, enjoying the last of the fishing season. Packed like sardines on the football terraces, throwing all sort of things at the ref. Learning Martial Arts at an Evening Class, so they'll be ready for the Bully on the Beach next summer. Or just dozing in the back row of the cinema as they watch "Enter The Dragon" for the 120th time . . .

WHAT THEY'LL BE WEARING

Spring's still a pretty cold time of year nowadays, so boys everywhere will be wrapped up warm in fraying sweaters, moth-eaten Parkas, football scarves and even woolly bobble hats (groan!). But don't despair, because just as a gorgeous butterfly will emerge from a crummy-looking chrysalis, a moth-eaten Parka can give way to better things . . .

SPRING SMALL TALK

Right, now you're about to stroll along to where you know the boys will be . . . Stuck for something to say to them? You mean you don't know the kind of small talk that's suitable for spring? Well, here are a few openers that ought to come in handy!

To the boy in the cinema:
"Excuse me, can I borrow your (sniff!) hankie?"
"Is that Bruce Lee or the Dragon?"
"I'm scared! Mind if I hold on to you?"

To the boy on the riverbank:
"What's the biggest fish you've ever caught?"

"What's the biggest lie you've ever told?"
"Are those really maggots?"

To the boy on the football terraces:
"Who's winning?"
"Why's that one dressed all in black? Has someone died?"
"Who's that one in the cage down the far end?"

SPRING THINGS TO DO

Once you and your boy are going steady, you'll need some ideas for things to do — public places to go to have fun, and private places for whispers and tender moments . . .

PUBLIC FUN

Spring can be cold or mild. So indoor and outdoor things are both needed. Fancy learning judo together? Or swimming? Or gymnastics? Weight-training? Or something gentler, such as jewellery-making or pottery? Why not enrol together at night school? It's great fun, and courses are in full swing in the spring.

As for the great outdoors, wrap up warm and go out in search of the first ducklings (parks and riverbanks), daffodils (council flowerbeds) and cowslips and harebells (the wild, wild woods). Go and see the animals in the zoo (you're bound to find one that looks just like him).

PRIVATE MOMENTS

It's hard to find places to be private in, unless the weather's very mild (in which case, wander along to the wild, wild woods again). A city's best, really, as there are lots of steamy, cosy little cafes you can cuddle up together in.

HOW TO END IT

If it all starts to go wrong, and he begins to say things like "Cowslips remind me of you . . ." **(Cow's lips — how dare he!)**, then it's obviously time to Spring Away in the other direction. But how? Tell him you're giving him up for Lent.

If you're the gentle, lying type, tell him you're going to Switzerland on a long Easter holiday, and he mustn't ring you up for at least three weeks. Then when he phones again, tell him you met a wonderful Swiss boy called Hans Kneesanboompsadaisy or Heinz Fiftisevenvarieteez, and that you're terribly in love!

BE—WHAT WEARING CATCH THEM!

As the year wheels round and the seasons change, boys change too. They look different, they do different things, and if you want to catch one of them and turn him into a super boyfriend, you'll have to adapt *your* technique to the time of year too! Study our special Boy Calendar for all you need to know about boys and their habits — all year round!

SUMMER

BIRDS, bees, flowers and cricket umpires are blossoming all over the country. Summer's a lovely, idyllic time of year . . . but are all those boys ready for their idyll?

WHERE THEY'LL BE

Playing football or cricket in the park, lying in the sun outside the pub, lying in the dust under their motor-bikes or lying in a puddle of chlorine by the swimming pool. Gathering on the beach for a game of Frisbee, going for long hikes along the Pennine Way . . . Or even, if they're studious, in the library, 'cos it's exam time, too, you know!

WHAT THEY'LL BE WEARING

Summer's the only time most boys look good. You can't go wrong with a T-shirt and jeans, can you? A stripey T-shirt shows he's a sporty type. A T-shirt with a rude message on shows he's a rude boy (but some rude boys are in disguise!). A T-shirt with arrows on it shows that he's escaped from jail.

SUMMER SMALL TALK

OK, so you're all togged up in your prettiest summer clothes! If you teeter over to his motor-bike and he *still* doesn't look up, you'll need some summer small talk—
To the bike boy:
 "What does two-stroke mean?"
 "What a beautiful bike!"
 "What's the fastest you've ever gone on that thing?"
To the studious boy swotting for his exams:
 "Would you like an iced Coke?"
 "Can I sharpen your Biro for you?"
 "Shall I test you on Julius Caesar?"

To the boy lying in the sun:
 "Gosh, you're really brown! What suntan oil do you use?"
 "Excuse me, would you mind rubbing oil on my back?"
 "Are you asleep?"
 "Do you mind if I join you?"

SUMMER THINGS TO DO

Once the exams are over and everyone's gloriously *free*, you and your boyfriend will have the long summer days to get to know each other, in all sorts of different places!

PUBLIC FUN

Now's your chance to get out and enjoy the sun (or cloud). Go swimming, walking, sailing, boating, biking. (You can hire boats, bikes and even boots.) Take

crazy photos of each other paddling in streams and falling off haystacks. Have a picnic with your mates out in the country. Collect wild flowers (and tame ones). Make him a daisy chain. Get a tan together. Go to London or the nearest big city for the day and wander about sight-seeing.

At night try the disco, and if it's too steamy for that, have an open-air barbecue! Go to an open-air play — there are masses of them on all over the country. Go to a pop festival if you can afford it. Try camping with some friends, if you've never tried it before. Britain's full of beautiful places. Or go abroad (a day trip to France if you're broke — bring back some smelly cheese for Dad).

PRIVATE MOMENTS

Well, you've got the whole of the countryside for your private moments. Walking around a rose garden at twilight is glorious — the scents are perfect.

And if you're on holiday, meet on the beach at 6 a.m. when everyone else is still asleep . . .

HOW TO END IT

Summer romances are notorious for being short and sweet. If a sour note begins to creep in, take action! If you met him on holiday, tell him you've got a steady boyfriend at home. If he *is* the steady boyfriend at home, tell him that you met someone on holiday (even if you didn't)! If he keeps phoning you, tell him you've got sunstroke (*especially* if it's cloudy). If he keeps writing to you, return the letter unopened, marked "GONE OFF." Well, you may not have gone *away*, but you've certainly gone *off* him!

BOY CALENDAR 1980

WHERE THEY'LL THEY'LL BE —AND HOW TO

AUTUMN

AH, autumn, the "season of mists and mellow fruitfulness," as someone once wrote . . . The season of going back to school, college, or work. Of new beginnings. And maybe new boys!

WHERE THEY'LL BE

It's the start of the football season (enough said). And the fishing season. Plays and concerts really get going in the autumn, so he could be rehearsing. Or you might find him sweeping up dead leaves and building a bonfire. Or jogging. Or taking his dog for a walk. Or writing poems about mists and mellow fruitfulness.

WHAT THEY'll BE WEARING

If they've got protective mums, they'll be wearing their winter vests (not that you'll be able to tell, thank goodness). Now's the time when cuddly, brushed-cotton tartan shirts, Fair Isle pullovers, boots instead of sneakers, and last year's bomber jackets (some of them look as if the bomb's already dropped) begin to appear.

AUTUMN SMALL TALK

As you saunter about looking stunning, don't forget you'll need some juicy pieces of small talk to get him well and truly hooked. Try . . .

To the boy walking his dog:
"What a beautiful dog! What's his breed/age/name?"
"Can I throw a stick for him?"
"Does he do tricks?"
To the boy building a bonfire:
"Is this for Guy Fawkes Night?"
"Can I help?"
"Need any potato-bakers?"

To the boy jogging:
"Are you training (puff, pant)?"
"Tell me, where did you get your lovely — gasp — track-suit?"
"You're not Brendan Foster's brother, are you?"

AUTUMN THINGS TO DO

Once you've joined your jogger, hooked your fisherman or prised your poet away from his pen, what can you do to make life lively in

autumn? Well, there's . . .

PUBLIC FUN

Autumn's full of celebrations. Most places have Michaelmas Fairs in October. So eat candy floss together. Go on the Big Dipper together (and be sick behind the Rifle Range together). Then, there's Hallowe'en. You could have a ghoulish party, or do "Trick or Treat" with the neighbours. And then there's Guy Fawkes Night,

when you can cling to him (your Guy) as the rockets take off, and share a baked potato in the glow of the bonfire.

Autumn's when evening classes start, too, and if you're interested in drama, most local groups start rehearsing for their pantos now. How about you as Cinderella and him as an Ugly Sister? Sell poppies together on Remembrance Day. Go apple-picking together. Make sure you go to the disco regularly — jogging's not the only way to keep fit, you know!

PRIVATE MOMENTS

Why not meet in the churchyard on All Hallows' Eve (you might not be alone, though!)? Wandering around the country lanes is lovely at this time of year, too — there are haystacks to sit behind, and the fields are all warm from the summer sun. If you're stuck in the town, find a sheltered corner of the park and whisper sweet nothings as the leaves fall all around you . . .

HOW TO END IT

If, as the weather cools, so does your passion, you'll have to do something about it! Tell him you've got to concentrate on some work and you'll see him again at Easter! Make a Guy Fawkes who looks just like him and see if he twigs! Ask him to pose as a model for your turnip-lantern on Hallowe'en . . .

If none of these delicate hints gets through his turnip-head, tell him that you've got an evening job and can't see him any more. If he suggests weekends, tell him you've got a weekend job, too. And if he asks what the job is, tell him it's as a Boy Disposal Officer!

BE — WHAT WEARING CATCH THEM!

BOY CALENDAR 1980

WINTER

WHEN icicles hang by the wall in winter-time, the problem is to find a nice warm boy to cuddle up to. So . . .

WHERE THEY'LL BE

Wherever it's warm! Herded together at pop concerts, discos, record shops and cafés. Christmas is a great time for meeting boys, as there are lots of parties, and plenty of mistletoe about. New Year's Eve is great, too — once you join hands for "Auld Lang Syne," hold on tight and don't let him go! If it snows, you'll find lots of boys out in the park, throwing snow-balls and making snow-women . . .

WHAT THEY'LL BE WEARING

Long coms, if they've got any sense! Luckily, most boys don't have much sense, so you'll find them in their usual winter gear or lumberjack shirts, cowboy boots, soldiers' jerseys and donkey jackets (which, unfortunately, all look better on lumberjacks, cowboys, soldiers and donkeys).

WINTER SMALL TALK

As you bear down on him in your winter woollies, try some winter small talk . . .
To the boy in the record shop:
"Excuse me, what's the difference between the Four Tops and the Three Degrees?"
"May I look while you flip?"
or even, "Is this a record?"
To the boy standing alone at a party:
"Haven't I seen you some-where before?"
"I don't know anybody here — do you?"

"You're not quite under the mistletoe — move a step to the right!"
To the boy at the pop concert:
"You're standing on my toe!"
"May I sit on your shoulders to get a better view?"
and, when the band starts,
"----- -- ----- --- ------?"
(these bands are really LOUD!).

WINTER THINGS TO DO

The world can be a winter wonderland with the right boy at your side. Here's how to get your-selves organised and enjoy it!

PUBLIC FUN

Go carol-singing together for a chance to hold hands in the dark and sing in close harmony (you don't get that sort of chance often!). Then, go to all the Christmas parties, even if you have to gatecrash! Carol Services are pretty nice if you fancy a serious evening. And put the decorations up together. He can hold the ladder steady and catch you if you fall!

If it snows, chuck snowballs at each other. Make a snowboy and snowgirl. Go sliding on the ice. Cook potatoes in their jackets and hot soup when you get back. If there's a blizzard outside — play Monopoly, or Mastermind, or even a game of Snap!

PRIVATE MOMENTS

The occasional moment behind the Christmas tree (with your own bit of mistletoe) isn't going to last very long. For a real bit of privacy, go to the public library and hide behind the stacks. Or take a round trip in a country bus (on the back seat!). Or find one of those cosy cafés with seats in alcoves . . .

HOW TO END IT

If you want to ring out the old and ring in the new, it's not difficult to think of an excuse. Tell him you're making a New Year's Resolution to give up boys altogether. Send him a Christmas stocking filled with all his old letters and presents to you. Tell him you haven't got a fairy for the tree so will he volunteer instead? Give him a Monster Plant with a card that says, "This plant reminds me of you." If that doesn't do the trick, tell him you're more interested in an Older Man at the moment (Father Christmas, to be exact!).

CATCH THE PARTY FEVER!

THE best party always turns out to be somebody else's. All *you* have to do is turn up looking ravishing (and feeling ravenous), while the poor mug who organised it is standing around perspiring like mad and feeling totally shattered after spending the whole day preparing the food and drink.

Sooner or later, though, someone will notice that you've never held a party and sooner or later they're going to suggest that you change the situation. When this happens you've got two choices . . .

1. Leave town, find a new group of friends somewhere else and start going to their parties. Or —

2. Have one!

Those of you who haven't left town, read on:

There are five things to consider before you start wildly scribbling invitations, and they are: *Why, What, Where, When and Who.*

WHY are you having a party? You must have an excuse.

WHAT kind of party will it be?
WHERE is it going to be held?
WHEN is it taking place?
WHO are you going to invite?

WHY? It's not essential to have a reason to throw a party. You

could just say, "I've got a great idea! Let's have a party!" But having a reason does help to explain why you're doing it in the first place and also stops anyone wondering if you're only giving it to make up for something awful you've done that they haven't discovered yet.

If it's near Christmas, call it a Christmas party. If it's Midsummer, make it a Midsummer party. Almost anything will do, from Guy Fawkes to the anniversary of the day you gave up your grottiest boyfriend.

Birthdays, though, are always the best reason. That way you may even get a few presents as well.

WHAT KIND OF PARTY? You could make it fancy dress except that boys are always more embarrassed about dressing up than girls are. Tramp parties are quite popular, as no-one seems to mind "dressing up" as a tramp.

If you're feeling really extravagant you could splash out and hire a disco for the night. If, however, like most of us you're not exactly loaded with spare cash, you could solve the problem by having a Bringalong party! Ask everyone to bring something for the party, salads, cheese, sandwiches, crisps, (caviare?), cans of Coke or anything else.

Then all you have to do is set out some plates and glasses and sit back — leave the rest to the guests.

IF you're having your party at home and you live in a flat, you'd be better off without the disco — unless your neighbours above and below are disco fanatics, in which case you could even invite them along.

Even if you don't live in a flat you're still likely to have a few problems. Like not waking up your kid brother or sister or both.

Try to persuade your parents to have a night out, too — you'll feel a lot more relaxed and so will your friends if you don't have them breathing down your neck. If, however, they insist on being around because they've nowhere to go or they don't trust you, or your guests, try to manoeuvre them into another room or the wardrobe or even outside to the garden shed.

Get them to take the furniture with them if and when they go, so you've got room to dance and less things to wreck!

WHEN? It's not much good holding a Christmas party in July or a Hallowe'en party in February. Parties for occasions like these ought to be held at more or less the right times.

There's no law about it,

though. If you want to hold a New Year party in October, go right ahead. Though don't be surprised if you get laughed at.

Spring always seems to be a popular time to have a party as it cheers everyone up after the long, cold Winter, and when Summer's over and there's nothing to look forward to until Christmas, an Autumn party is great fun and everyone will enjoy it all the more because there's nothing else going on.

NOW that you've sorted out why, where and when you're going to have your party you can get down to the serious business of *who* you are going to invite. The success of your party depends a lot on who your guests are and it's up to you to make sure you get it right.

If some of your friends aren't going out with anyone try to invite plenty of unattached boys along so you don't end up with a room full of wallflowers. If you *really* want to enjoy yourself don't, whatever you do, invite too much competition.

Your friend who looks like Debbie Harry's twin sister might be good fun but her presence could spoil your whole evening!

When it comes to boys, the same thing applies! If you invite

the local Casanova, even if you fancy him yourself, you're asking for trouble.

If he starts his romantic antics with some of your friends there's always the possibility that their boyfriends won't like it too much. Punch-ups at parties — especially yours — are no fun!

If this hasn't put you off the idea of having a party, then — what's stopping you? There's probably no reason why you shouldn't go ahead and throw a really great party. Being prepared means *you* should be able to enjoy yourself as well as your guests. So next time you're complaining that there are no parties to go to, take the plunge and have one yourself!

Take a very close look at your thumb. Did you know that its shape reveals a lot about the kind of person you are?

The shape of your thumb — whether it's small, large, fat or thin — tells you what makes you tick! So get to know your thumbs and gain an insight, not only into your own personality, but into those of everyone around — including the boy in your life!

THUMBS UP!

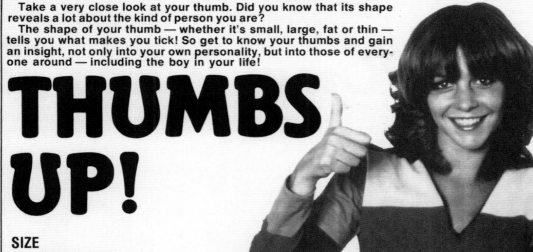

SIZE

If your thumb is Small

A small thumb means you're a romantic at heart. You love watching soppy old films on TV and you often let your heart rule your head — so watch out!

Long

Long thumbs show an interest in the mysterious, sinister things of life. You too tend to be a bit mysterious and don't like giving away much of yourself. You're highly sensitive to those around you and will defend or protect your friends no matter what the cost.

Large

If you have a large thumb you have a strong will. You believe in yourself and won't let anything or anyone stand in your way. Try not to be so ruthless, and you'll find you'll make a lot more friends!

Short

Short thumbs mean a quick temper. You're always ready for action and don't have time for those with less enthusiasm for life than you have. Try to control your temper a bit and you'll be lots happier!

SHAPE

If your thumb is Pointed

You have an ability to make people do what you want — and as a result, you usually get your own way! As you're a sympathetic listener, you're very popular with others, and you never have too little time to advise or help someone in trouble.

Straight

Persistence and stubbornness are two of your most noticeable traits. Once you've made up your mind, there's no changing it! Life might sometimes be a bit dull for you — but that's what you want. Anything unusual scares you.

Square-tipped

Square-tipped thumbs are a sign of ambition and intuition. You know instinctively which is the right path to follow, and you'll keep going till you get there. Everything you plan is carefully thought out before you decide what to do!

Waisted

Waisted thumbs — those which narrow in the middle — show a strong will and unending mounts of patience. You lead a very active life and have a love of all sports and out-of-doors activities. You're a romantic — but no-one is ever likely to have you under their thumb!

Almond shaped

You're full of energy and your whole life is spent in a state of disorganised chaos! Your impulsiveness often lands you in trouble and you're never quite sure how to get out again.

Your thumb is divided into three parts called phalanges. The first — the bottom one — shows willpower, the second reason and determination and the third, love and affection.

If your first phalange is the longest you have a bossy streak and tend to take the lead in any relationships. If it's short, you're the type who keeps your emotions to yourself and enjoys the air of mystery this creates.

The second phalange — if long, means you're obstinate — if short, it shows lack of judgment which can lead you into trouble.

The third phalange, at the top of your thumb, if long, means you have a romantic streak and you're always falling in and out of love. A short one, though, shows you're quiet, reserved and very fussy when it comes to choosing your friends.

Now that you've thumbed through our special feature, you should be an expert in thumbonology! So take another look at everyone you know, especially those you're close to, and find out thumbthing about them!

★ Do you wish upon wish that you could lose weight every time you bite into yet another cream doughtnut?

★ Do you wish upon wish you could put on just a few more pounds every time you pick and fiddle with your food?

★ Do you feel really guilty each time you gorge your way through yet another packet of chocolate biscuits?

Do You Know When To

If you answered yes to just one of these questions, then you're a foodaholic — you eat *not* because you're hungry, or because you physically *need* to, but because something's wrong with your life . . . In short, the way you eat, and the amount you eat — far too much, or far too little — is saying much more about the state of your mind and your emotions than words could ever say.

So just why do *you* nibble or gorge yourself when there's no need for it? Here's exactly what your eating habits tell about you — and how to eat your way back to health and happiness, the *right* way . . .

WHEN you were little, your mum probably gave you a sweet for being a good girl, or to comfort you when you fell over and grazed your knee. So it's natural that you should associate food with reward and pleasure, and with love and security.

At the other extreme, although you probably don't realise it, eating too little is a subconscious way of *punishing* yourself. This again goes back to childhood when Mum said, "No, you naughty girl, you don't deserve a sweet/doughnut/toffee-apple/strawberry!" So denying yourself the pleasure of enjoying your food can be a sign that you're angry with yourself, and are in fact trying to punish yourself because you feel guilty about something.

Any kind of emotional stress is likely to make you change your eating habits too — either by over-indulging yourself, or depriving yourself.

Are You Feeling Sad And Lonely?

YOU can see exactly how food is related to your emotions if you follow this girl's thoughts as she absently-mindedly works her way through a load of sweet treats!

Her name's Julie. She's going through a bad patch right now — it's Saturday night, and she's stuck at home with nowhere to go and nothing to look forward to. Her mum's out. She feels really sad and lonely.

"I feel rotten," she's thinking. "Nothing seems to have gone right lately. I'll have a cup of tea and a biscuit to cheer myself up . . ."

Then she thinks about school, about how badly she's doing in her Maths class and

how she thinks the teacher hates her. She's getting more and more depressed.

"I'm still hungry, I'll just have another biscuit, and some of that cake left over from tea yesterday . . ."

Next, Julie thinks about her best friend, Jenny: "She promised to ring me and she hasn't. Perhaps she doesn't like me any more, and I haven't seen Rita for *ages*, either. She's probably avoiding me, too. No-one seems to like me any more . . ."

Then she remembers a box of chocolates her mum got from an aunt. "Well, she won't mind if I just have one or two . . . Strawberry cream, my favourite!"

Now Julie starts to worry about Dave, the boy she fancies: "I really thought he was interested in me, he was always chatting me up, but then he did have to go and take that creep Linda Smith out, didn't he. Just my luck. I can't understand what's *wrong* with me . . .

"Oh God, I've eaten all the strawberry creams, plus two hazel whirls, two toffee crisps and a peppermint crunch — Mum'll be *furious*!"

Do you recognise yourself when, like Julie, you're going through a bad patch emotionally, and compensating yourself with food? The trouble is, though, the comforting effect doesn't last for long, and it's an easy temptation to eat more, and more, and more . . .

Are You A Greedy-Guts?

EMOTIONAL over-eating can become a habit which can be very hard to break . . . Take Sue, for instance. She's fifteen and very self-conscious about being overweight, even though she admits she's a bit of a pig with her food.

"The trouble is, the more I worry about

being fat the more I seem to eat," she told us.

"The funny thing is, that when I go away on holiday it's completely different — I don't think about eating at all. We went to Cornwall last summer and it was smashing — I came back all lovely and slim. But as soon as I came back home, I put it all on again . . ."

You can understand Sue's food problem if you look at it from an emotional point of view. Sue's become dependent on food as a way of coping with stress, because eating has a soothing effect on the body and emotions.

The point is, when Sue goes on holiday she's relaxed and free from stress anyway, so she doesn't need the calming-down effect of compulsive eating.

So if *you've* got into the habit of over-eating, the best cure is an interesting life! Try rushing round being energetic and doing things, being interested in things, enjoying yourself.

Are You Lovesick?

EMOTIONAL stress can also make people go to the other extreme of under-eating. If you're nervous and anxious, you'll feel too wound up to bother to eat anything.

An extreme emotion like being lovesick for someone can change you from a happy, bouncing girl to a mere shadow of your former self. That's what happened to Pam, who fell in love with a fantastic boy — but he, unfortunately, didn't feel the same way about her . . .

"It was terrible when Greg left me for another girl," she told us. "I could hardly sleep and I could hardly eat.

"I had no appetite for anything. If you'd put my favourite dinner down in front of

Stop ?

me I would have pushed it away in disgust.''

Gradually, Pam's feelings about Greg got less intense until she actually started to forget about him. She started going out and getting interested in other boys, and of course, her appetite came back.

So if *you're* off your food you can be sure there's something worrying you — maybe just minor worries, an argument with Mum, a bust-up with a friend, being up-tight about exams — all these things are likely to spoil your appetite. But, usually, as soon as the cause of stress is removed, you can go back to your three square meals again!

Are You Starving Yourself To Death?

JUST as over-eating can become an emotional habit, so can the Skinny-Liz habit of neglecting yourself by not eating enough. Like 16-year-old Wendy, who'd love to put on weight but can't help her fussy, finicky eating habits . . .

"My mum's always nagging on at me because I don't eat enough," Wendy told us. "I'd love to eat more and put on weight, but the more Mum nags the more I go off my food."

Wendy is the nervous type who reacts to stress by rejecting food. As a personality, she's inclined to put herself down and have a poor opinion of herself.

It's also significant that her mum's nagging only puts Wendy off her appetite more. **Food is a symbol of love,** and Wendy is rejecting her mum's love when she rejects the food her mother puts in front of her. It's a way of rebelling.

So if *you've* got into the habit of eating mouse-sized meals, your food problem can be cured by building up more self-confidence and a better opinion of yourself. Be nice and kind to yourself, indulge yourself with new clothes, perfumed baths, funny films, outings, treats, *anything* that'll make you feel better.

You'll have more energy, you'll look healthier and soon eating will become a pleasure rather than a pain. And most important of all, you'll start liking *yourself* a lot better too!

*   *   *   *

So you see, the way you treat your body is a reflection of the way you feel about yourself.

But if you at least *know* why you overeat or undereat, it's much easier to change your attitude to food.

Once you've sorted out your nosh problems, you can afford the occasional luxury of a doughnut binge or a greedy feast without feeling guilty, and you can also afford the occasional bout of keeping going on nothing but a crumb or a crust because you're so busy and hectic and life's so exciting you can't sit still for long enough to eat a meal.

And if you want *more* food for thought, always remember that your eating problems are in your mind, *not* in your stomach!

HOW SWEET ARE YOU?

Had a good sniff recently? No, we don't mean a good cry . . . we mean have you noticed any nice smells around? Delicious perfumes, sweet-smelling flowers, your favourite foods. There are super smells all around you . . . so start now and sniff out some of the nicest ones!

TOWN smells aren't always pleasant, there are just too many cars and dustbins around. The nicest smells come from baker's shops where they bake their own bread and cakes (don't go in!), perfume counters in department stores and coffee shops where you'll smell the wonderful whiff of freshly-ground coffee beans.

Country air is good for your sense of smell except when you pass a pig-farm or a dung-heap! Better to head for the woods with the tangy whiff of pine needles, the smell of woodsmoke from a cottage, the hedgerows in summer with all the flowers and newly-mown hay (fine, unless you get hay-fever!).

Now that we've reminded you of some of the delicious smells around, you'll start noticing others. How does your boyfriend strike you these days?

Does he smell irresistible and manly? Or does he just smell rather peculiar most of the time?

If he's not very sniffable you could try a campaign to change all that by buying him some aftershave or talc powder you'll both like. A little patchouli oil can smell good on boys . . . you'll find it at Indian shops.

Another good wheeze is to get him to try a super-smelling shampoo . . . Earthborn Apricot, Apple and Avocado shampoos smell great on boys!

You'll have to make sure *you* smell good, too, of course, which means finding a cologne or perfume to suit you. If you've no idea where to start, then why not choose one to suit your personality? Check with our list and see what's right for *you!*

SWEET DREAMER?

If you're the shy, quiet and dreamy type, try floral perfumes on a single note . . . Boots Original Formula Lavender or Rose, for instance, or Mary Quant country-sweet oils in Honeysuckle or Country Garden.

SPORTY TYPE?

Are you a sporty outdoor girl? Fond of horses or a keen football fan? Try Revlon's Charlie which is sweet but tangy, or go for Smitty or anything lemony and fresh.

MYSTERY GIRL?

If you long for faraway places, want to travel and see the world, try special oils such as patchouli, ylang-ylang or vetivert. Go for Stowaway or a French perfume spray, too.

A RAVER?

Are you the life and soul of the party? The girl who's always ready to dance the night away? Try Mary Quant's Havoc or any of the Musk perfumes. Try Rive Gauche by Yves St Laurent, too . . . it's very sophisticated. Look for sprays on offer!

GIVE your bedroom a romantic Eastern atmosphere by burning joss-sticks. You can buy them in lovely perfumes such as Mimosa, Ylang-Ylang and Frankincense! If you want something a little less heavy, try scented candles — poppy-scented perhaps?

For the sweetest dreams, try a herbal pillow as a very special treat. These are available in different sizes, from a normal pillow size down to a tiny size which will cost around £2.00 from craft shops. Kitty Little has a range of herbal pillows available all over the country. Re-fills are usually available when the pillow seems to lose its freshness.

Surround yourself with delicious smells and give your nose a *real* treat!

When Steve went away, Julie promised she'd love him for ever. Then she met Martin . . .

I Really Thought I Loved Him...

STEVE'S letter arrived on Saturday morning, just as I was leaving the house to meet Martin.

I've been away a long time, Julie. It's been hard for both of us. I just can't believe what you say – I can't believe it's over.

He was coming home. He had leave due and he was coming to see me, to try to sort things out.

We'd been in love, Steve and I. Really in love. Or it had seemed that way . . .

Joining the army had always been part of his plan. We knew it would be hard being apart, but we'd have letters, phone calls.

And the times we did spend together would be extra special because they were so precious . . .

Only, it didn't work out that way . . .

Sitting in, night after night, had driven me right up the wall.

When I couldn't stand it any longer, I phoned up my best friend, Jacqui, and we arranged to go out to a disco.

I chatted up a boy with dark hair. He danced like a dream and we spent the whole evening together.

I liked having him chat me up. I liked letting him take me home.

I liked the way he kissed me . . .

I felt a pang of conscience when I got ready for bed that night, though, and I couldn't write my usual letter to Steve.

What was the use of a letter? I was lonely. I missed having someone around, someone to hold me, to kiss me.

I didn't mean to go to the disco again. But I couldn't help it. Suddenly I was having fun again.

I thought it could go on like that forever — playing games, having fun. A different boy every week.

Nothing serious, nothing that could harm me and Steve.

Martin changed all that. When he asked me out I didn't even think about Steve once.

Martin was different from the others. I knew there was no way I was going to be able to forget him . . .

IN the end, I had to write to Steve, telling him it was over. I posted the letter right away, glad it was done, glad he would soon know where he stood with me.

And now — now when I was on my way to meet Martin — I had to read Steve's reply. Oh, if only he would stop being so stubborn and just accept things!

Martin sensed there was something wrong as soon as he saw me.

"Hey, what's up, Julie? You look like you're on your way to somebody's funeral!"

I tried to grin, but my mouth trembled a bit and Martin's arms tightened around me.

"Come on — we'll go for a coffee and you can tell me about it."

We found a little corner table in a cafe and sat down. I looked at Martin, just not knowing where to start.

In the end, I just pulled Steve's letter out of my handbag and gave it to Martin.

I watched him as he read it. He folded it up and put it down on the table

"I didn't know," he said.

I stared at the letter, unable to say anything.

"He's got a nerve," Martin said, after a while. "Don't see him, Julie."

"I feel — I have to, Martin. I owe it to him, I suppose. And maybe then it'll be straightened out and I'll feel better . . ." My voice cracked. "I — I'm sorry I didn't tell you before . . ."

He leaned over and kissed me.

"It doesn't matter," he said.

I REALLY dreaded having to see Steve again. He'd said he'd come to the house and I walked round all that morning, not able to sit down even, because I was so tensed up.

And it turned out to be worse than I thought . . .

He came to the door and he looked really nervous. We just couldn't seem to talk to each other at all.

"Julie, let's get out of here," Steve said. "It's no use trying to talk here."

I nodded. "All right."

We turned into the park, and Steve shoved his hands into his pockets.

"Julie, you know how I feel about the army, but if it comes between us, it's just not worth it. It's not worth anything."

I turned to him, dismayed.

"It's what you've always wanted, Steve! You don't mean that!"

"I mean it. You come first with me."

"Don't talk rubbish," I said and pulled away from him. I walked on a bit, and there were tears in my eyes because I knew he wasn't talking rubbish, that he

meant every word he said.

He came up behind me, and I started to cry. His arms went round me.

"Forget about me, Steve," I whispered.

He tilted my face up towards him and began to kiss me. Slowly my arms went round him till I was kissing him back.

Then he held me away from him.

"Don't throw it all away, Julie, it's too important. OK, so things have gone wrong between us, but we can put them right again.

"Because get one thing straight, Julie, I'm not going to lose you . . ."

HE kissed me again and smiled at me. I buried my face in his chest, crying with relief because I knew now Steve had been right to trust our love. I'd made such a mess of things. Convinced myself it was Martin I wanted. But he'd just been there when I needed somebody.

"There's just one thing I've got to know," Steve said. "Do you love me, Julie?"

"Yes, I do love you, Steve . . ."

He held me very tight, and then he said, "Let's hang on to that, then."

I knew, of course, I'd have to try to explain everything to Martin. It'd be difficult — he loves me and he believes I love him. After all, I told him I did, didn't I?

How could I have made such a mistake? It's Steve I really love — only I was almost too late in finding out.

I just hope Martin will understand . . .

A Reader's True Experience

TAKE A GOOD LOOK!

If you always want to look your best, two different looks are all you need – one natural for any time at all and one dressed-up look for special occasions. Follow our step-by-step guide to these two perfect make-up looks designed specially for Jackie by make-up artist Mary Vango. The looks are easy to follow – and they'll give you lots of helpful tips on skin and make-up!

The NATURAL LOOK

The natural look means clear, healthy skin, shining eyes and just a little make-up to define eyes, cheeks and lips. Skin care is really important and a regular cleanse, tone and moisturising routine is what you need to keep your skin clean, soft and healthy.

Remove eye make-up with an eye make-up remover lotion. Soak a pad of cotton wool in the lotion and hold it over your eye — never rub the delicate skin around your eyes.

Use a lotion cleanser or cleansing milk to clean make-up from the rest of your face, then wash gently with a very mild soap and water to remove dirt and grime.

Tone with a gentle toner for your skin type, then moisturise with a light moisturiser for your skin type. Even greasy skins need a little moisture!

Make-up should be really light and fresh for the natural look. It should be used to help make the best of your features — not to cover up blemishes! A greasy skin should be treated with great care and kept really clean — use medicated products for cleansing and treat existing spots with a treatment cream.

A great number of spots which never seem to go away could mean that you have acne. The best idea is to visit your doctor as there are several treatments available for acne now in different forms from special lotions to courses of tablets.

Whatever your skin type, your skin and hair can be improved if you eat a balanced diet, take regular exercise, get lots of fresh air and lots of sleep. Be kind to yourself and cut out sugar and processed foods which are so full of additives that their natural goodness has disappeared completely.

Now, follow these simple steps to perfect make-up and a perfect natural look!

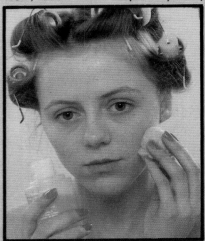

1. Make-up artist Mary Vango cleansed, toned and moisturised model Arabella's skin. The moisturiser makes a smooth surface for the base colour.

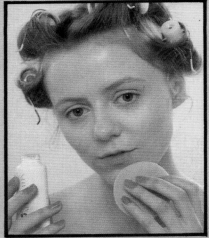

2. Base colour is a cream in ivory-beige shade, applied all over face and neck with a dampened cosmetic sponge for a really smooth finish.

3. Next Mary used a cream blusher in a dusky pink, applied with a sponge from cheek-bones to temples. The edges are blended so there aren't any hard lines.

4. On eyes Mary used a golden brown for lids and a frosted ginger shade for brow bones. Powder colours, applied with a brush, last longer than cream colours.

5. Black mascara next, with two coats for a perfect finish. Allow the first coat to dry before you apply the second – the last thing you want is thick, clogged lashes.

6. Lip colour is the final step and Mary used a russett automatic lip colour to give colour and shine.

7. The finished look – with hair styled on rollers for a bouncy, natural look!

CREDITS: Make-up from Boots 17, Max Factor and Lancôme. Blouse from a range at Laura Ashley.

The DRESSED-UP LOOK

The dressed-up look also calls for clear skin, of course, and more make-up. Using more make-up takes time and needs practice to get it right. The trick is to build up the layers gradually, especially on eyes.

The colours you choose are important, but sometimes it's difficult to know which ones will suit you. There are some special rules to follow, though. Here's some to help you.

Choose a foundation colour according to your own skin tones. Test it on your *face* if you can, and if you *can't* see the colour, it's the one for you. A base colour is used to even up skin tones and cover tiny blemishes — *not* to add unnatural colour, while blusher should be chosen to tone with skin and to go with lip colours. Lips and nails should tone with the clothes you're wearing and should go with your skin tones, too. For instance if you have quite sallow skin and dark hair a blue/red lip colour will look terrible! Colours should look good on

your skin and should make it look warm and glowing.

Eye colours are perhaps the most difficult to choose because there aren't any proper rules. There may be one shade that makes your eyes look *really* amazing — a shade that perhaps tones with the little flecks in your eyes. A green shade may bring out the flecks in hazel eyes, for instance, and a lilac may be just the thing for grey/blue eyes.

Mascara depends very much on your hair colour as well as your skin tones and eye colour. Dark hair usually means black mascara, brown, auburn or ginger hair means browny/black or brown mascara, light brown to blonde means brown or russet mascara, or perhaps navy.

Once you've chosen your colours, practise until you're really good at putting them on. And now, here's how Mary created Arabella's dressed-up look, step by step!

1. After cleansing, toning and moisturising the first step is the base colour. Mary used an ivory liquid foundation applied with a dampened cosmetic sponge all over face and neck.

2. Translucent powder went over the foundation before the powder blusher. Blusher is a light tawny colour carefully blended from just below cheek bones in a V shape out towards temples.

3. Eyes are all important and Mary used a light brown on the inside of each lid, applied with a brush. Next came a soft green applied to the outer lids and just under the lower lashes.

4. Arabella has quite deep lids, so Mary used a soft brown to shade along the socket-line, following the line of the brow bone.

5. For a special effect Mary used a soft green pencil along the lower rims of each eye. She then added two coats of black mascara.

6. Lips come last and Mary carefully outlined the lips with a lip pencil, then filled in with a deep red-rose lip colour applied with a lip-brush for a perfect finish.

7. The finished look with hair rolled back on each side from a centre parting. The side sections are secured with combs and topped with yellow flowers.

CREDITS: Make-up from Evette, Lancôme and the Babe range by Fabergé. Blouse from a range at Top Shop.

WANTED

ROD STEWART

LOCATION — Of Northern British origin, also known as The Tartan Terror, this species migrates between the United States and the U.K. mainly returning to let his thousands of followers catch a glimpse of his leopard-skinned, tightly-clad body and hear his incredibly sexy, husky voice. He's usually accompanied by a blonde — having fun.
THE CAPTURE — Adopt Scottish nationality. Bleach your hair — although if you're not also a willowy 5ft. 11in. this won't work too well. Say you're a distant relative of Kenny Dalglish — this may well work. Never *at any time* mention Argentina or Britt Ekland.

JOHN TRAVOLTA

LOCATION — Easily the most popular of the Travolta species. Can be found in America on film sets, or at private airports — this one loves flying. He may though, only be interested if you're an older, mature female. But you can always try to change his mind!
THE CAPTURE — You'll need to be nimble on your feet. Win "The Disco Dancer Of The Year" contest and be introduced, or pretend you're over 30 and just love young, dishy males with gorgeous blue eyes. Tell him you know all about how to pilot a Cessna 100 or whatever. As long as you don't actually have to *do* it, he'll be impressed, all right!

BOB GELDOF

LOCATION — This species is Irish, full of fun, and a bit of a rogue — so watch out! He's an incredibly nice rogue, though, and his roving eye will pick you out in recording studios, TV studios and generally every party that's going.
THE CAPTURE — Tear up a John Travolta poster in his presence. He'll love you for it! Make no mention of any similarity between himself and Mick Jagger. He'll hate you for it!

LEIF GARRETT

LOCATION — Usually found in discos or on TV and film sets. At one time he spent a lot of time in skateboard parks — now he gets around in fast sports cars. A youthful member of the species — noted for his good looks and his dancing ability.
THE CAPTURE — Go to New York and learn the New York Hustle. Or fly to California and live on the beach outside his home. Practise with hair-dryer in front of mirror to get that "windswept" look that goes so well in an open sports car. Thumb a lift in any sports car emerging from this wanted male's house.

PRINCE ANDREW

LOCATION — Any old palace or castle. His country seat! On the High Seas . . . this creature's pretty hard to track down! Often seen with his mother or brothers. Tweed jackets and a behind-the-back-with-his-hands stance is often adopted.
THE CAPTURE — Throw on all your diamonds and make sure that you're in the vicinity if there are any film premiers to attend or bridges to be opened — or even the odd ship being launched. Read up on polo and rugger. Being filthy rich and royal would be a real asset here.

MEN!

John Travolta, Rod Stewart, Bob Geldof — what have they all got in common? Apart from the fact that they're all magnificent specimens of masculinity, they're all among the world's most wanted men! Wanted by us, of course! So if *you* want to know how to go about locating — and capturing! — some of the world's most wanted men, read on . . . If you can actually manage to catch any of them, we bet you'll find it a rewarding experience!

MARK HAMILL

LOCATION — Often to be found with his head in the clouds and stars in his eyes, this one! One of the characteristics of this gorgeous creature is its fascinating blue eyes — hypnotic if you get too close. He's a little old fashioned really and has an incredible desire to rescue princesses . . .

THE CAPTURE — Either take up spaceship maintenance or hang around looking like a princess who needs rescuing. If you're also incredibly brave and not at all afraid of space creatures or being followed around by a film crew all the time, this will be a real asset.

PARKER STEVENSON

LOCATION — This one's a keep-fit freak and often found to be doing all sorts of energetic things to keep itself in shape (and what a shape!). You'll tend to find him around in secluded areas of Beverly Hills involved in an ancient rite called jogging! His eating habits are quite definite as well — lots of healthy wholemeal bread and yoghurt and salads and yoghurts and salads and . . . Anyway.

THE CAPTURE — The first thing to do is attract him to you by wearing a track suit and bobbing up and down, shouting "Who's for a quick one round the park, then?" Once you've caught his attention you could then make sure he's firmly yours for ever by presenting him with a huge tuna fish salad (we have it on good authority that that's his favourite).

THE FONZ

LOCATION — Fairly limited species this — in fact, it's nearly extinct. One last outpost where it's still hanging around is a hamburger joint called "Arnold's." It generally dresses in black leather and denim and can move at high speed, especially when it's on a motorbike. One of the quirks of this chap is his desire to stick both thumbs in the air and utter a kind of strangled yell.

THE CAPTURE — Read up on twin overhead cams and sprockets and always carry a selection of spanners around. Enjoy running your hands through greasy hair (your own if you've forgotten to wash them after fixing the bike!) and learn to survive totally on Coke and hamburgers. It also helps not to be too jealous as this male tends to attract hundreds of members of the opposite sex wherever it goes.

RICHARD HATCH

LOCATION — On a battlestar called Galactica — you mean there isn't a battlestar stop near your house? He's generally to be found with some sort of beautiful creature wrapped around him, fighting off monsters and looking stunningly attractive — clever chaps these Hatches . . . And if he's not doing that he's likely to be swimming, playing tennis, jogging or admiring cats — they *love* cats.

THE CAPTURE — Hire a panto cat outfit and fling yourself off the roof at him the next time he's jogging past. Admit that you don't know a *thing* about anything even remotely energetic but you're *awfully* willing to learn. Oh, and if you happen to be a beautiful star maiden who's looking for help and a bit of romance, it might stand you in good stead for capturing the heart of this particular battlestar trooper.

CAN YOU MAKE FRIENDS?

DO you want people to love you instantly? Do you want to be surrounded by warmth and friendship wherever you go? Do you want to feel relaxed, at ease, charming and sympathetic the moment you're introduced to someone?

If you've answered "yes" to all three questions then you're just the same as everyone else who belongs to the human race! You want to be liked and appreciated by other people and make a good impression on them.

The first impression you make on someone, though, is very important, because that is the one that tends to stick in their minds until they get to know you better. And, of course, their first opinion of you will determine whether or not they *want* to get to know you better!

For this reason, meeting new people can be fraught with worry and difficulty. The great temptation is to put on an act to convince people what a super person you are, and to hide your real personality by presenting an image which is very misleading.

It's odd how many people think they can make a good impression by putting on an act. The truth is that an insincere or defensive act is hardly ever impressive and is most likely to turn people *off* instead of *on*.

Just take a look at some of the most common mistakes people make when they're trying to impress someone and, if you recognise yourself — be warned! Remember — the simple fact is, the most impressive person to be is — yourself!

Are You A GUSHER?

Gushing takes the form of treating the other person like a god. A warm-hearted person with a genuine sympathy for others, who's naturally outgoing and really likes people, can be so desperate to be liked that she'll launch off into a stream of senseless gush, totally embarrassing the other person, and just making a complete fool of herself.

She currys favour with phrases like: "Oh, what a beautiful dress — you make me feel so dowdy — can you make apple flan, that's so wonderful, I really admire people who can do that . . ."

But in her heart of hearts, she doesn't, you see, and the person she's telling is even less convinced.

People see through overdone charm, and have no respect for you for over-praising them. In the process, too, the gusher is also putting herself down, and so presenting a completely false picture.

This is unfortunate, because the gusher does mean well, and she genuinely wants people's friendship. She has a lot to offer, but it's her lack of self-confidence that has got her into the habit of thinking that people will only like her if she falls at their feet and worships them.

So if you find yourself gushing, cool it! Get rid of the gush — people will appreciate you much more, and your warm and friendly nature will be revealed.

This way, too, you can still compliment people, and they'll know you *really* mean it, and like you even more!

Are You TOO TIMID?

Are you an individual with strong views and opinions of your own, who just hates smalltalk? Then make sure you're not falling into the trap of coming across as a very ordinary person, responding weakly to witty remarks, when in fact you could be sparking off a stimulating discussion.

Show your real personality for what it is — unusual and fascinating. You're interesting and original, a great conversationalist on a deep level, so get involved in the kind of conversations that *you* like — if people aren't keen to comply, they'll just make a polite excuse, and walk away.

Besides, you'll be surprised how many other people get tired of silly chatter and would long to share a good conversation with someone like you!

Are You BOASTFUL?

The person who comes across as boastful tends to be very insecure and feels that they're so ordinary they could never make a good impression on anyone.

In reality, if they would only see it, they're kind, good company, and fun to be with. But to make up for that bad opinion, they boast, and their poor victim is given a blow by blow account of love conquests, amazing accomplishments, privileged childhoods — all totally false.

The person being spoken to is also aware that the boaster isn't interested in them as a person, so there's no real basis for a relationship at all.

But if you boast, you're being your own worst enemy. If you could present your real self, you'd realise that you're not any more ordinary than anyone else. And you're hiding your good qualities, too — cheerful temperament, sense of humour, vitality and enthusiasm.

You'd realise, too, that your real personality is far more impressive than your big boasting act!

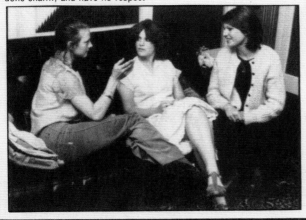

Your Special Jackie POP-A-CROSS!

CLUES ACROSS

1. Pretty fair band (7).
4. Ma Bakers' kids (5, 1).
7. You can't play noughts and crosses without it! (1).
8. --creatures Great and Small? (3).
9. Idol band (10).
13. Speedy group (5).
16. ? and behold he's a record producer with 17 (4).
17. A Christian name that sounds like steal (4).
18. A Christian Reg Dwight? (5).
20. A record label that sounds painful! (5).
21. She limited herself to Nutbush City initially (1, 1).
22. Reverse veteran horror film actor (1, 1).
24. These two letters make up Abba's name (2).
25. Starsky and Hutch's base (1, 1).
26. Queen once had a day at them (5).
30. Band's name needing assistance (1, 1, 1).
31. Well, Elvis C. likes them . . . (11).
35. Joins many lead singers to their groups?! (3).
36. Fonzie's nephew? (4).
37. Dury, and others, answer to this? (3).
38. Michael's speedy film manoeuvres? (3).
40. You're a hit if you're in this one? (3).
41. A blond, fun-loving football fanatic? (3).
43. Marie's big brother (1, 1).
45. American band that sound like The Motors (4).
46. What you did with Noakes? (2).
47. Zuko's pal? (5).
48. Three lovely ladies just above freezing point (1,1).
49. He rode to fame on the motorway? (1, 1).
51. You'll be ecstatic about this band! (1, 1, 1).
52. Laboratory measure that added to 40 across makes a band? (1, 1).
53. Tough TV brothers? (5).
55. Child-like lookalikes? (5).
57. Phil kept his whiskey here! (3).
58. Fan club members are "wild" about *this* group (5).
59. Supergroup's kid brother? (4).

CLUES DOWN

2. What joins Dave Travis together? (3).
3. This band sounds hungry! (5).
4. We're not saying Ian's band are stupid, but . . .! (10).
5. --,honestly,John Alderton appeared in it! (2).
6. Old "Rubberlips" first name! (4).
9. You'd slip a disc(o) if you stepped in it! (6).
10. A common greeting and band name? (1, 1, 1).
11. "Happy Days" Ritchie's real name (3).
12. Potsie's initials off the set (1, 1).
13. This Ray's always "darting" around! (4).
14. Actors do this! (3).
15. Village People stay here (1, 1, 1, 1).
19. Richard's "stand and deliver" role (6).
22. Superman's *first* lady (1, 1).
23. A precious stone and a Wings hit (3).
24. Dirk and Richard operate on one of these? (10).
27. A star is Shaun? (7).
28. Barbra Streisand was born one? (4).
29. Geldolf, Dylan, and Monkhouse have it in common? (3).
32. The real Mike Upchat (1, 1).
33. Sha -- na! (2).
34. How Baccara would say "Yes, I'm a lady" (2).
37. Take the first letters of The Saint's real names . . . (1, 1).
39. Currently one of the most electrifying bands around?! (2, 2).
40. See 49 across . . . again!
41. Ferry's band rocks on (4).
42. Hit the deck and add on A for a record company (5).
43. This band shouldn't be thrown at bullseyes!! (5).
44. Blame it -- the Boogie (2).
48. What Officer Dibble calls Boss Cat. (1, 1).
50. Initially The Sundance Kid (1, 1).
53. If you get this one you're laughing! (3).
54. Low-voiced singer once with Darts (3).
56. . . . and the Sunshine Band (1, 1).
57. Initially he wrote Annie's Song.

Solutions on page 36

A READER'S TRUE EXPERIENCE TOLD IN PICTURES

My sister, Vicky, was a couple of years older than me. But sometimes I really hated her—as far as Mum and Dad were concerned, she couldn't do anything wrong . . .

I'M GLAD I WAS THE ONE WHO TOLD MUM AND DAD THE TRUTH. IT WAS GREAT OF VICKY TO PROTECT ME, BUT I REALLY REALLY DESERVE TO BE PUNISHED FOR WHAT I DID TO HER . . .

THERE SHE GOES AGAIN! IT REALLY MAKES ME SICK THE WAY SHE CARRIES ON! SHE'S ONLY HELPING MUM SO THAT SHE CAN GET ROUND HER FOR THAT NEW DRESS SHE WANTS.

I HAD TO GET EVEN...

Fiona had had enough of being treated as the baby of the family—so she set out to get her revenge . . .

Whereas Mum was always picking on me . . .

HOW MANY TIMES HAVE I TOLD YOU NOT TO DO THAT, FIONA? YOU'LL RUIN THE CAKE. WHY DON'T YOU MAKE YOURSELF USEFUL, LIKE VICKY!

VICKY . . . IT'S ALWAYS VICKY! YOU'D THINK THEY DIDN'T WANT ME AT ALL THE WAY THEY GO ON . . .

I KNOW SHE'S MY SISTER, BUT SOMETIMES I HATE HER! I MEAN, WHY CAN'T MUM AND DAD TREAT ME LIKE A PERSON, TOO? THEY STILL THINK OF ME AS A LITTLE KID, RUNNING AROUND IN ANKLE SOCKS . . .

DEAR LITTLE VICKY WOULDN'T LET BUTTER MELT IN HER MOUTH! BUT THEY'RE ALWAYS TELLING ME HOW IMPOSSIBLE I AM . . .

I had to share a room with her, too—worse luck!

WHAT'S UP? YOU DON'T LOOK VERY HAPPY, FIONA!

THERE'S NOTHING TO LOOK HAPPY ABOUT! NOBODY ROUND HERE CARES ABOUT ME—I MIGHT AS WELL BE DEAD FOR ALL YOU LOT CARE!

It certainly made a change from being pushed around all the time . . .

IT'D BE EVEN BETTER IF I COULD START GOING OUT WITH VICKY AT NIGHT—THEN I COULD COME HOME LATE TOO! AND SHE CAN HARDLY REFUSE, CAN SHE . . ?

She must have been really stuck on Dave! Over the next few days she really made me feel glad I'd found out about them . . .

THIS ONE'LL DO PERFECTLY, VICKY. AND IT'S SO NICE OF YOU TO BUY IT FOR ME!

IT- IT'S A BIT EXPENSIVE, FIONA . . . BUT I- I SUPPOSE I CAN MANAGE IT.

Even at home things were better!

. . . BUT YOU PROMISED I COULD GO TO THE PARTY WITH YOU, VICKY!

DON'T BE SO SELFISH, VICKY. YOU CAN TAKE HER JUST THIS ONCE. ESPECIALLY IF YOU SAID YOU WOULD . . .

OH, WHY DON'T YOU ALL JUST LEAVE ME ALONE!

IGNORE HER, FIONA—SHE'S GOING THROUGH A PECULIAR PHASE. I DON'T KNOW WHAT ON EARTH'S GOT INTO HER!

AND YOU WON'T EVER FIND OUT— BECAUSE VICKY COULDN'T POSSIBLY TELL YOU. NOT AFTER THE WAY DAD BLEW UP WHEN I TOLD HIM ABOUT DAVE— HE'D GO CRAZY IF HE KNEW SHE WAS STILL SEEING HIM . . .

But I got to go to the party, of course! It was a bit boring until I noticed this boy on the other side of the room . . .

HE-HE'S REALLY SOMETHING! MUCH NICER THAN ANY OF THE BOYS MY AGE—I'LL HAVE TO GO AND INTRODUCE MYSELF . . .

HI! I'M VICKY NELSON'S SISTER, FIONA. NICE PARTY, ISN'T IT . . .

I DON'T THINK I KNOW VICKY, BUT HI, ANYWAY! I'M GRAHAM WALKER.

OH, THIS IS MY FAVOURITE RECORD—LET'S DANCE!

YEAH, WELL . . .

We were together most of the evening, and when the party finished . . .

BYE, FIONA—I'LL SEE YOU AROUND SOMETIME?

SURE! AFTER ALL, I'LL BE AT THE DISCO TOMORROW . . . AND SO WILL YOU, WON'T YOU?

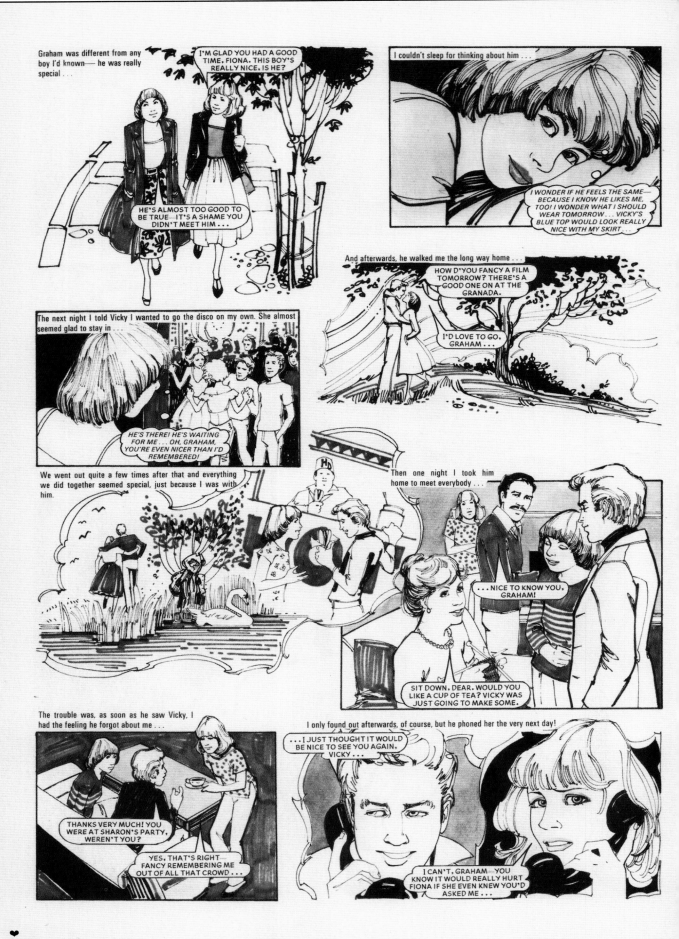

Graham just ignored me after he'd been told the truth about Vicky and Dave. I know I should have let it drop, but I couldn't bear to think of Vicky with my boyfriend. So . . .

. . . I DON'T KNOW WHAT'S THE MATTER WITH HER. SHE KNOWS HE DRINKS TOO MUCH AND STARTS ACTING STRANGELY! AFTER ALL, THAT'S WHY I STOPPED GOING OUT WITH HIM . . .

And as soon as Vicky got home . . .

I'M WARNING YOU, VICKY. YOU'RE NOT TO SEE HIM AGAIN! FIRST DAVE AND NOW THIS! I'D HAVE THOUGHT YOU HAD MORE SENSE!

BUT DAD—YOU'VE GOT TO LET ME EXPLAIN! THERE'S SOMETHING YOU DON'T KNOW ABOUT—

NO EXCUSES! JUST GET UP TO YOUR ROOM!

But then, just when I thought I'd got away with it . . .

VICKY! THERE'S A MR BATES HERE TO SEE YOU— HE SAYS IT'S IMPORTANT!

OH, NO! C- COMING, MUM . . .

It was Dave's probation officer—he couldn't have picked a worse time!

I JUST WANTED TO THANK YOU FOR ALL YOU'VE BEEN DOING FOR DAVE, VICKY. WE REALLY APPRECIATE THE ENCOURAGEMENT YOU'VE GIVEN HIM.

DAVE? THAT YOUNG . . . WHAT'S GOING ON, VICKY?

DAVE'S HAD HIS PROBLEMS, AS YOU KNOW, MR NELSON. VICKY WAS THE ONLY ONE WHO SEEMED TO GET THROUGH TO HIM— LISTENING TO HIM WHEN HE WANTED TO TALK, OFFERING HIM ADVICE. WELL, I JUST WANTED YOU ALL TO KNOW THAT HE'S FOUND A JOB, A GOOD ONE.

COME AND SIT DOWN, MR BATES. THERE ARE ONE OR TWO THINGS I'D LIKE TO ASK YOU . . .

. . . UNLESS VICKY DOESN'T TELL THEM WHAT I DID TO HER. SHE ONLY NEEDS TO EXPLAIN ABOUT DAVE, SAY I WAS WRONG ABOUT GRAHAM . . . I'M SURE THEY'D FORGIVE ME FOR THAT. IT WOULDN'T TAKE MUCH FOR HER TO HELP ME . . .

B-BUT WHY SHOULD SHE HELP ME . .? AFTER ALL I'VE DONE TO HER, I DON'T DESERVE ANYTHING FROM HER . . . HOW COULD I HAVE TREATED HER THE WAY I DID . . . OH, VICKY, YOU'VE GOT TO FORGIVE ME! I'M SO SORRY, VICKY . . .

OH, NO! THEY'RE BOUND TO FIND OUT THE TRUTH . . . THEY'LL BE FURIOUS WHEN THEY KNOW WHAT I'VE DONE TO VICKY . . .

THE END

IF IT'S SNOWING

WHAT TO WEAR:

Wellies and jeans, a big warm sweater, a scarf and a woolly hat with a bobble on it. Fluffy ear muffs are rather *sweet* so wear a pair if you've got any. If not, you can get the same effect by strapping two of your long-haired guinea-pigs to the sides of your head.

WHAT TO DO:

Enlist the help of a small brother or sister. No brothers or sisters? Then bribe a neighbourhood kid to accompany you.

Choose a nice snowy area and start building a snowman, keeping your eyes peeled for passing dishy males. When you spot one, attract his attention by catching him just below the ear with a well-aimed snowball, then blame it on your small companion.

Explain that small companion is rather fed up as you're not very good at making snowmen.

In no time he'll have forgotten whatever it was he was planning to do, and will be happily piling up snow — while you babble happily into his uninjured ear about how kind he is!

If it's snowing hard, you don't need a small child with you. All you need is a bewildered look.

Approach any likely guy and tell him you've been wandering around in the snow for an hour and you're completely lost and exhausted. Let him lead you home/to a nearby coffee bar/ to the disco and *insist* he stays with you until you've recovered.

If the worst comes to the worst and the other two approaches fail, borrow or steal a sledge and rocket down the side of a hill at any passing boy and flatten him. If you're profuse enough with your apologies and you haven't actually broken any bones, he'll at least agree to give you sledge-driving lessons. If nothing else.

IF IT'S COLD AND ICY

WHAT TO WEAR:

A big fluffy fake fur coat and hat. These will make you look soft and cuddly and remind him of a childhood teddy bear he once loved dearly . . .

WHAT TO DO:

Make a really slippery slide at the end of the road and wait. It may be a little while before a suitably dishy guy comes along but you can pass the time until then by helping up the milkmen, postmen, little old ladies and various other people who will have accidentally tested your slide.

When the right boy does turn up, you'll be expert enough to save him before he does himself a permanent injury. He'll be grateful, of course, and what with the added advantage of reminding him of his much-

HOW TO MAKE HIM WARM TO YOU IN WINTER!

Just because the warm days are over and winter's well and truly here, it doesn't mean you have to hibernate. This is, in fact, one of the best times of the year to meet boys! So stop sitting in front of the fire wishing for summer to come round again — instead, put on your fur-lined underwear, step outside, and grab a guy! Here's how!

loved childhood teddy bear, you should have a friend for life.

If it's really slippery underfoot, a simpler and more effective way to attract his attention would be to cling to a lamppost in the centre of town, looking helpless just as he comes along.

"It's so slippery," you gasp when he pauses to ask why you're holding the lamppost up, "I'm afraid to move." He'll either pass on with a comment like, "Don't worry, the weatherman says there's a thaw on the way," in which case he's not worth bothering with, or he'll offer to hold you up and help you to

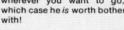

wherever you want to go, in which case he *is* worth bothering with!

IF IT'S SLEETING AND HAILING

WHAT TO WEAR:

Wellies, an ankle-length plastic waterproof coat and a waterproof hat with a big brim. Carry an umbrella.

WHAT TO DO:

Stand around, keeping a beady eye open for a suitable boy. The suitable boy will have a drowned-rat appearance. He will have come out unprepared for the weather and

will be wet through and in the first stages of double pneumonia.

Kindly offer to let him share your umbrella. He'll be touched by your kindness and remember you with gratitude when he's got over his pneumonia. If he gets over his pneumonia.

If it's windy as well as wet, let your umbrella turn inside out and wrestle with it in a hopeless kind of way. The passing boy won't be able to resist proving his superior strength and he'll stop and give you a hand.

By the time you've triumphed over the umbrella, especially if it's blowing a gale, you'll be practically old friends.

Or wander into the disco, dripping water, and shake your coat over the nearest good-looking male. Then look horrified, go red and apologetic.

He'll forgive you — probably — then you can discuss the appalling weather and you can tell him how brave he is to have come out at all. The next thing you'll know is that he'll be buying you Cokes and dancing with you. Boys are easily flattered.

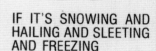

IF IT'S SNOWING AND HAILING AND SLEETING AND FREEZING

WHAT TO WEAR:

Your warmest, fleecy nightie and two dressing-gowns.

WHAT TO DO:

Make a list of all the boys you used to know and still fancy. Then phone them up one at a time and ask them how they're getting on.

With luck, one of them will remember you well enough to want to relight the old flame and you can arrange to meet up as soon as the weather breaks!

So, you see, winter isn't such a bad time after all, is it? By taking advantage of the weather instead of just dreaming about summer, you'll be one step ahead of all the girls who spend their time dreaming about summer instead of taking advantage of the winter weather! By the time they come out of hibernation and start looking around, they're going to find that all the best guys are already hooked. And serve 'em right!

The way to his heart!

"Come round to my place, and we'll have something to eat" — sounds good, doesn't it? But there are distinct disadvantages to making too much of this kind of invitation!

For a start, you don't want to spend hours slaving over a hot oven and find that when everything's ready, you just can't face eating it yourself! Neither do you want to find that, once you'd paid the earth for your elaborate meal, you'll have to starve until pay-day comes round again!

So it's important to choose food that's easy on the budget, fun to cook AND delicious to eat — and that's not as difficult as it sounds, if you try one of our special recipes . . .

THE REAL THING!

MAYBE you're really looking for the works -- sitting down, with knives, forks and soft candlelight, no less! Well, here's a winner — but don't mess things up by trying to go too far and serving anything before the main course or after it, which will only add to the work. This is quite a substantial meal, so if you want a three-course job, all you really need is grapefruit or melon to begin, and cheese and biscuits to end, neither of which take any cooking.

Ingredients:
1 large potato per person
Chicken joint per person
2 oz. butter
lemon juice
1 tablespoonful flour
½ pint milk and water mixed
2 oz. grated cheese
1 large onion, sliced
mushrooms, sliced
salad or peas

First, scrub a large potato each, rub the skin with a little cooking oil, then wrap loosely in aluminium foil and put at the top of a hot oven (400⁰ or gas mark 6).

Next, fry the chicken joints in a pan with 2 oz. butter and a good squeeze of lemon juice. Shake the pan and stir the joints about, turning them until they colour lightly on all sides. Lift the meat out, and put in individual ovenproof dishes. Leave on one side. Add 1 tablespoonful flour to the juices in the pan, and stir until well mixed in. Slowly add the half pint of mixed water and milk, stirring all the

time, until you've got a smooth sauce. Turn the heat even lower, and add the grated cheese. Add a dash of salt and pepper. The mixture, when again smooth, should be like thick custard, not solid and not runny. Add more water if necessary, or cook for a little longer if it needs to be thicker. Scatter the peeled and sliced onion and the sliced mushrooms in the bottom of the dishes, around the meat. The amounts aren't important — use as much as you like. Pour the cheese sauce over, so it covers the meat and the excess runs into the bottom of the dishes. Cover with metal foil.

★ ★ ★ ★ ★ ★ ★ ★ ★ ★ ★ ★ ★ ★

When the potatoes have been cooking for about half an hour, put the covered dishes into the oven under them, and continue cooking for a further hour at the same temperature.

When everything seems ready, put the meat at the top of the oven, and the potatoes below. Remove the foil over the meat dishes, to let the cheese sauce brown. Now's the time to prepare a green salad, or cook some frozen peas, whichever you prefer. When this is done, the meal will be ready to serve!

Before going to the table, you should unwrap the potatoes, make slits in the top and insert a small piece of butter OR a small piece of cream cheese. If you want to be really impressive sprinkle a teaspoonful of chopped green chives or half a teaspoonful of finely chopped raw onion on top of the potatoes. Delicious!

FLIP IT AND FILL IT!

You can't beat pancakes for a meal that's fun to make and good to eat. If you think ahead and get all the separate ingredients prepared in advance, nothing could be easier.

It can be romantic to have a pancake supper for two by candlelight, or you can cater for as many as you like, and have stacks of pancakes and a choice of fillings for a party. You can make all the fillings 24 hours ahead — even the batter.

The basic batter is easy. Just put 4 tablespoonfuls flour into a bowl with a pinch of salt, mix one egg with about half a pint of milk-and-water, and start adding the liquid slowly whisking it up with a fork or an egg beater, rotary whisk or electric beater as you go. You should finish up with a thin, creamy liquid. If you're preparing the batter in advance cover it and put it into a cold place. This makes enough large pancakes to feed two or three people.

Fillings can be sweet or savoury, hot or cold. The hot fillings can be made in advance, and reheated gently.

FILLINGS

Chocolate and nut: Mix 1 tablespoonful cornflour and 2 tablespoonfuls drinking chocolate to a paste with a little cold milk. Heat half a pint of milk, and pour it slowly on to the paste, then pour the hot mixture back into the pan and re-boil, stirring all the time, for one minute. It should be quite thick, but smooth. Pour a dollop inside the cooked pancakes, roll up, and sprinkle nuts on top. Add whipped cream if you're feeling really gluttonous.

Cheese and egg scramble: Beat up an egg with a little milk and a pat of butter, and cook over gentle heat, stirring, until it's just turning into scrambled egg but not completely set, and then remove from heat. Chop up a couple of little cheese triangles, stir into the egg mixture, add salt and pepper and use to fill the pancakes.

Cherry and ice-cream: Have some vanilla ice-cream to hand, and as the pancakes are prepared, put a spoonful of the ice-cream on the centre of each, and pour a little cherry pie filling (from a can) on top — then roll up the pancake quickly and eat right away.

On the night, have everything set out easily to hand. Heat a thick frying pan until hot, drop in a *small* piece of butter or a *little* cooking oil, and when this smokes LIGHTLY, add just enough batter to cover the pan.

If the batter was made the day before, beat it up well before using.

When the first side is set, flip it over or turn with a spatula, and cook the other side.

You can either cook the pancakes one at a time, and get your boyfriend to fill them, or stack them up as you cook them and, once the batter's finished, let everyone help themselves to the fillings, which can be dished up into large bowls for serving. That way you can be sure you'll get to taste your creations, rather than standing in front of the oven all evening!

How's Your Dream Life?

Dreams tell you a lot about what's going on in your mind and are dead give-aways to all your secret hopes and fears! Some dreams are so obvious they don't need any interpretation — say, for example, you dream that you've fallen in love with a gorgeous boy you know . . . well, it's obvious that in real life, you probably fancy him a lot! This is called a Wish Fulfilment dream, for obvious reasons, and you don't need anybody to interpret that for you!

Other dreams aren't so easy to see through, though. Read on and see if any of your dreams are here — and find out what they might be telling you about your life and your love life!

FLYING

SOME people dream that they can fly, zooming and swooping about in the sky!

THE MEANING of this Science-Fiction fantasy come true is that you're a pretty lucky girl. You're free and independent in spirit, and feeling adventurous. Nothing will hold you back. You'll enjoy yourself in life without feelings of guilt or duty to spoil it.

The flying in your dreams represents this lovely, free-flowing energy that you have — so be grateful, and enjoy it!

CLIMBING

YOU could be going up steps, or climbing a mountain, or just going up and up a winding path.

You might dream that you're carrying a heavy bundle with you, and it's definitely hard going — a bit of a struggle. You won't be afraid of **falling** in this dream, so much as afraid that you'll never get to the top . . .

THE MEANING of this dream revolves around **getting to the top.** You're an ambitious soul, and you've set your sights on something big — success in exams, getting a really good job, or maybe attracting a really super boy who's really way out of your class! Whatever it is, you're stubborn and you're not going to be put off! You're obviously finding it a bit of a struggle, though!

FALLING

DREAMING that you're falling or tripping up is very common. For instance, you might dream that you're walking on the edge of a cliff when suddenly your foot goes over the edge.

Or you might be walking about in a building which has rotten floors — gaping and paper thin. You're sure you're going to plunge through and, suddenly, it gives way under you — and you do . . .

Or you might find yourself dreaming about crossing a deep chasm, and the only way to get across is by a rope-bridge. You can see right through it. It's swaying about dangerously, and you can see it's all thin and fraying . . . Help!!

THE MEANING of dreams like these is that you're feeling very insecure about something. It could be that you've got some big challenge ahead – such as

exams, organising something, or sorting out an emotional tangle with your best friend or boyfriend — and you're really scared because you've got no confidence in your own ability to sort it out. You're terrified of failure. You're sure you're going to let yourself down, and so you dream about **falling** . . .

The dream is just bringing the problem to your attention, so try to face up to it as best you can, and solve it!

BEING CHASED

THIS is really more of a nightmare than a dream. Maybe you're all alone in some creepy place — like a deserted street, or a dark, ploughed field, and all you know is that somebody's after you!

You're not too sure who they are, or why they're after you, but you're absolutely desperate to escape. As you try to run away, though, your legs get heavier and heavier, your knees go weak, and you feel as if you're sinking into the ground. Meanwhile, your dreaded pursuer is getting closer and closer.

THE MEANING of this dream can be quite complicated. It might be that you're trying to ignore something which you feel is threatening you in real life.

Or it could be that what's threatening you is actually inside yourself – feelings of some sort that are just too much for you. Maybe you want something too much, and you're afraid to face up to it.

Whatever it is, it's really troubling you – so much so that you feel, in your dreams, that it's actually **chasing** you. Think deeply about your life and your problems. You may be able to identify who or what your mystery pursuer is, and then you can start to work on it!

Most of these dreams are rather anxious ones because they're usually the hardest to understand — it's easy to see the meaning in a nice dream! Let's hope most of your dreams are sweet dreams, though, but if they're not — try to work out what it is they're trying to tell you!

STAR SP★T

How well do *you* know your favourite stars? Try our quiz and find out! You could be in for a few surprises!

Superhunk

This handsome hunk is really a mixture of the eyes, nose and mouth of *three* goodlookers — who are they?

WHO'S MASK-ERADING NOW?

Who are these masked marauders? And which one's the *real* Dick Turpin?

EYE-CATCHING BLONDES!

Whose eyes are these? Clue: They're all blondes!

Penny For The Guy!

What we all wouldn't do to have lots and lots of lovely money . . . or a guy with lots of money to share it with!

But money's supposed to be the root of all evil, and it's true it can do strange things to people — it can certainly bring out the very worst in them! Money also tells us a lot about *boys*, according to their attitude to it . . .

So, depending on how important money is to the boy in *your* life, here's how to make him fall *wildly* in love with you, also how he's likely to treat you once you've captured him, *and* how best to get rid of him — if you need to!

MEAN MIKE

He's the boy who just won't spend money. While other boys have masses of pens and Biros, Mike just has one grubby old pencil, and while other boys are flashing their calculators around, Mike's adding up his sums on his grubby little fingers.

HOW TO DAZZLE HIM

So far, Mike sounds pretty repulsive. But what if he's gorgeous, has a dazzling smile and is great company? You'd want to dazzle him, right?

Well, it's going to cost you, because you'll have to keep reaching down into that purse of yours. Every boy has his price — and once Mike realises what a Generous Girl you are, he's yours!

HOW HE'LL TREAT YOU

A mean person basically can't give — financially or emotionally.

And that means that you mustn't expect too much of Mike. Oh, he can load you with compliments (they cost nothing), but when it comes down to the real nitty-gritty of your relationship, he'll avoid getting serious — and he'll change the subject if anybody mentions love.

HIS ADVANTAGES

Mean Mike won't ever get into trouble with the police, scream at you in a public place, or slip on a banana skin. He's far too cautious to look a fool . . .

HIS DISADVANTAGES

What fun is a guy who won't ever scream at you or slip on a banana skin?

HOW TO DITCH HIM

When you're finally sick of having to pay all the bills and disgusted by his birthday present to his mum (a tiny hankie) just stop paying. And he'll stop playing!

MONEYMAKING MARK

Mark could well end up as a millionaire. He's got that moneymaking bug, you see. He's full of bright ideas, but they're always leading in the same direction — money.

HOW TO DAZZLE HIM

First of all, try to give him the idea that you're rich — or at least, that you've got a millionaire Great-Uncle Fred who lives in Miami.

And throw out the odd remark about "Aunt Emily's Emeralds" and "Cousin Monty's Mercedes." That'll intrigue Mark.

HOW HE'LL TREAT YOU

Mark will see you as a girl of many talents. If you don't exactly look like the back of a bus, he'll be sure you could be a fashion model.

If you occasionally sew a Snoopy badge on to your T-shirt, he'll be sure you could be a great designer. If you can stagger through a couple of reggae tracks at the disco without actually falling on your bum, he'll assure you you should be in Legs & Co. All this worship will be quite nice . . .

HIS ADVANTAGES

He'll make you feel pretty, clever and talented. A real investment . . .

HIS DISADVANTAGES

Millionaires (and boys who are going that way) are usually single-minded – and incredibly boring.

HOW TO DITCH HIM

Tell him you dream about living on potato soup in a primitive village in the Shetlands, and knitting jerseys for a living. And that'll be the last you'll see of him!

SPENDTHRIFT STEVE

Money runs through Steve's fingers like water. He just can't resist temptation — anything with a price tag on it he must have.

HOW TO DAZZLE HIM

The quickest way to get yourself noticed would be to have yourself gift-wrapped with a price tag saying, "Special Offer £4.99." But that might make you feel a bit . . . well, cheap.

Instead, cultivate a bit of variety. That's what Steve really likes. Dress up as a punk one day, then at the weekend, put on your prettiest, daintiest dress. Steve knows a bargain when he sees one — two girls for the price of one!

HOW HE'LL TREAT YOU

Life with Steve will be a lot of fun. He always acts on impulse — there's never a dull moment with him.

One minute you'll be planning to go to the movies on Saturday . . . next thing you know, he's dragging you off to a party he's just heard about.

HIS ADVANTAGES

If you like your life to be a whirl of frenzied activity, Steve's the boy for you. He's always

hurtling off after the latest thing that's caught his eye.

HIS DISADVANTAGES

The latest thing that's caught his eye might be blonde and beautiful . . . yes, he's a bit of a flirt, and among the many new things he can't resist are new girls.

HOW TO DITCH HIM

No problem here. Wear the same old dress every time you see him, chew gum and look vacant. Then he'll ditch you!

GENEROUS GRAHAM

Graham likes spending money, too — but not on himself, like Steve! Oh, no. Graham's generous — and that means he feels he must give people things (whether they want them or not!).

Admire Graham's tie at a party, and he'll whip it off and give it to you. (For goodness' sake, don't admire his trousers!) Say you love the soundtrack of "Superman" and it'll appear on your doorstep, wrapped in pink tissue paper. Say you like pink tissue paper and a huge, gossamer-light parcel will arrive on your doorstep . . .

HOW TO DAZZLE HIM

Graham likes giving because it makes him feel important, powerful and appreciated.

So whatever you do, keep accepting his gifts. Don't get embarrassed and send them back. As you unwrap a pair of hideous purple leg-warmers, cry, "Oh, Graham, you shouldn't have! You're wonderful!"

HOW HE'LL TREAT YOU

Graham likes to dominate. In a way, his constant buying and giving is a way of imposing himself on you.

HIS ADVANTAGES

Are obvious. He likes to give. He'll give you lots and lots of love, but he'll want you all to himself.

HIS DISADVANTAGES

Graham's basically trying to buy you, to make you all his. And just let anyone else try and buy you things! Graham'll punch him in the wallet!

HOW TO DITCH HIM

Send all his gifts back to him gift-wrapped, with a copy of the Beatles' old song, "Can't Buy Me Love." He'll get the message.

COULD YOU LIGHT HIS

1. You're invited to your friend's bonfire party. Would you plan to wear —
- c. a new jumper you've just bought — you want to show it off,
- a. a pair of old jeans, leg-warmers, an extra jumper and a duffle coat,
- b. your usual autumn outdoor gear — you don't really give it much thought,
- d. something really wild — dress up as an old tramp or a Guy Fawkes?

2. When you arrive at the bus stop, you discover you've missed the bus. Do you —
- d. burst into tears and kick the bus stop,
- b. set off to walk, telling yourself you'll soon be there and it's good exercise,
- c. try thumbing a lift, though you're a bit nervous and don't really want to,
- a. phone up your friend and ask if her parents could come and fetch you — after all, you're their guest?

3. When you arrive at the bonfire party, the first thing you notice is —
- c. the dangerous-looking, badly-organised bonfire,
- d. the way everybody seems to be standing about shivering and looking miserable,
- b. the fantastic smell of baking potatoes, hot soup, and frying onions,
- a. a group of people you've always wanted to get to know — and now's your chance?

4. The party seems to be getting off to a pretty soggy start — it's drizzling and cold. Do you —
- b. begin to wonder if you'd be better off at home watching TV,
- a. decide it's up to you, and run around slipping hot spuds down people's backs to get them going,
- c. lose interest in the party, and nip off towards the house — maybe there's a stereo unit and some LPs in there,
- d. sink into a really bad mood, glare at everybody, and swear when a firework singes your eyebrows?

5. Suddenly, a dark handsome boy comes up and says, "Do you want a hot-dog?" You hate hot-dogs but you really like him. Do you —
- d. say, "Ugh! No thanks!" but offer to hand them round,
- b. shake your head but give him a lovely smile, and ask him what else there is,
- c. ask, "Do they bite?", giggle, and run off,
- a. refuse, but decide he's the only decent-looking guy around, and ask your friend who he is?

6. An almighty Russian Thunderer goes off right behind you. Do you —
- c. scream with terror and fling yourself into the arms of the nearest dishy-looking boy,
- a. feel a bit startled, and decide it's time to follow the hot-dog boy into the house,
- b. tell the people who are running the party that you think it's getting a bit dangerous,
- d. feel like exploding yourself?

7. A lot of rockets are soaring into the sky, and the hot-dog boy is standing quite near you. Do you —
- b. ask your friend to introduce you,
- c. grab him by the arm and then say, "Oh, — sorry — I thought you were my brother,"
- a. go up and ask him a few questions about

A Jackie Quiz

40

 **FIRE?**

Do you light up people's lives wherever you go, or do black moods often engulf you and put a damper on everyone's enjoyment?

In short, are you a sparkler, or more like a damp squib?

Try answering our special fireworks quiz to find out the secrets of your personality, and how you get on with boys . . .

rockets, hot-dogs, anything you think he'll know about,

d. creep up beside him and ask him what he's doing next weekend, 'cos you've heard there's this great disco happening?

8. The hot-dog boy (who's called Tony) seems to be pretty popular. A girl comes up, gives him a sparkler and tries to wriggle in between you and him. Do you —

c. decide you're wasting your time and flit off to try your luck elsewhere,

d. give her a few smouldering looks and if she doesn't get the message, spill hot soup down her anorak,

b. give up trying to chat him up and start a conversation with your friend instead,

a. stay around and eavesdrop, to try to figure out just how well she knows him and what chance you've got?

9. Suddenly, the bonfire flares up, and the Guy (the real Guy, not Tony!) goes up in a sheet of flame. His hat explodes and his hair shrivels up. Do you —

b. think how sad it is, really — and feel a bit sorry for the poor old Guy,

d. feel quite excited — the more lifelike the Guy is, the more thrilling it is,

a. have a good laugh — he looks really funny with his hat over one eye,

c. feel quite upset — the way he twisted up and writhed about was really horribly life-like?

10. Finally, towards the end of the party, you really get talking to the dishy Tony, and find you have a lot in common. But he still hasn't asked when he can see you again. Do you —

d. gaze deeply into his eyes and whisper, "This has been a fantastic evening, don't you think?"

b. decide that this is one time you can't hope for more, and say goodbye gracefully,

c. get nervous and flirt with him like mad, hoping he'll ask you out,

a. mention casually that you'll be having a party soon, and ask him for his address so you can invite him?

11. The last sparkler's sparked, the bonfire's dying down, and you stare at the scene before you go. You'll never forget —

b. what a great time you had — despite the awful weather. Food, fireworks, fellas — it was perfect,

c. how terrified you were when the banger exploded just behind you,

d. how sexy the hot-dog boy was — and how furious you were when that other girl tried to pinch him,

a. it was the night you met Tony — and you've got *plans* for him — even if he doesn't know it!?

12. You get home much later than you'd promised, and Mum yells at you. Do you —

a. just relax and let her shout — she'll soon get over it,

b. feel guilty, apologise, and try to think of ways of making it up to her,

c. get really rattled, and have a row with her,

d. say nothing, but sulk about it all the next day?

13. As you drift off to sleep, you dream about —

d. the row with Mum — you're still seething,

c. the beautiful shapes of the shining, shimmering fireworks,

b. flickering fires and someone's arms around you,

a. meeting Tony again, and how you're going to sweep him off his feet?

If your answers were mostly a:

You're a rocket! You just trust to chance when it comes to the future — you always plan ahead, and because of this, you're very much in control of your life. When unexpected things happen it can throw you, but you soon bounce back and re-adjust to new situations.

You're pretty ambitious, too, and when you've set your heart on something, you won't be budged — whether it's an exam result, a career, or a boy you've set your sights on. And when it comes to boys, you attract them because of your energy and your common sense.

You share ups and downs like anybody else, but you're usually confident and optimistic, and you can take disappointments well.

If your answers were mostly b:

You're a sparkler! In other words, lively, charming and attractive, but not terribly ambitious. You enjoy the domestic side of life and you're very fond of people — especially the very old and the very young. You have a protective instinct towards them.

In fact, you're a pretty positive character through and through — popular with boys and girls alike, and often relied upon to help other people sort out their lives and problems!

You're very rarely bad-tempered, and you hate rows. You're capable of taking an easy-going view of things. So things don't go your way, you can be quite obstinate, but basically you're cool and calm, and you're usually confident and optimistic, and you can

If your answers were mostly c:

You're a Jumping Jack! Totally unpredictable, you shoot from one mood to another. You're a fairly nervous character, and you react strongly to whatever happens. You're very lively, though, and enjoy people's company — and they enjoy yours! But they sometimes feel a bit uncertain with you.

You're quite a flirt where boys are concerned — sometimes you can do and say quite mad things you don't really mean. When you're in the mood, you can attract boys with your sheer vitality — other girls probably envy you for your quick wits.

Although you tend to be nervous, you've got quite an adventurous attitude to life. You can be quite daring, and that often gets you into trouble. But you're always likely to do something that'll give you a laugh —

If your answers were mostly d:

You're a squib! Squibs smoulder quietly for a while and then — POW! They explode. And that's the way you react to things. You're a girl of extremes — either up in the air or down in the dumps. And when you're down, you're really down. You're capable of sulking for hours if something really upsets you.

You're capable of really turning on the charm when boys are around, but although boys are instantly attracted to you, they often find you hard to get on with because you're so unpredictable and moody. So you probably find you have no trouble in attracting boys, but have quite a lot of trouble keeping them!

You can be quite aggressive when you want to be and you're not afraid of having a blazing row once in a while if necessary. People probably think twice before inviting you along to their parties, in case you have a bad day and pick a fight with somebody!

However, when you're in a good mood, you can be really great. You've got a creative, imaginative attitude to life and you really know how to enjoy yourself. In fact, you can create real fun like no-one else. The problem for other people is trying to keep pace with your moods!

Your modest ways and good humour make boys feel protective towards you. You like them to do the running — you just don't feel right making the first move. In fact, you're quite shy — a real old-fashioned girl too, and people really appreciate it. If a problem arises, your reaction is to do the reasonable, commonsense thing, and not to fly into a panic or lose your head. All this means you're very sweet and affectionate nature. You're not at all proud or sulky, in fact, you're quite shy — a real old-fashioned girl too — you just don't feel right making the first move.

You strongly dislike rows and would do almost anything to avoid them and keep the atmosphere pleasant. You're not at all proud or sulky, in fact, you're quite shy — a real old-fashioned girl too, and people really appreciate it.

You've got a very sweet and affectionate nature.

Sometimes you find it hard to concentrate on things however crazy. With you, life is never dull! Sometimes you find it hard to concentrate on things and get bored for a long time. You soon lose interest and get bored easily. Basically, you're a bit lacking in self-discipline, and can let people — and yourself — down.

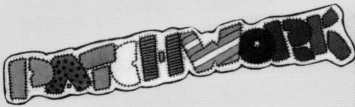

Have you ever felt you'd like to give someone a little present just to say, "Thank you" or "You're nice" or even, "I'm sorry"? The trouble is, it always seems to be just those times when you're stony broke and next pay day seems like a million years away!

So why not make your own presents? It's true that a hand-knitted egg cosy or a home-made bookmark aren't exactly the stuff dreams are made of, but there are things you can make that are original and attractive — and what's more, you don't have to be an artistic genius to make them! So read on and have a go — you might surprise yourself!

HANG IT!

A PENDANT is dead easy to make, and doesn't look any different from a bought one, as long as you don't finish it off with an ugly, lumpy knot! There's a neat trick to avoid this, which is easily done.

First, though, assemble your bits and pieces! The actual pendant motif could be an unusual button (keep an eye on market stalls, junk shops and jumble sales for those), a large bead, an initial traced from a capital letter in a newspaper or magazine, and cut in leather or suede, a small bell, or an interesting shape twisted in wire, or cut out of plastic or card and covered with self-adhesive plastic or glued-on fabric.

If you aren't good at thinking up shapes, look at things like the patterns on a blouse or wallpaper. Pick out a simple shape and keep it roughly oblong, oval or triangular, in other words, something which is longer than its own width, then it'll hang nicely.

Next you need to choose what the motif is to hang on. Use odd lengths of narrow chain, from an old belt or broken pendant, or narrow thongs cut from leather. Or you could use narrow ribbon, gold or silver-covered string, wool or embroidery silk in a suitable colour, plaited or twisted to the right thickness for the pendant. This is important — if your pendant motif is small, the chain must be light-weight, and if the pendant is heavy, the chain must be thick.

Now to make the pendant look professional! Thread the cord or chain through the motif, and make a tight, small knot that lies flat (a reef knot, as illustrated, is best). Snip off the loose ends, fairly close to the knot, and dab a little glue on the knot itself.

If the pendant is a bead, or something similar, force the knot into the bead, using a knitting needle or a skewer, and then the glue will hold it there, unseen. If the pendant motif is a flat object, like an initial, cut a small circle of paper, fabric or self-adhesive plastic, (glue it unless already self-adhesive), pull the knot into position and press the circle over it, hiding the knot completely. And that's all!

If you're making a pendant from a large bead, or several beads, and want to have your string or chain with the bead suspended from it, rather than running through it, here's how. Take the chain or string through the large bead, and then make a knot, and thread the chain back through the bead, so that the knot wedges just inside the bead.

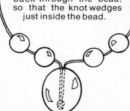

If your chosen chain is too large to go through the bead, tie a thread round a small bead and pull it through the large bead, so that the small bead jams at the bottom of the large one. Tie the thread to the chain and pull it through the large bead again, pulling the chain slightly into the hole at the top of the large bead. Knot firmly, and cut off the end.

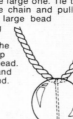

IT'S A MUG'S GAME

TRY handpainting mugs. Buy some plain ones, and make your own decorations. You can buy suitable paints in craft shops, and you can also get transfers suitable for use on china and glass.

If you don't want to buy special paints, you can use nail varnish, though it tends to wash off after a time. Still, it's easy enough to do again!

BITS AND PIECES

KEEP your eyes open for really nice pictures on old Christmas and birthday cards, from magazines, calendars, and so on. Cut them out carefully, and ink in the cut edge with a red, purple or black felt-tip pen. Cut a small square of foam rubber or card, about 1 cm thick, and glue to the centre back.

Cut out a piece of cardboard a good bit larger than the picture, and cover it with hessian, lining silk, self-adhesive plastic in a plain colour, or with glued-on wallpaper in a plain design, and then glue the small square of foam rubber or card exactly in the centre.

Add a loop for hanging, and you've completed the picture!

GET SHIRTY!

BUY some plain T-shirts and decorate them, the next time you're racking your brains for a special gift for a friend who's got everything (we can all do with just one more T-shirt!).

You can use paint-on fabric dyes, from Dylon stockists (full instructions come with the dye).

You can also buy a special transfer pencil from good haberdashery counters. Draw your design on greaseproof paper — it's very easy to trace the design with the pencil — from anything you like. Now pin the greaseproof paper in position on a T-shirt, or pillowcase, or anything else you want to decorate. Iron over — and the design is transferred!

You can embroider over the design or sew on small beads in lines or blocks, or colour with fabric to make it more lasting.

Another good gift idea is a Krazy Karpet. You can often buy very small squares of carpet cheaply – from carpet shops' sample books, or on sale in carpet shops as off-cuts and on market stalls.

Cut the pieces into fun shapes, to make unusual bed-side rugs. How about a pair of giant feet – one on each side of the bed? Or a mouse, with a string tail?

COVERED IN BEADS!

USE lots of tiny beads to brighten up plain clothes or bags. You simply sew the beads into a pretty pattern on a pocket, cushion, skirt or a velvet bag.

It's easy, once you know how to sew on the beads so they don't shift about afterwards. Use a back stitch — bring your threaded needle up through the material, place the bead on top of the material, to the LEFT of the needlepoint, take the needle through it and down through the material. Take a long stitch to the RIGHT, on the underside, place the next bead to the left of the needlepoint and so on.

There's also a quick way to sew on beads if you want to work in straight lines. Thread them all on to a thread that fits the holes in the beads fairly tightly, and arrange this thread on the surface, as you want it.

Now thread the needle with a much finer matching cotton, bring the needle up from underneath the material, and just catch down the thick thread between the beads with a small stitch every four or five beads. Make sure the thread is fastened off underneath the material.

You can also glue beads on things like glass, china, leather, plastic, etc., for a decorative effect — use a glue suitable for the material. Pretty up an old plain plate either by sticking on beads in your own design, or use the design on the plate already, and fill in areas with tiny coloured glass or metallic beads.

A Time For Love!

What was it like to be a girl in the past? Was it really as romantic and glamorous as it seems? Or was it a very uneasy time, threatened by illness, wars and cruelty? We've had a look back through time to see just how different life would have been if you'd been growing up then. So read on — and find out if *you* could have survived in the past!

Roman

IF you were a Roman girl, you'd wear cool, comfortable dresses, enjoy heated rooms and hot baths and probably be a lot cleaner than any girls for the next 1900 years!

You'd certainly be courted. Ovid, the Roman poet, wrote a book called "The Art of Love" telling all would-be lovers how to set about it! One of his recommendations was that you should write messages to your lover on your maid's back in milk. Then he would rub her back with coal which would make the words visible. You'd have had to watch out, though, that your maid wasn't prettier than you!

Medieval

THIS was the age of courtly love. While the husbands and fathers were away at the Crusades, the women made full use of this chance to enjoy themselves. With your hair hanging in plaits or ringlets to your waist, and dressed in a close-fitting dress with fur-trimmed cuffs, you'd enchant every young man within miles.

This was the age of real Romantic love. Your lover would write poems to you, and sing sad songs beneath your window. It was almost your duty to be cruel to him — for a while, at least!

Part of the reason for all this intense passion may have been that life was very uncertain. The plague was everywhere, and once it got into your town, you wouldn't last more than a day or two. So perhaps it was a case of making the most of things while you could . . .

Puritans

OLIVER CROMWELL soon changed all this. If you'd been a Puritan girl your hair would have been pulled back out of sight under a modest cap, you'd wear a thick black dress up to your chin and as for make-up, well, any girl daring even to think of it, was sure to go *straight to the fires of hell*! (In fact, doing just about anything seemed to guarantee you a place there, in Cromwell's time!)

Any kind of contact with boys was a sin. Punishments for "wicked behaviour" included head shaving, being ducked, and being put in the pillory or stocks for people to pelt you with rotten eggs. Merely talking to a boy

was enough to get you into serious trouble. Better to sit at home reading the Bible, and let your parents arrange a marriage for you with some religious man who was probably forty years your senior, and who wouldn't have any ideas of fun even if it had been allowed, anyway!

Regency Times

IN the early nineteenth century, life was delicious. You could have your hair cropped, curled or wear it long. Your dresses were of featherlight muslin — so fine that they could be passed through a ring.

Courtship was open and daring. The Waltz — the new dance which was all the rage — enabled you to drift around the ballroom in a close embrace. The wildest place in Britain was Brighton, where the Prince Regent led a life of wine, women and song. It probably wasn't a good idea to pursue the Prince, though; he was vastly overweight, and *very* sweaty.

Victorian

AS usual in history, people soon reacted against a period of wild fun. If you'd been alive in Victorian times, you'd have been corseted more tightly than ever — women often fainted from tight-corseting and sometimes even had deformed ribs!

You'd have to stay at home all day — surrounded by potted plants and furniture that had skirts on to hide the legs! You'd only be allowed out with a chaperone: usually a crotchety middle-aged spinster with eyes like an eagle.

Marriages were usually arranged by families, and even if you happened to *like* your fiancé, your behaviour with him even when you were engaged would have to be absolutely perfect. "Courtship in public is selfish, vulgar, indelicate and offensive" — or so they believed. So your idea of fun was likely to be a quick giggle with your sisters over your embroidery. A pretty limited life!

Well, that's the way it was. Do you wish you'd been there? Or does it make you realise just how lucky you are to live in our pulsating, punky, plastic, dare we say, perfect age?

A Happy New

January

BE AN ICE MAIDEN

It's the month of frosts and glittering snows . . . So why not be an Ice Maiden, someone who's pale and interesting, with a not-quite-real, fantasy atmosphere about her? With just a *touch* of frost, of course!

LOOKS: Hair. If you've got long hair, wear it pulled over to one side. If your hair's short, give it a blonde rinse (the sort that lasts for 3 to 4 shampoos). For evenings, sprinkle a little glitter dust over it.

Clothes. Stick to ice-cool colours — blues and whites. If you've got any satin clothes, or glittery tops, wear them. Silvery accessories look really good with this look.

THE WAY YOU ACT. Try to be a bit more mysterious than usual. Talk less, and listen more. Watch people and study their reactions. Don't get too carried away by your emotions. Read a lot more than usual, and try to find out as much as you can about subjects you're interested in. That way, you'll not only look interesting, you'll sound interesting too! Make a point of listening to all-sorts of music as well — not just the sort you know you like. Don't let people upset you and *don't* get angry — remember, you're staying SUPER COOL!

February

BE A VALENTINE

Try for an early thaw by becoming every boy's ideal Valentine for this special month of love — sweet, gentle, and tender-hearted. Be a bit of a romantic, and terribly feminine . . .

LOOKS: Hair. Something soft and feminine will do the trick. If your hair's naturally curly, great! If you've been wondering about a light perm, go ahead! And if your hair's dead straight and staying that way, soften it up by wearing a flower attached with a hairslide just behind the ear, or even a pretty clasp.

Clothes. Wear something pretty and flowery — maybe a Laura Ashley dress or blouse. Choose warm, delicate colours — pink, rust, brown, warm greys.

THE WAY YOU ACT. After the January freeze-up, let your emotions thaw! Watch sad movies and have a good weep. And laugh till you cry if you really feel like it. Get a hyacinth in a bowl and put it by your bed, so every night as you doze off to sleep, the sweet smell of spring will creep over you. Tell your family how much you love them. And if you're too shy to tell them — *show them,* by running errands for them . . .

March

BE A MAD MARCH HARE

March is the traditional month for going mad — and why not, once in a while? Live it up, really have yourself a ball and be outrageous!

LOOKS: Hair. If you're brave enough, have something really wild done — a wild gipsy perm, or a really short cut. If you've always hankered after a pink streak, now's the time! But if you don't fancy that, go for hats — knitted hats, tweed hats, Mum's old hats from the Sixties, bowlers, berets. Try a different one every time you go out.

Clothes. Well, it's your mad month, so anything goes! Try out male gear — ex-Army combat jackets, boiler suits, basketball boots. Or go off wildly in the other direction and try out fishnet tights, stilettos and satin skirts. Root around Army & Navy Stores, and market stalls for medals, badges, interesting beads and belts, and make your own accessories!

THE WAY YOU ACT. For once, don't worry what people think, just do what *you* want to do! (Unless it's downright dangerous, of course!) So go for a run in the park, play on the kids' swings, have a bonfire, write a fan letter to Prince Andrew, hold a jumble sale — and liven up the neighbourhood in any way you like!

44

You!

— A NEW YEAR'S CALENDAR OF COOL NEW LOOKS — JUST FOR YOU!

It's fun trying out new ways of looking and acting. So why don't *you* ring the changes throughout the coming year, and have a New Look and a New Style for every month of the year? Here's how!

May

BE QUEEN OF THE MAY

Traditionally, the May Queen is crowned with flowers and led in triumph through the streets. She's definitely the First Lady for a day, and you can certainly take a few tips from her!

LOOKS: Hair. May stunners should make the most of their hair. Try rolling it on big rollers if it's long, and see what a headful of tousled curls does for you. If it's short, try the effect of a daisy chain round it, or a twisted silk scarf, or thongs and beads.

Clothes. Got any really *nice* dresses? If not, now's the time to look out for a few. The second-hand market stalls usually have some. Romantic ones are nice for summer, and always look good.

THE WAY YOU ACT. Forget your usual shy self and be really outgoing. And that means smiling at people as often as you can. They'll smile back, and it feels great to spread a little happiness. And ask that boy you fancy to come out with you. He may be dying to get to know you better but be too shy to ask. Give a party. Tell people what *your* ideas are, for a change. Make them sit up and take notice!

April

BE A COUNTRY GIRL

With spring beginning to — er — spring in every hedgerow, why don't you turn yourself into a true nature-lover, and be a real country girl?

LOOKS: Hair. It should be casual, natural, and gleaming with health, of course. Treat it to lots of lovely herbal shampoos, such as Wella's, or Boots *Original Formula* range. And try the super range of shampoos by Leryss.

Clothes. You'll go for lovely, practical, warm country clothes. Casual, brown and green jumpers and tops, tartan shirts worn with waistcoats, and good, warm boots — the sort you can walk in for miles, which won't let the mud in. (Hush Puppies are best, and Kickers look really smart.) Stick to natural fabrics: things like wool, cotton, corduroy.

THE WAY YOU ACT. Really look at the natural world all around you for once — the trees, the rivers, the grass, and all the newly-growing plants. Get out into the country if you can, and watch the fields being sown and the birds building their nests. And then look up into the sky and find time to wonder at what's behind it all . . .

June

BE ON FIRE FOR FLAMING JUNE

Flaming June it's supposed to be — but so often it's soggy and disappointing instead. So why not become flaming June yourself — a fiery girl who'll send everyone's temperature soaring, even if Wimbledon's rained off!

LOOKS: Hair. If you've never tried henna, now's the time to try it out! If you're a blonde, though, don't go for the red henna unless you want to end up with bright orange hair, 'cos that's how it'll turn out! But Henna Hair Health Ltd. make a Golden Henna now, specially for blondes, which gives shine and condition.

Clothes. Cut a dash. Choose strong, bright, dramatic colours. Go for something really sharp, a white suit, maybe. Or if it's really hot, a billowing red or white chiffon dress.

THE WAY YOU ACT. Now's your chance to really come on strong, to get ahead, to be always on the move. Make a point of exploring new places, going out as much as possible, planning a foreign holiday, maybe. And try to get to know a lot of new people, by going to lots of summer events, fairs, jumble sales, cricket matches, sports events . . . there's lots going on!

45

A Happy New

July

BE A BIKE GIRL

July's the month of the open road, the start of the holiday, and get-up-and-go. So get your own looks together around the idea of the road, and bikes!

LOOKS: Hair. You don't want to do anything too elaborate with your hair. Shove it away under a cap or scarf. Short hair is really best for this look. If yours is long, make bunches or tie it back.

Clothes. Shorts are a must, for this look! Look out for vests, plain white T-shirts, towelling tops and sandals, too.

THE WAY YOU ACT. Put aside your ultra-feminine feelings and go in for a bit of adventure. Try out things you've never done before. Also, get fit by jogging or weight-training. Working out at the gym can be fun — think of all those glistening musclemen!

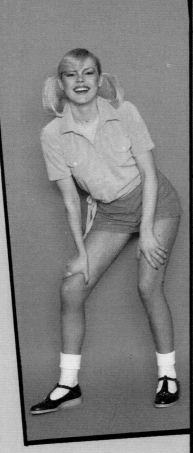

August

BE A BEACH BELLE

Even if you're not going anywhere near the sea, now's the time you should be cultivating that sun-kissed Californian beach-girl look . . .

LOOKS: Hair. If yours could possibly be called fair, try and bleach it in the sun. If the sun won't come out, go to the hairdresser and get a few streaks put in. It'll make you look really good. If you're dark, make your hair gleam with lots of conditioner and the occasional application of henna.

Clothes. When you can't actually wear your bikini, go for really cool, casual looks. Look for off-the-shoulder T-shirts in pale, sun-bleached pastel colours, shorts, sandals and skirts which show off your bronzed, beautiful legs!

THE WAY YOU ACT. You're a Beach Belle now, and your job is to relax to the very depths of your being. If you haven't tried yoga, make a start on it now! As you lie back and soak up the sun, too, let your mind swim idly around all sorts of subjects . . .

September

BE A SUNBURNED GIPSY

The month of fairs, and the end of summer. Say goodbye to the sun in style and be a gipsy — even if you're not travelling anywhere!

LOOKS: Hair. If you're blonde, cover it up with headscarves! If you're dark — great! Dark curls clustering around the face are really flattering.

Clothes. Colours should be bright, and patterned. Shawls go well with this look, so do headscarves and big, chunky earrings. Try boots if the weather's cold — if not, it must be bare legs and flat sandals!

THE WAY YOU ACT. The gipsy life is very simple, and close to Nature. Try and live simply. Really learn to appreciate the basic pleasures of life — being warm, the smell of cooking, good company . . . And have a look at that other gipsy thing — the supernatural . . .

46

You!

November

BE A SPARKLER

This is the month of Guy Fawkes and Bonfire parties. So make sure you're a real fire-cracker — bringing dazzle and sparkle everywhere you go.

LOOKS: Hair. Make sure it's in tip-top condition and try out lots of new looks — hairslides, hair ribbons, little hats. If it's long enough, try lots and lots of fine plaits. Or get some little beads and thread them into your hair (specially nice if your hair's crinkly).

Clothes. Go for a cuddly-but-dazzling look. Lacy jumpers, gloves, jeans worn inside boots. Ankle boots go well with this look.

THE WAY YOU ACT. You're a fire-cracker, right? So you've got to be very *sparky!* Keep smiling. Laugh at people's jokes — even if they're a bit weak — and whatever anybody suggests, react *positively.* Keep your energy level high with lots of exercise. Spring a few surprises on your friends and family — pleasant surprises, that is!

October

BE A FORTIES FLIRT

By October, the best of summer's gone and we're all back at work. A time for looking back, a mysterious month of shadows. Take your own look back, too . . .

LOOKS: Hair. Basically, try out hairstyles from the past. If your hair's very long, try putting it up. Or try a Fifties pony-tail. If your hair's short, get that Twenties look with a really close, boyish crop. If it's mid-length, try some of those Thirties and Forties looks — with little rolls and quiffs.

Clothes. Go round all the second-hand clothes stalls, jumble sales, and Oxfam shops. They really are a gold mine! You can find wonderful clothes at very cheap prices there. Beautiful crepe dresses for 60p or £1 . . . amazing hats with birds and feathers on . . . old fur coats for £8 . . . Go along and see what you can find!

THE WAY YOU ACT. This month's all about the past, so why not read a historical novel and be a bit more aware of history all around you? And think about your own history. Ask Mum and Dad to tell you what life was like when they were young. And go browsing through the photograph albums!

December

BE A CHRISTMAS CRACKER

This is a magical time of year, with parties, presents, and a very special atmosphere. It's time to try out a new, sparkly, crackly look . . .

LOOKS: Hair. If your hair's long enough to put up, try it, and show off the shape of your neck and ears. Maybe even put some silver or gold sparkle in it for special parties (but first make sure it's a spray for *hair!*).

Clothes. Try to find something really out of this world. An old silk dressing-gown. maybe. or a satin dress or an old lacy blouse. Any of these, worn with silvery sandals, would be stunning.

THE WAY YOU ACT. If you want to be a Christmas Cracker, you'll have to sparkle! So try to liven things up wherever you are! Sing in the bath, be nice to everyone, organise parties and carol singing and generally be sweetness and light to everyone. And don't worry too much about all this niceness — when it's time for a Christmas party you can get up to a little naughtiness — just to liven things up!

Everybody talks about it, everybody sings about it and most of us think about it . . .
What is it? Love, of course! But what exactly *is* this thing called love? There are lots of experiences that feel a bit like love, and lots of different *kinds* of love, so it's all pretty confusing and not at all straightforward . . .
Here, we talk to some girls who've all had different experiences of love. Hopefully, their stories will help you decide what it is *you're* feeling — and what it'll be like once you do fall in love!

This Thing Called Love...

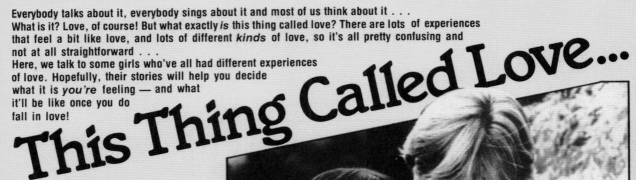

UNREQUITED LOVE

. . . IS when you care very deeply for someone who doesn't care at all about you. It's a very painful experience. Carole, who's 16 now, knows all about the hurt of unrequited love . . .

"I was about thirteen when I met Mark. He was in the Sixth Form at school — a lot older than me and he seemed very grown-up. He wasn't at all like the boys in my class, who were pretty awful. I got to know him through being in one of our school plays.

"I always made sure I was sitting in a group around him, so I could be near him. I remember the time I realised I was falling for him — it was during one of the rehearsals. Mark had arrived late — and suddenly, I went weak at the knees when I saw him. He never ever noticed me, of course, but I couldn't take my eyes off him . . .

"We got to know each other quite well during the play, and he said some nice things to me. Then there were the Christmas holidays."

'HE NEVER NOTICED ME — BUT I COULDN'T TAKE MY EYES OFF HIM . . .

"When I went back to school, I had to face the fact that I'd hardly ever see him — the play was finished and his Sixth Form had their own block and everything.

"He always smiled and said hello, and that kept my hopes alive. But then he started going out with a girl in the Sixth Form. It felt like the end of the world. I was so miserable.

"I've got over him now, of course, but I don't think I'll ever forget him, or ever feel as deeply about anything or anyone as I did for Mark . . ."

Carole's experience is very normal. It's natural when you're 12 or 13 to fall for much older boys — simply because boys your own age are still so much more immature than you are.

If you find yourself feeling this way about a boy, content yourself with harmless daydreaming about him, but just don't kid yourself that anything will ever come of it — though it might, of course, but it's unlikely to happen for a while, until you're much older, anyway . . .

PHYSICAL LOVE

WHEN you're young, it's pretty hard to make sense of all the different feelings you have about boys. Di, who's 14 and recently finished with her boyfriend, Ricky, explains the physical kind of love she experienced.

"Right from the start, it was the way Ricky looked that attracted me. He was gorgeous.

"When he came up at a disco and asked me to dance, I felt great! And when he asked me out, I felt on top of the world. I was so happy. I used to love just looking at him, his

eyes especially.

"After a while, though, I began to notice something. Whenever we were together, I'd listen to what he'd be saying without actually listening, if you know what I mean. I didn't concentrate on what he was saying, I was just looking at him.

'I USED TO LOVE JUST LOOKING AT HIM . . .'

"Once I'd realised that, it made it pretty hard to carry on. I still fancied him like mad, the way he moved and looked, but it just isn't enough, is it? In the end I chucked him, I still fancied *him* — but not his mind, if you see what I mean!"

Just fancying someone — being fascinated by their looks and wanting to touch them — is great in itself.

But there's got to be a lot more to a relationship for it really to take off. For a start, there's got to be a lot of interests to share, and a real ability to communicate and stay interested in each other — absolutely vital if you're going to build a relationship that really lasts.

PLATONIC LOVE

. . . IS when you love a boy the way you love a brother. It's what you feel for a guy you're fond of, but whom you don't really fancy. Some girls find they feel this way about their boyfriends — especially towards the end of a relationship — but it's more usual to feel this way about guys who are just friends. Listen to Janice who's 16 . . .

"I was 14 when I got to know Terry. We were both pretty serious people and we used to spend hours and hours sitting talking about anything and everything under the sun.

"I did love him, but in a very straightforward kind of way, like a brother, only without all the irritation you sometimes feel for your brother. Once I'd realised that Terry fancied me though, I began to get really nervous.

"One day, the inevitable happened — he started to tell me how he'd really fallen for me and how he'd like us to start going out properly. I didn't know what to say, so I kind of went along with him.

"The trouble was, it never felt right. I did love him in a way, but not the way he wanted. I wanted to talk to him and be

'I DID LOVE HIM IN A WAY — BUT NOT THE WAY HE WANTED'

with him but that was all. And when I was pretending it was more than that, it all seemed horrible — the really nice, affectionate way I felt about him kind of sank under a feeling that it was all wrong.

"So I told him. It was awkward for a while but we managed to get back to our old relationship. In the end, too, it was better than ever, simply because we'd got the physical thing out of the way."

Janice and Terry were lucky that their relationship was strong enough to withstand that sort of strain.

But then, Platonic love really is strong. It's sexual feelings that usually cause trouble in a relationship.

You can discuss things without feeling the strain you might with a boy you were physically involved with. You can ask his advice about how boys feel and about their problems, and tell him about girls, without feeling embarrassed. In fact, it's a lovely feeling! So if you've got any boy friends (as opposed to boyfriends!), look after them!

IS IT THE REAL THING?

WELL, maybe there isn't such a thing as "THE REAL THING." There are lots of different ways of feeling real love, and a lot of people go around really worried because they think they haven't felt "it." What Penny felt, though, is obviously the "Real Thing," despite the times she had a lot of doubt and anxiety . . .

"I met Martin when we were both on a course at a big house in the country. It was a really romantic place to meet: trees, a lake . . . fantastic! I noticed Martin straightaway and he noticed me, too. By the first coffee break we were chatting away to each other.

'I WAS SCARED IT WOULDN'T LAST'

"We seemed to like so many of the same things, it was . . . well, weird! I seemed to know exactly what he was thinking.

"When the course finished, we had to part. But we only live ten miles away from each other, so we still meet a lot. I was scared stiff that it wouldn't last, but it has. We see each other at weekends — and from time to time in the week, if there's a chance. It's eighteen months now since we met.

"When I'm going to see him I feel really excited. When he looks into my eyes I feel myself sort of melting inside. And I sometimes feel agonies of jealousy if I think he might be falling for another girl. He hasn't yet, thank goodness!"

Penny and Martin are obviously in love — they've got a lot of common interests, a similar outlook on things and an almost telepathic ability to read each other's thoughts! The fact that Penny still feels excited when she's going to see him shows their love is still fresh, though it's perfectly possible to enjoy a gentler kind of being truly in love, where you don't feel your heart turning somersaults as soon as you see him! That exciting stage is usually only at the beginning of a relationship, anyhow.

It must be clear from all these girls' experiences that there's a huge range of feelings possible in your relationships with boys. The great thing is to be able to recognise what you're feeling and not mistake it for something else.

The sort of love that's going to last must include physical attraction, similar interests, and the ability to talk honestly together. But if what you're sharing with a boy doesn't quite come up to those high standards, don't worry – enjoy it anyway!

Are You Charming Enough?

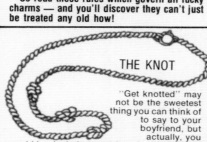

Are you a little bit short of luck at the moment? Maybe you need some help with your love life? — or a bit of protection from the "Dark Forces"? Well, here's how to charm your way to success!

From the very beginning of civilisation — even before people got round to wearing clothes! — people have been wearing lucky charms.

Nowadays, though, we tend to take lucky charms for granted without realising their true significance and their strong astrological connections.

Unlike lucky stones, charms can be very ordinary, commonplace objects, and the same shapes and symbols appear again and again throughout history as bringers of luck, with magical properties.

So read these rules which govern all lucky charms — and you'll discover they can't just be treated any old how!

★ No charm which has been obtained unjustly can be a bringer of good fortune.
★ No charm will bring good fortune to one who is unworthy of it.
★ No charm must be allowed to touch the ground. If it falls accidentally its luck will be lost, for a time at least.
★ Charms are more powerful when worn on the left side of the body, rather than the right.

Got that? Good. Now all you have to do is to find out what objects are most likely to be lucky for **you** — it all depends on your astrology sign, and what area of your life you need some help with!

THE KNOT

"Get knotted" may not be the sweetest thing you can think of to say to your boyfriend, but actually, you could be declaring your love for him! A knot stands for the joining of things, and is particularly useful for a girl who wants to draw a certain boy to her. Everyone has heard of the "true lover's knot" and a particularly effective charm is to get hold of a tie he has worn and tie three knots in it, while saying: "Three times a true-love's knot I tie secure, Firm be the knot, firm may his love endure." Usually, the knot should be made of silver and it particularly favours those born under *Gemini* and *Pisces*.

THE PADLOCK

It might seem strange as a lucky charm, because to some people it suggests locking up, or loss of liberty. But, in fact, when it comes to love and romance a padlock is very lucky. Especially when used to fasten a bracelet or bangle, it is a securer of affection, the lock that holds romance safe and also brings long life and happiness. It's especially fortunate for *Taurean* girls.

THE FOUR-LEAVED CLOVER

This charm is of Irish origin and is still commonly held throughout Ireland to have luck-bringing powers. Each leaf has a separate meaning.

The first leaf on the left of the stalk helps to bring fame; the second moving clockwise assists in the obtaining of wealth (i.e., it helps you get rich!), the third to the right brings a faithful boyfriend and the fourth, on the right of the stalk, brings good health.

This charm is particularly associated with the signs *Cancer* and *Pisces*.

THE HEART

The heart as a mascot stems from Ancient Egypt where they believed that people's hearts were weighed before they were accepted into heaven! Now, of course, it's a symbol of true love and affection, and is especially fortunate for *Leo* and *Libra* people.

THE FROG

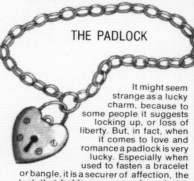

You may think these are pretty ugly-looking creatures, but right back through the ages they turn up in myths and fairytales, magic spells and brews — remember the one that turned out to be a prince? Frogs are small but powerful! Small frogs in gold or gilt metal are amulets against illness, or may be worn to speed recovery from disease or injury. And to kill or hurt a frog in any way is supposed to bring illness and ill-fortune.

THE KEY

In ancient Greece and Rome the single key was the most important of all mascots as it was the oldest mascot known to them, and was a symbol of life and knowledge.

A key is particularly suitable as a lucky mascot for *Virgo*, *Scorpio* or *Aquarius* people and should be gold, silver or stainless steel.

And one last tip: gipsies say that if you hang a door key upside down near your bed you will be safe from all forms of evil, including Mare, the evil spirit of the night — the bringer of "nightmares"!

Catch Him If You Can!

Most boys are sportsmen at heart — tennis players, footballers, boxers, cricketers, bikers, skateboarders, fishermen — and most of them play the love game the way they play their favourite sport, to win!

Find out the rules he follows to win your heart, and you'll find out all about the kind of boy he is — and the kind of game *you* should play to win *him!*

THE FAST BOWLER

Tell him by his fixed and glaring eyes, the way he scowls to try and terrify the opposition (you — or any other half-decent girl who's within 3 feet of him), and the restless way he prowls around while he's waiting to pounce on you!

How he'll treat you
His aim is to bowl a maiden over. He'll shower you with compliments, send you flowers, buy you lots of lovely pressies — in short, bowl you right off your feet. If you show signs of resistance, he'll just keep on trying and trying . . .

His interests
A physical type, he's attracted to a nice pair of legs — that's why he seems obsessed with legs before wickets!

If you like him
Make it easy for him to ask you out. It's worth the effort, as he's quite a catch himself.

If you don't like him
Tie his bootlaces together, so he'll slip and pull a tendon.

THE CLEVER BOXER

Tell him by his dead classy, ever-so-clever bobbing and weaving style. He's a real knockout, but what he enjoys is all the slippery-footed dancing about that leads up to it.

How he'll treat you
He'll dance round you, all lively, and soften you up with lots of clever little jokes and cunning moves. Then, when you're getting a bit weak at the knees, and a bit groggy from all his charm . . . WHAM! You'll see stars, 'cos he'll have moved in for the kill.

His interests
What he relies on is his speed and fitness, so all his spare time is spent getting into shape — sharpening up his chatting-up and exercising his girl-hypnotising footwork.

If you like him
Box clever and don't pull your punches and you could be *his* champion!

If you don't like him
Tell him you're going to float like a butterfly — right out of his reach!

FISHERMAN

Tell him by his calm, peaceful, very patient look as he sits hunched up, waiting for the Big One (you) he knows sooner or later he's going to land . . .

How he'll treat you
The fisherman's cunning approach is to cast handfuls of bait to get you interested. Cinema tickets, invitations to discos, cups of coffee, spearmint chews. If this "ground bait" works, you'll be nicely lined up for something really tempting — a double album, or a trip to London to see a live Elton John concert. Then, you're hooked!

His interests
He's a guy who can relax and take his time. He's not going to rush after you when he can tempt you right up into his backwater just by playing his cards right.

If you like him
Swim right up to him with a saucy flick of your fins and let him land you.

If you don't like him
Be the one that got away!

THE LONG-DISTANCE RUNNER

Tell him by his slow but steady trot, his lean and hungry look, and the way he hangs back and bides his time while lots of other fellas are buzzing around you. He's saving himself for the last straight.

How he'll treat you
His technique is to stay with you, gently pottering along in the background for weeks and weeks, as flashier boyfriends come and go. In the end, he's usually rewarded for his stamina.

His interests
Since his effort depends upon stamina, what he really needs is lots of sweetness — from you — to keep him going. A smile here, a compliment there, and a friendly pat on the head now and then ought to be enough to fuel his fires and keep him interested for months . . .

If you like him
Ask him: "Is this the last lap?" — and then jump on to it!

If you don't like him
Tell him he's for the High Jump.

HAVE YOU GOT BAD TABLE MANNERS?

Whether you're a chomper, a guzzler or a nibbler, the way you eat your food is a dead give-away to your personality. Read on and taste the difference . . .

SWEET SHARON

How She Eats — She's always sucking sweets, chewing gum, and slinking into the corner shop to stock up her rations. She doesn't eat very much at meals (not surprising, really. Could you, with a hundredweight of gob-stoppers rattling round inside?), but between meals, her jaws are never still!

Her Character — It's obvious she likes to indulge herself and this extends to other things, too. She'll put off even the tiniest of chores, as she's so lazy. If you're relying on her to do something for you, forget it — *she* certainly will! She's very affectionate, though, and makes you feel needed.

Her Attitude To Boys — This girl is boy mad and spends most of her time dreaming about some guy or other! She can be very faithful and stick to one guy for months on end, but, there again, she can also fall madly in love three times a week, if the mood takes her! Boys like her, because she's sweet and attractive, but they soon tire of her because they can be clinging and possessive.

Her Disadvantages — She won't do a thing for herself and relies on her friends and family. Sometimes she puts on an act of being a helpless fluffy little creature who's totally incapable. The truth is she hasn't really grown up and still yearns for Mummy to come and sort things out for her!

GUZZLING GERTIE

How She Eats — She positively wolfs down her food. Great forkfuls of pies and tarts, huge forkloads of roast beef — all disappear without trace! It's not that she's *greedy*. She doesn't

eat *more* than other people, just *faster*. (Twenty times faster!) By the time most of us are halfway through our soup, she's licking her pudding spoon.

Her Character — She's really ambitious and doesn't waste time on such unimportant things as eating — not when there's the rest of life to get on with! She wants to go far and do great things. She's got bags of energy, and she's the sort who could walk 20 miles, swim 40 lengths, and run 10,000 metres in the same afternoon! Nobody ever finds her hard to talk to — she's very outgoing.

Her Attitude To Boys — She doesn't wait for boys to chat her up. If she fancies one, she'll dive straight in and ask if he wants to join her rock-climbing club, squash team or drama society. When she hasn't got a boyfriend (which isn't very often), she doesn't bother to think about them. There's plenty of other things to do and say!

Her Disadvantages — Guzzlers suffer from indigestion. And she gets it in lots of ways! Often she rushes into things without enough thought, and then finds herself in circumstances beyond her control. She's not very tactful and tramples on people's feelings quite often.

FANATICAL FRAN

How She Eats — Her attitude to food is *all* that's important. She has theories about it. Maybe she's a vegetarian, or a wholefood fanatic, or even a macrobiotic freak? Or it could be she's into one particular kind of cooking — Chinese, French or Greek.

Her Character — Her head just buzzes with ideas. What's more, she's very strong willed and can follow an idea right through, against all sorts of difficulties. You might call her a bit of an intellectual, and in fact, she's certain to be interested in all sorts of things — books, plays, politics and science.

Her Attitude To Boys — She sets her standards pretty high. She finds boys easy to talk to and get on with, but she can be fooled by a guy who's just ordinary. She sees things in him that aren't there and when she realises she's wrong, she blames herself for her foolishness. In fact, she feels quite a lot of guilt generally — about things in the wider world, like whaling and conservation, as well as in her own life.

Her Disadvantages — She can be a little out of touch with reality. Sometimes she can be intolerant and difficult to persuade about things, too. But in general she's a really great girl — a good mate and an inspiring girlfriend!

NIBBLING NORAH

How She Eats — She goes around the house like a mouse nibbling an apple here, a bit of chocolate there, "tidying up" a piece of cheese that's been left on the kitchen table . . . she's never still. Or at least, her teeth never are!

Her Character — The most important thing about this girl is she's rather nervous and insecure. Really she's convinced she's fat and ugly (or thin and ugly, for despite all her nibbling, she *can* be thin because she worries such a lot). Or maybe she's always arguing with her parents, or doesn't get on with

her mates at school. Whatever the reason, she's lacking a little in confidence.

Her Attitude To Boys — She'd love to get to know some, and maybe even go out on a date, but at the moment that's unlikely, unless a guy's very determined to take her out. Unfortunately, she's so nervous and shy, she hardly ever opens her mouth when boys are about, except to pop a crisp or nut in it, of course! She's so tense she finds it very hard to talk to people, especially boys.

Her Disadvantages — Well, they're obvious! She's a bag of nerves, and however nice, gentle, charming, sweet and intelligent she is underneath it all — nobody's going to find out until she's managed to conquer her nerves and stand up to people.

TAKESTIME TINA

How She Eats — She cuts her food up into nice, even-sized chunks, chews each mouthful well, savours it, and enjoys it! She likes to put her knife and fork down from time to time just to talk. Sometimes while she's doing this, her food gets cold. But does she care? Not a bit!

Her Character — She's very secure, very relaxed and has been lucky enough to be brought up in a very happy home, so her reactions to most things are very even tempered. She's good in emergencies and always keeps her head — so if the soup boils over, she's the ideal person to have around.

Her Attitude To Boys — She's well adjusted to boys, too. But her only problem is she finds boys of her own age very immature, as she's particularly mature for her age. She's quite capable of falling head-over-heels in love with a guy, but she'd probably be quite successful at hiding it from her friends, and she'd certainly never do anything silly or make a fool of herself over him!

Her Disadvantages — She can be just the teeniest bit irritating! After all, she seems to find life *so* easy. If only she'd lose her cool now and then, she'd be a lot more popular!

WATCH THIS SPACE!

We've had superheroes and anti-heroes, space villains and good guys, princesses from far-flung planets and weird and wonderful monsters of every size, shape and description — not to mention a fair spattering of luscious space trekkers for us to drool over. Here we've taken a selection of films you've seen, some you'll be watching now, and even a sneaky peek at a few to come! Read on for stars in your eyes and a delicious floaty feeling!

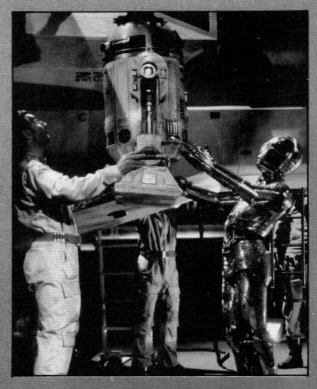

Set in a far-off galaxy, "Star Wars" was the perfect cowboys and Indians adventure — even the costumes were in keeping with the action — black for the baddies and white for the goodies. That all seems so long ago now, especially as the sequel to "Star Wars" has already been filmed. "The Empire Strikes Back" followed on where "Star Wars" left off. Once again starring Mark Hamill, Carrie Fisher and Harrison Ford — not to mention the evil Darth Vadar and the amusing C-3PO and R2-D2, this exciting film has all the action of its predecessor, and lots more!

Space ships are the "in thing" for the film designers. Who can forget that incredible mother ship which appeared in "Close Encounters Of The Third Kind"? CE3K, as it became known, really gave substance to the idea that the Planet Earth was being visited by beings from another world.

A similar visitation occurs in the film "Foes," which is about four people who become the focus of a destructive and tragic series of events, when extra-terrestrial aliens attempt to communicate with our planet!

It would be impossible, when talking about space ships, not to give a mention to perhaps the most popular vehicle of them all — the Starship Enterprise. Yes, the full-length film of "Star Trek" is proving as popular as it's TV brain-child, now a staggering ten years old! All your favourites are there: William Shatner, Leonard Nimoy, De-Forrest Kelley and as an extra bonus, former Miss India — Persis Khambatta, who plays an exotic and incidentally *bald* navigator called Ilia, who comes from the planet Delta.

Disney, too, has not forgotten his fans — "The Spaceman And King Arthur" has the unlikely situation of a spaceman who accidentally travels back in time to the court of King Arthur — and receives a none-too-friendly welcome. Look out for gorgeous Dennis Dugan in the leading role.

"Battlestar Galactica" is almost like a "Star Wars" spin-off, and was originally made for television. Once again the planetary powers are fighting their way into total oblivion. But the special effects, as always in this type of movie, are always worth watching — so is one of its stars — ex-Bond girl, Jane Seymour! Mind you, Richard Hatch and Dirk Benedict are the only two we've managed to see at all!

In "Buck Rogers," Gil Gerard plays an American astronaut whose space probe goes wildly off course and, although colliding with a shower of meteorites, hurtles him back 500 years in time. To help Gil through his troubles is a charming little robot named Twiki — he's played by Felix Silla — aww!

The Women's Libbers haven't been forgotten. "Outer Touch" is billed as a science-fiction comedy and it concerns the adventures of a space ship which has — wait for it — an all-female crew — and about time, too!

Following on from the hugely-successful "Capricorn One," a film about the faking of a United States space mission to the planet Mars, comes Farrah Fawcett-Majors, Kirk Douglas and Harvey Keitel in "Saturn 3." Our heroes and heroine are trapped in a distant space laboratory — sounds like fun!

Even our own James Bond is unable to keep away from sci-fi. His latest adventure "Moonraker" has a marvellous twenty-minute interplanetary battle fought between 007 — Roger Moore — and the evil Hugo Drax, played by Michael Lonsdale.

"Alien" which stars Ian Holm, John Hurt and Veronica Cartwright is a suspense thriller about five men and two women on board a star ship. They realise that, somewhere inside the ship is a horrific alien being — take a hunky boyfriend to hang on to....

So far, we've dealt with nothing but films, zooming to a close on that subject with a last, lingering look at Christopher Reeve, alias "Superman," and on to something that hit our TV screens in 1979 — Mork played by actor Robin Williams, who was the star of "Mork And Mindy" — an odd chap if ever there was one — which is as good a way to end as any!

DO YOU HAVE ANIMAL MAGIC?

THE way you react to, and behave with, animals tells you a lot about your personality. You might be the sort of person who'd run a home for strays if you had the space, or you could be the type who can't even sit in the same room as a cat!

Whatever your feelings about small or large furry animals, you'll find out a whole lot more about yourself if you try answering our fun quiz — it's all a question of that old animal magic, in the end !

1. Which of these pets would you most like to have?
a. A big, healthy, bounding dog.
b. A fluffy kitten.

c. A beautiful, proud Siamese cat.
d. A lizard.

2. Do you think the best thing about having a pet is —
c. being able to admire its beauty.
d. being able to observe how other creatures live and behave.
a. being able to run around and have fun with it.
b. being able to cuddle and love it?

3. Would you like a boy who —
c. painted exquisite pictures of multi-coloured birds.
a. had a horse and liked to ride it bareback.
d. kept snakes and made a record of their behaviour,
b. kept pigeons and looked after them meticulously?

4. Which of these would you find most sad?
c. A peacock which had lost all its tail feathers in an accident.
a. A cheetah or other fast-moving animal in a small cage.
b. A dog whose owner had recently died, returning to its old house.
d. An animal from a foreign country suffering because its owners didn't know how to look after it?

5. Do you think zoos are —
d. a good idea, because we can learn about lots of unusual species,
b. a bad thing — those poor animals can't be happy,
a. all right for some species, but for the animals who need lots of space to run about in, they're pretty awful,
c. if they're well planned and set out, they're a great idea because there's so much to see that most of us could never see in the wild.

6. If you could give a present of a pet to a boy you fancied, would you give him —
b. a lovable puppy,

d. some tadpoles,
a. a greyhound,
c. a brilliant Amazonian parrot?

Questions

7. If you could go on one of these holidays, which would you choose?
a. Pony-trekking.
b. Working at a kennels.
c. Bird-watching in the mountains.
d. A trip to the jungle to search for rare species.

8. What do think about wearing real fur coats?
b. It's awful because it means suffering for the poor animals.
d. It's a bad thing because certain species could become extinct.
c. You don't really approve, but you'd find it hard to resist if someone offered you one.
a. Men have always worn animal skins, so don't let's be over-sentimental.

9. What's your attitude to "creepy crawlies"?
b. You hate them — if there's one any-where near you, you have a scream-ing fit!
c. You're not hysterical about them, but they're not exactly nice to look at.
d. You're interested in them, and wish you had a microscope so you could examine them more closely.
a. You're not frightened of them, but they're boring because they don't do anything.

10. What would you think about watching a Chimpanzee's tea-party?
a. It's a crack-up!
c. There's something grotesque and rather nasty about it.
d. You'd rather see a film of them in their native habitat.
b. It's quite funny, and makes you think you'd like one for a pet.

11. What's your attitude to the controlling of rabbits?
a. If they have to be controlled, ferret-ing is the best way, because it's natu-ral.
d. They do have to be controlled, and we should do it the most humane, scienti-fic way.
b. Why do they have to be controlled? They're such sweet, cuddly things.
c. It's a shame rabbits have to be killed off, because it's such an ugly business.

12. Your attitude to hunting is —
b. it's absolutely awful, cruel, and you can't bear to think about it,
c. there is some cruelty, but a hunt can look very fine in a winter landscape,
a. whether or not it's cruel, it's a marvel-lous sport,
d. there are better ways of controlling foxes?

13. If you could come back to Earth as an animal, which would you like to be?
c. A bird of paradise.

d. A rare species of lizard.
a. A dolphin.
b. A fat dozy farm cat.

Now add up your score, mostly a, b, c, or d, and turn to the conclusions.

CONCLUSIONS

★ ★

If your answers were mostly a:
You're an energetic, action-packed girl. You're not over-sentimental — you take a realistic view of life and don't get led astray by your feelings. You appreci-ate natural things, and it's real nature that you like; not a watered-down pretty-pretty version. You accept that there's cruelty in life but because you're so clear-sighted you're likely to be able to deal with your own problems without being overwhelmed.

Boys like you for your energetic approach to life, and the fact that you'll probably appreciate sport. (We bet you're a football fan!) You've got none of the irri-tating feminine attitudes so boys won't tease you. They're likely to accept you as an equal. Another thing they like about you is your sense of humour.

Girls, however, may find you a bit too cool. They may find you hard and unfeel-ing but they'd be wrong. You're a lovely, lively, fresh, down-to-earth girl!

If your answers were mostly b:
You're a home-loving character. Very emotional and full of feelings. Your re-actions to things are very direct and full of warmth. You feel very protective towards children and animals. You're warm-blooded. However, your emotions often blind you to facts and make it very hard to look at things objectively. In arguments, you get het-up very easily and the strength of your feel-ings makes you easily upset.

Boys like you for your gentle, loving approach to life. They probably tease you, because your reactions to things are so predictably soft hearted and illogical. You sum up everything that they think of as feminine. Your gentleness and affec-tionate nature make you very appealing to all males — Dad and Grandad as well as boyfriends!

Other girls like you very much. You're totally at home in girls' company. You share their interests and reactions, and are sympathetic to their problems. You're the loving, muddle-headed girl everybody loves!

If your answers were mostly c:
The most important thing to you is beauty. You love it in animals, in nature, in the landscape, and in your life. Your reaction to nearly everything is deter-mined by the beauty of it — or otherwise. You don't react to things with violent emotion, but with a sense of whether it looks good or not. You're not sentimental about nature, and you know what you like. But you won't get involved in hot-headed arguments. It's much too undig-nified!

Boys admire your style. You know how to dress and emphasise your good features, but some boys may find you rather frightening — you're just a bit too stylish for them. So make a point of hang-ing around in scruffy old jeans once in a while — to prove you're human!

Girls like you. Some of them may envy your looks and style, others may imitate you, others may ask for your advice. You're certainly a trend-setter in your group!

If your answers were mostly d:
You're quite an unusual sort of girl. You have a great curiosity about the world and you're probably very inter-ested in the natural sciences — biology or zoology. You're highly intelligent, and very logical and careful in your approach to life. Nature is a ceaseless source of interest to you but you don't react emo-tionally to it — you'd rather find out about it. The more unusual a subject, the more it captures your imagination.

Boys may be a bit intimidated by you, but they'll certainly respect you and wouldn't dream of talking down to you or regarding you as less than equal — in fact, most boys probably think of you as downright superior! The really intelligent boys will be interested in you, but they may be a bit shy of approaching you. Other girls admire you and find you interesting. They'll feel in awe of your intelligence but they'll probably be proud to know you.

★ ★

ARE YOU A DATING DISASTER?

OK, so the boy you've been keen on for weeks (months? years??) has finally noticed you and asked you out. You think your troubles are over, that from here on in it's going to be moonlight and soft music and romance all the way. You *think*. But *is* it? Your troubles could be just beginning . . . and here's why!

LOOKING on the bright side, your first date could turn out to be absolutely perfect, of course. On the other hand it could turn into a *disaster!* The reason why a lot of dates go wrong is because the girl has used the three simple words, "I don't mind." He asks her out — she happily agrees — he asks her where she'd like to go — she says, "I don't mind," and instantly leaves herself wide open to any loony idea he may think up!

A lot depends on the type he is, though. And, as you obviously don't know him all that well yet, you don't know what type he is — yet. Don't worry. You soon will.

Here's all you need to know about dating disasters — and how to avoid them!

If he suggests A NICE EVENING AT THE ZOO

Fine, you'll think. He's an animal lover. As you're probably quite fond of elephants or duckbilled platypuses yourself, you won't mind in the least.

You'll happily follow him around until you suddenly find yourself in the reptile house with him cooing at the cobras and pythons and slithery vipers, and telling you how *crazy* he is about snakes. He's probably even got a pet boa constrictor at home he's just dying for you to meet.

DO NOT FEED

Or you'll find yourself in the very authentic Brazilian Jungle House, complete with dark undergrowth and creepers and even an authentic black widow spider crawling down your neck . . .

WHAT TO DO

Head for the elephant house. If the boy's really interested in you, he'll have guessed by now that you don't share his love of snakes or spiders, so obviously he'll come after you. If not, well, elephants don't mind being stared at for an hour or two, and thankfully the only dates they're interested in are the ones in cakes!

If he suggests A MEAL

This could mean prawn cocktails, mouth-watering tender steaks and strawberries in delicious ice-cream in a discreet, candlelit restaurant.

So you put on a slinky dress and make yourself up to look really cool and sophisticated. Then you find yourself in Greasy Joe's All Night Chippery eating sausages and chips. Or even standing around in the rain eating fish and chips out of a soggy newspaper.

WHAT TO DO

There's not much you *can* do, unfortunately. This boy is suffering from a fairly common complaint known as poverty. He may recover on pay day but don't count on it. If you like him, grin and bear it. At least he's not into collecting snakes or spiders. (You hope!)

If he suggests you GO TO THE PICTURES

Don't get carried away with the idea that you'll be going to see Superman II, Grease II or Star Wars XXI. You could be disappointed because some boys have funny tastes in films.

You're more likely to find yourself in a downtown flea-pit watching "Dracula Meets Frankenstein's Mummy."

Of course, he may be quite willing to let you choose the film. If he is, it means he's not in the least interested in it. His plan is to get you in the back row and eat you! Actually, he's not really intending to eat you at all — that's just the impression you'll get. You'll also get the impression he's got three pairs of hands.

WHAT TO DO

Watch the film. It's very off-putting for a boy to make amorous advances at a girl who's so interested in what's going on on the screen that she doesn't even notice him. It's also a bit unfair. You could say you can't see too well from the back row and insist on moving nearer the screen. This should slow him down. Eating sweets also slows down kissing activity. On the other hand, if the film is so boring, why put him off? If you like him, kissing and cuddling is a pretty nice way to spend the time!

If he suggests A NICE LONG WALK

Whether this is a good idea or not depends a lot on the time of year — and the weather. A nice long walk with an east wind blowing and hail pelting down, isn't going to be much fun.

A pleasant evening in spring or summer, on the other hand, could be very enjoyable. But why did he suggest a walk? You might find you're stuck with a fitness freak whose idea of a walk is a ten-mile trek over the hills. Or maybe he's got the same disease as the boy who suggests a meal which turns out to be fish and chips — poverty. Well, at least a walk is free! Or he could simply be the sort of guy who loves the great outdoors and birds and flowers and things.

WHAT TO DO

It all depends on what he does. If he turns out to be a fitness freak and sets off at a trot, go along with him for a while and then pretend you've twisted your ankle. Having to carry you home *ought* to slow him down a bit. If he's the outdoor enthusiast — enjoy the walk. You might learn something about flowers and birds. And if he's only suggested a walk because he's short of cash, go along with it. You don't want to embarrass him, do you?

If he suggests THE DISCO

This is more like it. Now you're getting somewhere. This guy either likes to dance or he knows you do.

It doesn't really matter which, unless he turns out to be the World's Worst Show-Off and only wants you to admire his style.

WHAT TO DO

Enjoy yourself, that's what! If he does turn out to be the World's Worst Show-Off, it doesn't matter too much. While he's busy showing off, you can be looking around at the talent. Maybe you'll be luckier next time??

The thing about first dates is that they don't have to lead to second or third dates. If the boy doesn't turn out to be quite what you were hoping for — make an excuse when he asks you out again. It's not so difficult to do and you won't hurt his feelings too much if you're kind about it.

Not that you'll need to make an excuse, will you? You will be the girl who gets the right guy first time, won't you? **Won't you?**

Something In The Way He Looks

Does he love you? Does he hate you? Do you bore him, drive him wild, or simply send him to sleep? You can find out all these things and more with the help of our extra special feature on body language! Here's everything you need to know about all those mysterious facial expressions of the boy in your life — and what they *really* mean!

1. THE DAZZLER

A dazzling smile, dancing eyes, not a trace of shyness or second thoughts about anything . . . If this is the way he looks when he meets you, well, you've got absolutely nothing to worry about! He's well and truly hooked. There's nothing false about the smile, so count your blessings — and smile back, of course!

2. THE DOUBTER

Oh, dear, what have you done? Let him down in some way, that's what! Could be he thinks you're lying; could be that you're saying or doing something he disapproves of. The under-the-eyebrows look shows that he's signalling to you to come clean, and his pursed lips show he's none too pleased!

3. LITTLE BOY BLUE

Downcast eyes are a sure sign of depression — and that he can't face looking you in the eye. There's a downward-turning, discontented look to his mouth, too, that shows all too clearly how cheesed off he is. If it's about you — put it right! And if it's about something else, force him to tell you.

4. LOVER BOY

He fancies you, all right, and what's more, he's pretty sure you ought to fancy him. His eyes have a thoughtful look — he's giving you the once over. He's looking confident and is obviously very sure of himself. You've certainly made an impression on him, and within 5 minutes he's going to make a pass, so . . . watch out!

5. THE SNEERER

This guy's feeling pretty superior. See the sneering half-smile playing around his lips and nose? And those sarcastically-raised eyebrows? He may be feeling hurt, angry, or just malicious, but whatever it is, somebody's going to get a mouthful of sneer any minute! If it's you, make a quick exit. You've got nothing to lose but a few insults!

6. THE GIGGLER

This guy's feeling absolutely fine — the way he's thrown his head back, showing all his teeth and opening his mouth means he's totally relaxed. Bright, sparkling eyes show he's feeling really good — and the whole impression is one of terrific happiness. Could you be the cause of this insane joy? If so, you're laughing, if you see what we mean!

7. THE THINKER

Touching his nose is always a sign of doubt. Basically he's pretty interested in something (or someone). You can tell that by the way his eyes are looking sideways into space. He has his doubts, though he's not too put off. He's likely to make a grab for whatever it is (Doughnut? Job? Girl?) pretty soon!

8. THE DOZER

Eyes closing, face slumping . . . either he's practising meditation, or yoga, or he's so bored with you, he's dropping off! So sharpen up your small talk quick, before he nods off completely! It could just be lack of sleep. Was he up all night writing love poems to you?!

9. SHY GUY

He likes you, he really does. But do *you* like *him*? He's not at all sure how you feel about him. He's smiling, but it's not a proper smile. His eyes are alert, open for any tell-tale signs that you don't really like him. Put the poor guy out of his misery — give him a great big hug, or tell him to go!

You just won't be able to resist the chance to own this pair — and they're so simple to make, too! We must warn you, though, that making Madge and Beryl is the easiest bit — it's once you've got them that you've got to look out! Make sure you've got a heavy-weight boxer on hand to separate them if any squabbles start, and for goodness' sake, don't you be the one to fall out with *them* — we hear they tear up all their enemies' weekly Jackies — a fate worse than death, as you're surely aware! Seriously, though, Madge and Beryl are an asset to any household, so get out your pins and start knitting!

BERYL BEAR

NEEDLES — A pair of 3¾ mm (No. 9) knitting needles.
WOOL — Sirdar Superwash Wool 4 ply, 2 (25 g) balls in Honey Beige (060) and 1 ball in White (051). Also a small amount of black 4 ply wool.
PLUS — A scrap of black felt, glue and kapok.
ABBREVIATIONS — K — knit, sts — stitches, beg — beginning, inc — increase by knitting into front and back of stitch, tog — together.
Knitted in garter-stitch (knit every row) throughout. When counting rows, remember that 1 ridge equals 2 rows.

LEGS AND BODY

FRONT
*With beige wool cast on 15 sts and K 4 rows.
Next row — Inc in first st, K6, inc in next 2 sts, K to last st, inc in last st (19 sts).
K 6 rows.
Next row — K2 tog, K6, K2 tog twice, K to last 2 sts, K2 tog (15 sts).
K 1 row.
Next row — K2 tog, K to last 2 sts, K2 tog (13 sts).
K until work measures 32 rows from cast-on edge.*
Break wool and push these sts to end of needle. On to same needle cast on 15 sts and repeat from * to *
**Work across both sets of sts and K 2 rows.
Next row — K11, K2 tog twice, K to end (24 sts).
K until work measures 56 rows from cast-on edge.
Cast off 7 sts at beg of next 2 rows.
Cast off remaining 10 sts.

BACK
With beige wool cast on 13 sts and K 32 rows. Break wool and push these sts to end of needle. On to same needle cast on 13 sts and K 32 rows. Repeat as for front from ** to end.

ARMS (2 alike)
With beige wool cast on 18 sts and K 1 row.
Next row — Inc in first st, K7, inc in next 2 sts, K7, inc in last st (22 sts).
K 6 rows.
Next row — K2 tog, K7, K2 tog twice, K7, K2 tog (18 sts).
K 1 row.
Next row — K2 tog, K to last 2 sts, K2 tog (16 sts).
K 18 rows, cast off.

HEAD (2 pieces alike)
With beige wool cast on 15 sts and K 2 rows.
Next row — Inc in first st, K to end.
Next row — K to last st, inc in last st.
Inc 1 st at beg of next 2 rows.
Repeat last 4 rows once more, then first 2 rows once more (25 sts).
K 8 rows.
Next row — K2 tog, K to end.
Next row — K to last 2 sts, K2 tog.
Repeat last 2 rows twice more.
Next row — K2 tog, K to last 2 sts, K2 tog.
Next row — K to last 2 sts, K2 tog.
Next row — K2 tog, K to end.
Next row — K to last 2 sts, K2 tog.
Repeat last 4 rows once more, then first row once more.
Cast off.

BRA
With white wool cast on 48 sts and K 6 rows. Cast off.

A JACKIE KNIT-A-BIT PATTERN

MADGE and BERYL

KNICKERS (2 pieces alike)
With white wool cast on 24 sts and K 2 rows.
K2 tog. at beg and end of every row until 4 sts remain on the needle.
Cast off.

TURBAN
With white wool cast on 50 sts and K 2 rows.
K2 tog at beg of every row until 2 sts remain on the needle.
Cast off.

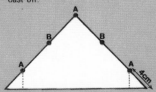

TO MAKE UP
Join body pieces together, leaving neck and feet open. Gather up feet openings and stuff neck with kapok. Join head pieces, leaving cast-on edge (neck edge) open. Stuff firmly and join head to body. Fold each arm piece in half lengthways and sew seams, leaving cast-off ends open. Stuff firmly and sew to body. Join knicker pieces by catching at each point with a couple of stitches. Join bra along short sides and gather seam. Make turban by following diagram, putting points A together and sewing seams AB. Gather along dotted lines. Embroider features on face and make leopordskin by making three beige satin stitches and surrounding with a single black chain stitch. Sew turban to head. Cut 4 small black felt ovals and glue to hands and feet.

MADGE DUCKWORTH

NEEDLES — A pair each of 3¾ mm (No. 9) and 3¼ mm (No. 10) knitting needles.
WOOL — Sirdar Superwash Wool 4 ply, one (25 g) ball each of Festive Scarlet (085), Royal (023), and Camel (041); Sirdar Fontein Crepe, one ball of Horse Chestnut (055); a small amount of emerald green 4 ply wool.
PLUS — A scrap of white felt, red and black felt-tipped pens, glue and kapok.
ABBREVIATIONS — K — knit, P — purl, sts — stitches, beg — beginning, tog — together, inc —

increase by knitting into front and back of stitch.

LEGS AND BODY (2 alike)
With 3¼ mm needles and blue wool cast on 9 sts and continue in stocking-stitch.
*Work 19 rows.
Next row — Inc 1 st at each end.
Repeat last 20 rows once more.
Work 10 rows (13 sts, 50 rows)*
Break wool and push these sts to end of needle. On to same needle cast on 9 sts and work from * to *
Work across both sets of sts and work 2 rows.
Next row — K2 tog, K9, (K2 tog) twice, K9, K2 tog. (22 sts)
Work 9 rows.
Change to red wool and work 14 rows.
Next row — Inc 1 st at each end.
Work 2 rows.
Cast off 4 sts at beg of next 2 rows; then 3 sts at beg of next 2 rows. Cast off remaining sts.

HEAD (2 pieces alike)
With 3¼ mm needles and beige wool cast on 10 sts and proceed in stocking-stitch.
Work 2 rows.
Next row — Inc in first st, K3, inc in next 2 sts, K3, inc in last st (14 sts).

Next row — Purl.
Inc 1 st at beg of every row until there are 22 sts on the needle.
Work 8 rows straight.
K2 tog at beg of every row until 12 sts remain.
Cast off.

NECK
With 3¼ mm needles and beige wool cast on 18 sts and work 6 rows stocking-stitch.
Cast off.

ARMS (2 alike)
With 3¼ mm needles and beige wool cast on 18 sts and proceed in stocking-stitch.
Work 2 rows.
Next row — Inc in first st, K7, inc in next 2 sts, K7, inc in last st (22 sts).
Work 5 rows.
Next row — K2 tog, K7, (K2 tog) twice, K7, K2 tog (18 sts).
Next row — Purl.
Next row — K2 tog, K to last 2 sts, K2 tog (16 sts).
Work 19 rows.
Change to red wool and knit 6 rows.
Cast off

FEET (2 alike)
With 3¼ mm needles and emerald wool cast on 32 sts and proceed in stocking-stitch.
Work 2 rows.
Next row — Inc 1 st each end.
Work 5 rows.
1st row — K2 tog, K to last 2 sts, K2 tog.
2nd row — P2 tog, P to last 2 sts, P2 tog.
Repeat first row once more.
Cast off 6 sts at beg of next 2 rows.
Work 2 rows.
Cast off.

HAIR
With 3¾ mm needles and rust wool cast on 18 sts and proceed in garter-stitch.
K 2 rows.
Inc 1 st at beg of every row until there are 40 sts on the needle.
Working on the first 20 sts only, *knit 2 rows.
K2 tog at beg and end of next and every following row until 10 sts remain.
K2 tog at beg of every row until 2 sts remain.
Cast off.*
Repeat from * to * working on remaining 20 sts.

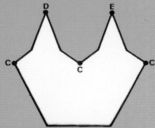

TO MAKE UP
Join body pieces together, leaving neck and ankles open. Fold feet in half and sew together, leaving tops open. Sew to ankles. Stuff body and sew up neck. Join head pieces, leaving cast-on edge open. Stuff firmly, join neck and sew to head, stuff and sew neck to body. Fold each arm piece in half lengthways and sew seams, leaving cast-off edges open. Stuff firmly and sew to body. Make hair by following diagram, putting points C together and sewing seams CD and CE. Sew to head. From white felt cut 2 ovals and carefully colour edges with a black felt tip. Allow to dry then glue to face and make a few black stitches in centre. Embroider mouth and eyebrows with black wool and make a nose with a few stitches of beige wool. Redden cheeks with a felt tip used very lightly.

Something In The Way You Look!

You may try to hide your feelings, but your eyes will always give you away! Your eyes are the mirrors of your soul, and just by looking deeply into them, other people will be able to find out what you *really* feel.

If you don't believe us, take a look at these pictures, and you'll see what we mean! And the next time that special boy looks into your eyes, remember, you might be giving it all away!

1. She's definitely pretending to be amused by the situation, perhaps because she wants to be polite, and she's certainly unsure. It's a very false laugh — her eyes still reflect bewilderment, and to a certain extent insincerity.
She's probably saying, "What's so funny about this? Well, I'd better laugh along with the rest so they don't think I'm stuck up, or a complete dummy." She's not very sure of the people she's with and wants to make a good impression.

2. In this picture she's showing a mixture of regret and confusion. Imagine your friend in the situation where she's just finished with her boyfriend.
She's probably regretting it slightly, although deep down she knows she's done the best thing. "Should I have done it like that?" she's probably saying, or, "Oh, well, it had to be done sometime — but I'm still not sure . . ."
She'd really like to think what's done is done, but a feeling of doubt creeps in, which shows all too clearly in her eyes. She could do with reassurance.

3. Someone's feeling pleased with themselves here! She looks as though she's managed to get to know the boy she fancies, and she's going to keep it to herself. "I've done it! He likes me enough to ask me out, but I'm not going to tell anyone about it yet!" she's thinking.
It's a look of triumph — she obviously feels that the boy in question was something of a challenge, and she's proved herself by attracting him!

4. This girl's in love! She's got a slightly dreamy, faraway look in her eyes which tells you she's thinking of him. Recognise the look?
Underneath the calm there's a feeling of excitement, though. She's trying to suppress it, but it still shows. She's probably about to meet him, and can't keep her thoughts off him, but along with the feelings of excitement and strong emotions are feelings of insecurity and worry.

5. She's looking very coy and charming, but there's a touch of nervousness here, too. "Can I get away with it this time?" she's thinking.
She's about to ask a favour which she knows may not be granted. But she knows how to use her charm to persuade — and hopes the whole scene will be over with soon.

6. This is the sort of look you'll see on a friend who's feeling very mischievous. She's spotted someone on the other side of the room and she's in a wicked mood and wants to say, "Why not take a chance on me then, big boy!"
Definitely light-hearted and flirty, this look is teasing and humourous. But deep down she's hoping that the game she's playing will turn into something a lot more serious.

MADGE and BERYL

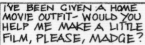

I'VE BEEN GIVEN A HOME MOVIE OUTFIT— WOULD YOU HELP ME MAKE A LITTLE FILM, PLEASE, MADGE?

OF COURSE, BERYL— CAN I BE THE STAR?

WELL... YES

OH, GOOD— AND DO I GET THE BEST DRESSING ROOM?

OF COURSE— I'LL PUT A STAR ON THE DOOR!

AND CAN I DESIGN MY OWN COSTUMES?

I SUPPOSE SO!

NOW, WHAT SORT OF ACCENT SHOULD I USE?

I'M AFRAID IT'S A SILENT FILM, MADGE

OH, WELL— NEVER MIND. IT'S LUCKY I HAVE SUCH AN EXPRESSIVE FACE!

NOW WE MUST WORK OUT MY CONTRACT!

I'D PREFER A PERCENTAGE OF THE BOX OFFICE RECEIPTS, PLEASE, BERYL!

MADGE! MADGE!

I'M ONLY A LITTLE BEAR, AND THIS IS ONLY A LITTLE FILM!

I CAN'T BE EXPECTED TO BE WONDERFUL AT IT, SO SOON!

I'M SORRY, BERYL— I GOT CARRIED AWAY!

HOW WOULD IT BE IF I TOOK THE FILM, AND YOU WERE THE STAR?

NOW, WHY DIDN'T I THINK OF THAT?

SOMETIMES I DON'T KNOW IF I'M IN CHARGE OR NOT!

When you meet someone for the first time you need all the clues you can to help you get things going. The easiest way to assess someone's character is, quite simply, to look them straight in the face — it's that easy!

Have a look at our Jackie guide to the face shapes below and make sure you're prepared next time you meet someone new . . .

FACE THE FACTS!

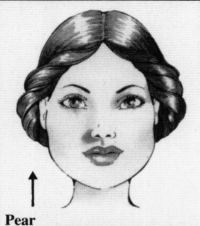

Pear

This is a slightly nervous character who has a tendency to shrink back and let other people take over and run her life. Very often there is an interest in creating things — from pottery to food. She is warm, loving and kind, with a friendly and modest nature.

Round

This shape of face belongs to a pleasure-loving and fun-seeking person who thrives on variety and change. She'll be easily pleased but just as easily hurt, because she'll rush into new romantic situations without thinking. She's always full of enthusiasm for new ideas, schemes and plans, whether romantic or otherwise.

Oval

The dreamers and the hopelessly romantic all have oval-shaped faces. They tend to be sensitive and highly strung, which means they're easily annoyed. This shape of face shows a character who needs attention and admiration. She tends to be idealistic about romance and is rather in love with love.

Square

This is a bossy type, although dependable and reliable as a friend. However, she always wants to lead rather than follow and enjoys getting her own way. She has strong will-power and so ends up being the dominant person in any organisation. She can't stand being ordered about or made to feel small.

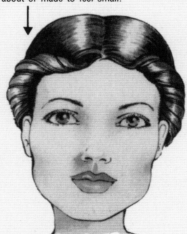

Heart

This face maybe looks really soft but, in fact, there's usually a very hard and determined nature behind it with a strong character. She's usually extremely affectionate and will have a well-developed, possibly off-beat, sense of humour. She'll be good fun to be with and rarely gets annoyed enough to hold a grudge.

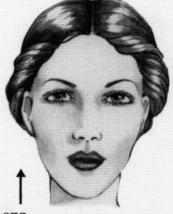

Long

This face reveals a forceful character who likes nothing better than to be physically active. She's always moving around and generally doing everything at the double. Usually with plenty of push and drive, she'll always be in a hurry to get things done and can't wait for tomorrow to come. She'll tend to make very quick decisions where affairs of the heart are concerned.

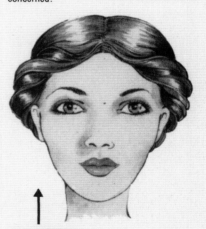

Triangular

Easy going, lovable and just a tiny bit lazy, that's what this shape of face reveals. Her nature is affectionate but she doesn't like making an effort in anything. Being loved and looked after appeals to her and it's very rare for this shape of face to become aggressive or anti-social in any way. Anything for a quiet life, that's this one.

Remember that although we've used girls' faces here, the shapes and rules also apply to boys. So, get out there and get looking for your ace-face!

Face Up To Them!

Have you had a good look at your face lately? That noble forehead, that resolute chin . . . have you ever thought that that strong, straight nose shows just what a strong, straight person you are? Well, analysing your face can give a clue as to what kind of person you are — so, we've taken some of our favourite people and given their features the once-over just for *you!*

Mark Hamill

HAIR
Mark has a high, slightly-pointed crown to his head, and this is a sign of a very active mind. His hair is light and fine, indicating a slightly lazy temperament at times.

HEAD
His heart-shaped face and broad forehead indicate his interest in self-expression and the artistic or acting world and there's a love of rhythm and movement in his very widely-spaced eyes.

NOSE
The bridge of his nose is wide and shows that he likes to feel secure in his relationships and he has the will to see a thing through once he's started it.

MOUTH
Mark has a long, thin upper lip creased at the corners, and this shows his off-beat sense of humour and ability to see the funny side of things. He has a thick protruding lower lip, indicating warmth, sensuality and generosity, plus a love of the opposite sex and flirting!

CHIN
His narrow chin is squared off with a flat base, and this demonstrates his hasty temper, which dies down as quickly as it flares up.

Summing up his personality, Mark has a great sense of fun, enjoys being the centre of attention and loves showing off a little.

Martin Shaw

HAIR
Martin has a squarish face and his thick curly hair hanging low over his forehead shows his vitality and energetic nature.

EYES
The eyes are set far apart, and this means that Martin is more of a giver than a taker. The tiny rolls of flesh under his lower lids are a sign of a warm, affectionate and deeply caring nature.

BROWS
His eyebrows show that he's slow to anger and prefers to use reason rather than force to put across his point of view.

NOSE
The tiny ridge across the bridge of his nose reveals curiosity and an enquiring mind, while the flaring-out of the nostrils is a sign of an open and friendly nature.

MOUTH
The wide, generous mouth with its dip in the middle of his top lip is a sign of individuality and shows Martin can be tender, constant and true.

CHIN
The square-shaped chin is a sign of determination and persistence, and the rather plumpish cheeks show a liking for humour and the simple things of life.

EARS
His ears are set low on his head, and this means he is capable of making quick decisions and isn't easily led by other people or their opinions.

Martin's overall personality is a capable, caring and sympathetic nature with a good sense of drama — but one who isn't likely to be carried away.

Lewis Collins

HEAD
Lewis has a pear-shaped face, and this is a sign of a fairly highly-strung person. It shows a lot of artistic talent and a romantic but down to earth streak.

EYES
Lewis has a longish forehead, and this shows his keen intelligence. His eyes are deep set, showing he can sum up people and situations quickly and he isn't easily taken in.

NOSE
His nose is thinner at the ridge, and this means he's extremely active with a love of attention and a need to show off sometimes.

CHIN
The chin comes to a point almost, and this shows that Lewis has a lot of attraction for the opposite sex, but is a bit of an idealist in his choice of partner.

MOUTH
His lips are tightly closed with the lower lip protruding a little, showing he can keep a secret well, and has a warm passionate nature with a need for harmony in his love life.

Lewis' personality is a curious mixture of the mildly aggressive and friendly-guy-next-door-type. But he is a man with a strong sense of responsibility, and this is something he wouldn't shirk, not with that well-formed head on his shoulders.

Dirk Benedict

HEAD
Dirk has a temperament that's a mixture of the dreamer and the action man. His head is shaped well, long and fine, and his hair laying flat against the crown shows that he enjoys physical exercise and has lots of energy and drive.

EYES
His widely-spaced eyes — large and clear — reveal a mind that likes to range over lots of subjects and show that he's quick, alert and fast thinking.

BROWS
The well-formed eyebrows coming to a point towards the nose show his sense of humour and love of life.

CHEEKBONES
His cheekbones are high, and this is a sign of an affectionate, loving and demonstrative nature with a need for close relationships.

MOUTH
Dirk has one predominant feature that stands out above all others and that's his mouth, beautifully shaped and turning up slightly at the corners, showing that he has a romantic soul.
His bottom lip is fuller than the top and has tiny perpendicular lines on it, indicating a passionate and ardent nature!

CHIN
His chin is firm and means that he has lots of willpower, even to the point of being obstinate at times when he wants his own way.

The overall impression of Dirk's head, face and hair is of a nicely-balanced guy with a love of beautiful things and a desire to achieve his ambitions.

Fozzie Bear

What an extrovert this bear is . . . . ! He loves to be in the limelight and enjoys being the centre of attention.

MOUTH
That huge gaping mouth tells us **all** about his personality, and how he loves to talk.

EYES
Watch those eyes set a bit too close together. They show he's great at getting his own way and he doesn't mind taking short-cuts to get it.

NOSE
He's a lovable, noisy, individualistic type who has a large nose for enquiring into other people's affairs, but he does it so cheekily no-one minds.

BROWS
Those high-flying eyebrows show he's always surprised at the way things turn out and he's certainly a character to be reckoned with . . . .

EARS
Those ears, almost large enough to take off, show his love of gossip and you'll always find Fozzie Bear where the action is!

Shaun Cassidy

HEAD
Shaun has a rounded head with a small round face, and this means that he's a romantic and a bit of a daydreamer, but with a practical streak, too.

HAIR
He enjoys an audience, and that thick hair shows his vitality and love of space and movement.

EYES
His eyes are "laughing eyes," very expressive, and show that his feelings are near the surface and he tends to be impulsive and spontaneous.

NOSE
His nose is full and has a very wide bridge, flattened at the sides of his nostrils, showing that he's a trusting, confiding and frank person.

MOUTH
The wide, generous mouth, that crinkles at the corners, demonstrates his amusing, sociable and friendly personality and extravagant, generous, ready response to people.

NECK
His neck is quite long, and this reveals his ready energy and love of action. Those dimples in his cheeks show affection and a loving disposition, tinged with a lack of caution at times in his friendships.

EARS
The ears are forward and low on the side of his head, giving away his love of music, singing and dancing.

CHIN
Shaun doesn't keep many secrets to himself because he enjoys sharing them, and his well-formed chin also shows he has many ambitions for the future.

Nicholas Ball

HAIR
Nicholas has a lot of vitality showing in his face, and one of the things that gives this away is his wiry, very much alive hair. It springs back from his forehead and upwards, showing lots of physical energy and drive.

BROWS
The heavy, thick shaggy eyebrows meeting almost over the bridge of his nose indicate a temperament that's thoughtful, deep and passionate.

EYES
The deep-seated eyes are a sign of persistence and the ability to be practical when necessary. They also reveal an impressionable nature with a genuine curiosity about the world and people around him.

NOSE
The slightly broad top to his nose is a sign of a person who uses the talents given to him to the best of his ability.

MOUTH
The thinner upper lip shows his sensitivity, and yet he has a temper when crossed or under tension, and the fuller lip tells of his generous disposition and sympathy.

HEAD
The overall impression of his face denotes his artistic and creative talents, his imagination, and desire to express his personality through his acting.

Nicholas is emotional, has a slightly sentimental streak, and there's a lot of understanding in his nature, but he's not the type to form superficial attachments. He likes to choose his close friends with care, and he's a difficult person to get really close to.

ARE YOU NICE

THERE are two sides to human nature — the nice, kind, good side and the nasty, mean, bad side. Most of us are a mixture of both good and bad — but what kind of mixture are *you*? Are you a goodie or a baddie? Nice or nasty? Just how do you see yourself and, more important, how do *other* people see you? Well — now's your chance to find out! Just try our fun quiz and find out how nice (or nasty!) you are — and what that means about your relationship with boys!

1. Before an important interview, would you . . .
  a. be so nervous you'd feel positively sick,
  b. make sure you have a good night's sleep and a good breakfast beforehand so you'll be at your best,
  c. keep your fingers crossed and carry your good luck charm with you,
  d. say a quick prayer as you go in, and then leave it all in the hands of Fate?

2. If you were visiting an old church while on holiday, what would you be most likely to think?
  a. It's got a really weird atmosphere.
  b. Just think of all the people who've been here over the years.
  c. Gosh! It's freezing cold in here.
  d. What beautiful colours those stained-glass windows are.

3. There's a market in the town where your friend lives, and you like going there. Which stall would you find most interesting?
  a. The second-hand clothes stall.
  b. The antiques stall.
  c. The flower and plant stall.

  d. The pets and petfoods stall.

4. If you're watching TV with your family, and a sexy statue of a naked woman is shown, would you think . . .
  a. what a lovely body! Wish I looked like that!
  b. gosh, this is a bit embarrassing,
  c. I wonder what Mum and Dad are thinking . . .,
  d. that statue is a really beautiful work of art?

5. While your steady boyfriend is away on holiday, you're asked out by a boy you've fancied for ages. Do you . . .
  a. feel it's wrong, but go anyway, unable to resist him,
  b. indulge your feelings and have fun without feeling guilty,
  c. say no, with a lot of regrets, and still think about him,
  d. say no, but go on feeling guilty for being tempted?

6. When you say hello and goodbye to family and friends, do you . . .
  a. give them all big hugs and kisses,
  b. feel you want to kiss them, but be too shy,
  c. give your mum and dad a peck on the cheek, but that's all,
  d. not kiss or hug anybody: it feel wrong and you don't want to?

7. How would you most like to spend a summer afternoon?
  a. Swimming and sunbathing on a deserted beach.

  b. Having a picnic on a riverbank with friends.
  c. Lying on your back in a sunny park, listening to the sounds all around you.
  d. Taking a neighbour's children to the park to give her a break.

8. What do you think of poetry?
  a. It's OK sometimes — when it's funny.
  b. It's a load of old rubbish.
  c. You like reading it; it fills you with ideas and feelings.
  d. You even *write* it sometimes! You like expressing your feelings in this way.

9. Music's something you probably enjoy. But what's the thing you like most about it?
  a. The great, foot-tapping rhythm of it.
  b. The sheer exhilarating noise.
  c. The patterns you can hear in it.
  d. The words of the songs and the feelings they express.

10. You're at a party where most people seem to be kissing and cuddling. Is your reaction . . .
  a. to blush all over,
  b. to think it's embarrassing but a bit exciting,
  c. to want to join in,
  d. to wonder why they're all behaving like that?

OR NASTY?

11. Which of these would be your favourite smell?
- a. Roasting coffee.
- b. The smell of expensive perfume.
- c. The smell of honeysuckle by a cottage door.
- d. The cool fresh smell of lemon eau de cologne.

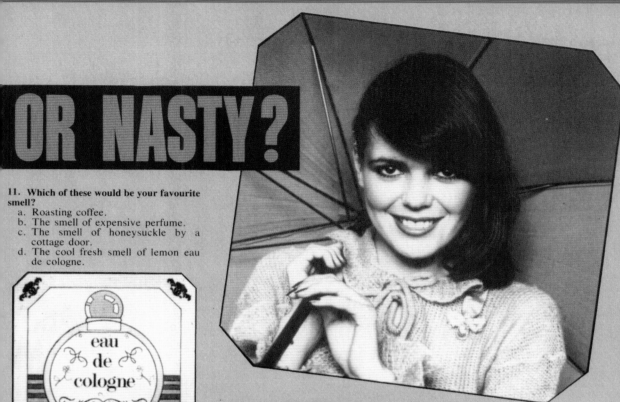

12. Are you attracted to . . .
- a. mainly good-looking boys,
- b. ugly boys sometimes — if they're interesting,
- c. only interesting boys — and you don't always fancy them, either!
- d. ugly boys quite often, 'cos they're usually nicer?

13. You're at a posh dinner and you want to go to the loo. What do you do?
- a. Quietly ask the nearest person where it is, and feel embarrassed.
- b. Go off and look for it on your own, too shy to ask.
- c. Announce, "I must go to the loo!" in a loud voice.
- d. Wait till you get home, even though you're bursting, rather than ask.

QUIZ CONCLUSIONS

Now count your score and turn to the conclusions.

SCORES

1. a-4, b-3, c-2, d-1.	7. a-4, b-3, c-2, d-1.
2. a-1, b-2, c-4, d-3.	8. a-3, b-4, c-2, d-1.
3. a-3, b-1, c-2, d-4.	9. a-3, b-4, c-1, d-2.
4. a-4, b-3, c-2, d-1.	10. a-3, b-2, c-4, d-1.
5. a-3, b-4, c-2, d-1.	11. a-3, b-4, c-2, d-1.
6. a-4, b-3, c-2, d-1.	12. a-4, b-3, c-1, d-2.
	13. a-3, b-2, c-4, d-1.

If you scored 40-52:

You're much more of a baddie than a goodie! But don't worry — all it means is that you're very basic and down-to-earth. You like to enjoy yourself, and your pleasures are eating, drinking, looking at beautiful things — in short, all the pleasures of the senses, including touching! This makes you very affectionate and warm. You probably come from a very cuddly, happy family — you're a lucky girl and a lovable one, too!

Your feelings are all very immediate, and even violent sometimes. You're quite hot-blooded really! You tend to fall suddenly and passionately in love, but you do find it hard to stay loyal for long. The trouble is, you just can't resist your feelings and get swept along by them. In fact, you haven't really got much self-discipline. You probably find it hard to concentrate on work for long!

You're a very physical person. Looks matter to you, you make the most of your own, and go for good-looking guys. You're also active — you enjoy the sheer sensation of swimming, dancing, and bounding around. In fact, you're a real bundle of fun! If people might whisper behind your back that you're a weeny bit empty-headed, or can't control yourself, what do you care?

If you scored 30-39:

You're mostly bad but with one or two good qualities thrown in! Which means you're a straightforward, pleasure-loving, warm person, but occasionally you are plagued by doubts or guilt or ideas which upset you. However, you're still much more likely to be swamped by your feelings than able to reason them away or rise above them. The result, more often than not, is a feeling of conflict — torn between the desire to do something and

the feeling that you mustn't. And you usually go ahead and do it, but feel guilty afterwards!

Boys find you a warm and friendly girl. Easy to get to know, and good fun to be with. As far as being faithful is concerned, you'd be capable of it if the boy was really your type. Try to find a boy who's fond of sports, dancing, and who has a good sense of humour. An intellectual type probably wouldn't suit you so well, and you'd fly off at the first chance — and feel guilty about it!

What you really need to do is work out what pleasures you're going to allow yourself, and enjoy them to the full. And be really firm with yourself about the ones you know you should resist! (Be they jam doughnuts or other people's boyfriends.) If you work hard to develop a bit more self-discipline, you'll be a really well-balanced person!

If you scored 20-29:

You've got your life pretty well sorted out! You understand yourself and your motives, you know how to enjoy yourself, and in some quite sophisticated ways sometimes. But you'd hardly ever let pleasure get in the way of duty. Which means that you're a very nice girl to know: reliable, loyal, and very considerate of other people's feelings. You think before acting and would be unlikely to commit yourself to a relationship with a boy who didn't suit you. And the sort of boy who wouldn't suit you would be a teraway, irresponsible and wild, even though he might be really attractive. Boys find you a bit shy but once they discover your warm, balanced personality, they find you pretty irresistible!

You don't chase after boys. In fact, though you like people a lot, you're also happy just being on your own. Peace and quiet, and a

chance to feel your own feelings and think your own thoughts, is what you need, just occasionally your shyness gets the better of you, and it could lead you to miss a lot of what's out there waiting for you! It might be, for example, that there's a boy who fancies you a lot and is just too shy to do anything about it! He needs encouragement, so try and become a bit more outgoing and confident!

If you scored 13-19:

Where are your wings and halo? 'Cos you're the nearest thing to an angel we've ever heard of! (Unless you cheated?!) This means that you're very highly disciplined. You have incredibly high standards for yourself and other people, and you take a fairly detached, cool and calculating attitude to life. Your sense of duty is strong — so strong, it often interferes with your pleasures. And you like reading, art, and learning more about life. These pleasures are pretty intellectual — you like to use the girl who can be totally faithful to her chosen boy. But that boy had better be pretty wonderful, 'cos you've got such high standards for him that he's almost bound to disappoint you. When he does, though, you'll forgive him . . . you're an angel, after all! The thing that's really missing from your life is good, strong, spontaneous feelings. You're never swept off your feet. (Have angels got feet, anyway?) Even when a really attractive, interesting boy comes along, you're very wary of losing your heart too quickly. A little tiny bit of you wants to — and it would do you good to indulge that little tiny spark from time to time. Go on, let yourself go and really enjoy yourself for once in your life! Otherwise, you'll end up just too good to be true!

65

The one thing there is never any point in doing is slobbing around thinking you're a failure! If you want that boy you fancy to notice you, if you want to be pretty, witty and full of personality, well, you can get halfway there at least by making the very most of things — including yourself! If you want to get the very best out of your life, make a start right now by following our extra-special A - Z which tells you all about how to make the very most of yourself!

A is for ACCIDENTS

Which *will* happen, and they aren't necessarily anyone's fault! So if you're freaking out at the disco, someone trips, and a glass of Coke suddenly pours itself down your new white dress — do *not* scream and collapse into tears! Also, do not immediately punch the offender on the nose! Soak the stain in cold water in the "Ladies," sponge yourself off, pin a smile on your face — and keep on dancing!

B is for BOYS

Without whom, frequently, life wouldn't be worth living! But if you haven't got a boyfriend, don't despair! It could be you just haven't found anyone you fancy enough yet. Boys need to be handled with TLC (tender loving care)! They must *always* be given the impression *they're* the ones doing the chasing! They must *never* be made a fool of in front of their mates! And you've got to remember that most of the time they're just as worried and scared as *you* are!

C is for COSMETICS

In other words, lipsticks, eye-shadows, cleansers, etc. Do not get conned into believing something in terrific packaging costing three times as much as anything else is the best thing out! Quite often own-make brands, like Boots, are *far* better — as well as cheaper! Basic rule to follow with cosmetics is find a make that suits *your* skin, find colours that compliment your own colouring, and stick with them for a bit. Who *needs* 50 different lipsticks, anyway?

D is for DAYDREAMS

Which everybody has, but never get so involved in a daydream you can't be bothered with the reality! Daydreams are great for getting you through boring moments at work or at school or on the bus. They're not so great if you drift off into one when your boy's whispering sweet-nothings in your ear and expecting you to answer him!

E is for EYES

Eyes can send a wealth of different messages from, "I love you" to "Get lost, you creep!" Make the most of yours by using complimenting eyeshadows, lashings of non-run mascara, and lots of fluttering! For tired, dull eyes, first rub a little cold cream round them. Dip some cotton wool in witch-hazel water. Lie down. Close your eyes and put the cotton-wool pads on the eyelids. Relax for ten minutes. If you haven't any witch-hazel, a couple of slices of cucumber will do the same trick!

F is for FASHION

And whether you follow it or not is entirely up to you! Always, though, buy clothes that actually suit *you*, and if they're really fashionable but look hideous — forget them! Keep watching Jackie fashion pages, too, for the brightest and best of what's around.

G is for GROWING-UP

Which is frequently a painful process. Try to remember, though, when Mum gives you a lecture for the 50th time, that *she* had to grow up once, too, and that *her* mum nagged *her*! All sorts of things happen when you're growing-up. Your body starts changing . . . you're happy as a lark one minute — in the depths of gloom and doom the next. Relax! You're normal! We've all gone through it!

H is for HAPPINESS

Which means different things to different people, so if you find you're at your most ecstatic catching falling leaves or cutting your toenails — ignore anybody who says you're a twit! Just go on being happy! Happiness brings a sparkle to your eyes, a bounce to your step, and generally makes you *feel* like a million dollars. And if you feel that way — there's a good chance you'll look it, too!

I is for INVITATIONS

And they're great things to get! But a quick word of warning. If, for example, you're invited back to *his* place to meet his folks —*do not* turn up looking like a Punk crossed with a Mod. This will only terrify his mum and worry his dad! So whenever you receive an invitation — try to find out about where you're going. You'll feel a right nanna turning up at a disco that doesn't allow jeans in your newest shrink to fits, won't you? And an even *bigger* nanna appearing on a cross-country ramble in footless tights and stilettos!

J is for JEALOUSY

Unfortunately, it's one of those feelings we all experience at some time or another. You can get pangs when you see your boyfriend grinning at his old girlfriend. You can be furious when your best friend starts going out with the dishiest boy in town and suddenly can't meet you every night. Panic not! Just try not to let it get on top of you, because if you're feeling jealous you can say, and do, things you'll later regret. So take deep breaths, think twice before you open your mouth, and *try* not to turn green. (It's a lousy complexion colour, anyway!)

THE MOST OF YOURSELF

K is for KEEPSAKE
In other words, that wilted daisy he gave you on your first date and that you've kept ever since! Keepsakes are great sentimental souvenirs — but they do have snags! If you keep *every* wilted daisy he ever gave you in your underwear drawer, you may not have room for your tights! And if you happen to stumble across one of these daisies two days after you've split from him, you'll just burst into tears. Face it — keepsakes will bring back memories, and they'll also be classified by your mum in sarky moments as "all that rubbish!"So clear them out occasionally!

L is for LOVE
Never underestimate the strength of it. Never play about with it. If you're *not* in love with a guy — don't tell him you are. And don't, either, ever fall for the old line of, "If you loved me, you would . . ." If *he* loved you, he wouldn't have said *that* in the first place!

M is for MONDAYS
And there is *nothing* good to say about them! They are vile, endless, dreary days, and the only thing you can do with them is get through them without screaming or killing someone! Try, therefore, to make Monday nights special nights, somehow. (Even if you only stay in, have a luxurious smelly bath, then nip early to bed with Jackie and a mug of cocoa-it's *something* to look forward to, isn't it??)

N is for NOTHINGNESS
That awful feeling quite often associated with Mondays! It's a sort of "ugh" where you don't think anything's going to be the same again, and you *know* nobody'll ever understand you — sniff! sniff! Rubbish! That is a very unpositive attitude and you've got to *do* something about it. Nothingness is a frame of mind, so go and spring-clean your wardrobe immediately, or bake a cake, or take the cat for a game of tennis! As long as you stay active — you'll keep the "ughs" at bay.

O is for OPPORTUNITIES
Which should always be grasped firmly with both hands. People who mumble, "I had the opportunity once . . ." are the saddest people around. Don't be like them! If the chance to do something, or go somewhere, or *be* something, crops up — grab it! It doesn't matter how nervous you feel. What *does* matter is that you don't just sit there thinking, "No, I could *never* do that!". That's just soggy! How d'you know anyway — if you don't try!

P is for PEOPLE
Of whom there are all sorts of different types — nice, nasty, and nothing-very-much. If you don't *know* many people — what're you sitting here reading this for? Go forth *immediately* and join a club full of the species! Or find a penfriend! Or start a "People Need People" Society! The more you know, the more fun you'll have — and the more friends you'll make.

Q is for QUARRELS
Not nice things to have. Somebody's granny once said, "Never let the sun set on a quarrel" — and she had a point! If you walk off in the middle, still yelling at each other, it's that bit more difficult to kiss 'n' make up. So avoid quarrels where humanly possible. If you really can't, have a violently spectacular yelling match and get it all out of your system as fast as possible! Then you can start to calm down — and find out what you're *really* arguing about!

R is for RAIN
Which is very damp, we know, but also does wonders for the complexion! All that soft water trickling down your nose may turn it a delicate shade of purple for an hour or two — but think how soft your skin'll feel! And if you don't believe us — try talking to the plants in the garden. They couldn't survive without the stuff!

S is for SLEEP
Which we all need in order to recharge our batteries. About eight hours a night is average, but some people get by on as little as six — while some need ten! Always have your bedroom window open a bit at night — if you go to sleep in a fugged-up room you'll wake up feeling *ghastly*! Don't have too many heavy bed-clothes — you'll just be uncomfortable. And never have a really heavy meal just at bedtime. Apart from stopping you sleeping, it'll very probably give you indigestion!

T is for TALK
Not the every-day, "How are you? Isn't the weather awful?" kind. More the kind when you're really worried or upset and need help. Finding someone you can talk to, and who'll actually *listen* to you, is worth a great deal, because once you've actually started to put what's on your mind into *words* — the worries and anxieties will seem that bit less.

U is for UGLY
Which you're *not* — even if you *think* you are! You may not have the most spectacular face and figure in the world, but d'you have a nice laugh? Are you good fun? Kind? Sincere? Willing to help people? Kind to dumb animals? Then you're *not* ugly!

V is for VICES
LIke stuffing yourself with cream-cakes when you're supposed to be on a diet! Buying *another* pair of jeans when you really need a dress! Playing disco sounds at top volume and giving the budgie a headache! Vices, little ones, anyway, are sort of self-indulgent things that don't really matter unless they directly affect someone else. But try never to let the *little* vices grow into *big* ones — or you could be in a whole heap of trouble!

W is for WEATHER
Or rather it's for feeling under it, the weather, that is — and if you're feeling ill, for heaven's sake tell someone about it! Don't be afraid to speak to Mum or go to your doctor — they are there to help, you know. And don't think it's smart struggling on with a streaming cold — it's not, especially when you infect everyone else . . .

X is for XMAS
Or one of the times of the year when you will *certainly* eat too much, drink too much, and have *far too many* late nights! If you want to make the most of yourself — don't accept the third slice of Xmas pudding (unless you want to make the most of yourself in a very *large* way!); do go on a diet on Boxing Day; don't go to parties *every* night of the week; but *do* have a thoroughly good time!

Y is for YOGA
And Yoga exercises are very good for trimming flabby figures, helping you relax, and generally easing aches and pains. Join a class and try. At least you'll meet a load of new people that way!

Z is for ZIP
Both the variety you find on the front of jeans — and the variety that means you're full of get-up-and-go! If the first variety doesn't meet — you *need* those Yoga classes! And if you've got plenty of the second kind — then you already *are* making the most of yourself!

Your Jackie Guide To... *Kissing!*

First off, it's not such a great idea to kiss a boy you're not all that interested in, even if he is great to look at. If you don't *like* him then you won't like kissing him, it's as simple as that. For any kiss to work, there's got to be some feeling behind it, so try not to kiss just any boy, especially pushy ones who try to Half-Nelson you into doing it, or you'll only end up regretting it and feeling really let down. Remember — your kisses are precious, they ought to be full of honest feeling, definitely not to be wasted on SLOBS!

OK? Now on to the fascinating subject of kissing and how to kiss . . .

YOU'VE probably imagined what it's like to kiss a boy. In your dreams, everything will be just perfect . . . In real life, though, it might not work out like that, so don't be too let down if it isn't all sweetness and light straight off. Here are a few tips to make all your first kisses that little bit special. Of course, there's no one right way to kiss but the following points to remember might help you out when it comes to the crunch, when he wants to kiss you and you think you might panic and run away from him!

Kiss your mum and tell her how much you appreciate her. Kiss your dad and tell him you think he's great. Kiss your boyfriend and *you don't have to tell him a thing* because here, actions speak much louder than words!

There are kisses and kisses though, and no two kisses are alike — a friendly peck on the cheek, for instance, is a million miles from a wild, passionate mouth-to-mouth clinch! So which kind of kiss should you use where and with whom, and, when you get right down to it — how should you kiss a boy in the first place anyway? Read our extra-special blueprint on all you need to know about kissing and you'll find out!

HOW TO KISS

★ *Be prepared for the fact that he probably* **will** *try to kiss you after he's walked you home, although it could happen any time, any place – at the bus stop, in the disco, in the street . . . It'll help if you remember he's just as nervous as you are, so . . .*

★ *Take a few deep breaths and try to relax.*

★ *Keep your head up, don't stare at the ground.*

★ *Look at him.*

★ *When he moves towards you, don't back away.*

★ *Tilt your head.*

★ *Contact! Your lips meet.*

★ *Move your lips with his, slowly.*

★ *Depending on how things are going, you can stop kissing him now and lay your head on his shoulder. That's all there is to it!*

Once you're with a real, live boy, you ought to find everything goes really smoothly. Just make sure you *like* the boy you're kissing in the first place.

IF YOU DON'T LIKE HIM

If you've only been out with a boy once, and he's taken you home, obviously expecting a late-night snogging session, things can be a bit awkward, especially if you don't want to encourage him. So, once you get to your front door, thank him for a really nice evening, say you'll see him around, then peck him lightly on the cheek, if you like, and go indoors.

Don't allow him to put his arms around you in the first place if you don't want him to, and don't let him kiss you at all if you don't want him to — it'll only make him think you really do like him. So be honest with boys, especially the boys who are nice, not pushy, but whom you don't really fancy.

IF YOU DO LIKE HIM, AND HE LIKES YOU

Here, you'll probably expect your first kiss with him to be out of this world. If it isn't, put it down to nerves and try again. The chances are, though, that your first kiss with a boy you like *will* be wonderful, simply because it's *him* you're kissing!

IF HE WON'T TAKE NO FOR AN ANSWER

If he's too pushy, and he tries to force you to kiss him and you don't really want to, you'll have to tell him to stop. A lot of boys just don't know what's expected of them and so they go completely over the top, especially on first dates. How do you handle a boy like this? You do *not* just stand there and let him do whatever he pleases, that's for sure! You teach him to kiss naturally, the way *you* want to be kissed.

Try to make a joke out of it — say something like, "That may be OK for a female gorilla but I'm a girl." Or simply tell him what he's doing isn't welcome. Ask him to cool it. Or be honest, and tell him you don't *like* it, and will he please stop.

There's absolutely no point whatsoever in pretending to like being kissed in a certain way if you really don't, so for goodness' sake say so. Your boyfriend will probably be glad of it because then he'll stop having to live up to a big he-man image.

KISSING AND LOVEBITES

A lot of girls think lovebites are great and a lot of girls think they're pretty ugly. A lot of boys think that once they give a girl a lovebite that she's his property, while a lot of boys are really turned off by girls with lovebites.

Well, it's up to you really. Most people think kissing is a pretty private and special thing, not something you tell the whole world about. Really, though,

lovebites aren't pretty at all. And do you *really* want your boyfriend to act as if he owned you?

Too obvious lovebites can cause a lot of upsets anyway — your friends think you're a show-off, other boys think of you as being not quite nice, maybe even a bit easy, and as for your parents — it'll hurt them a lot. So is it worth it?

If you don't want lovebites, then tell your boyfriend so.

FRENCH KISSING

French kissing is when you put your tongue into your boyfriend's mouth and he puts his into yours. To a lot of people it's nice and natural. To others it's disgusting. Some people aren't disgusted by it but still don't quite like it.

If *you* don't like it, don't do it, and don't let your boyfriend force you into doing it. He may just be doing it because he thinks that's what you expect or because he thinks it's more grown up, or even a tiny bit daring.

It can be embarrassing to talk openly about your feelings when it comes to the physical side of your relationship with a boy but it's always best to air your views rather than to carry on feeling used and miserable in silence.

So speak up. If there was something he didn't like about you, wouldn't you rather he told you? At least that way, you'd understand each other a whole lot better, and feel even closer than ever.

WHICH KISS SHOULD YOU USE WHERE . . . AND WITH WHOM?

THE FRIENDLY PECK ON THE CHEEK

Use it on a boy you don't want to get serious with. If your evening out together proved a disaster, or even just OK, it's ideal — friendly without being *too* friendly.

THE ROMANTIC KISS

Use it when you're with a boy you really like — one you think you might even get to love!

THE FRENCH KISS

Kiss a boy this way and it ought to mean you've known the boy for some time. French kissing on a first date is a bit pointless and not much fun at all. A lot of boys think you must be pretty experienced if you kiss like this. Well, are you? And can you handle the kind of boy it'll encourage . . . ?

Finally, here are a few do's and dont's to remember. Follow them and you'll keep your kisses really sweet!

Don't *chatter on and on and on because you're nervous at the thought of him kissing you — he'll only think you don't want him to kiss you.*

Do *close your eyes when he kisses you. You don't want any distractions!*

Don't *get into a really heavy session with someone you don't really care about.*

Do *smile or laugh it off if everything does go drastically wrong, if you gulp really loudly, or if your false tooth falls out! Show him you've got a great sense of humour and he'll come back for more . . . and more!*

HOW TO PUT HIM OFF YOU!

If you've fancied a certain boy for a while and you want him to start noticing you, it's up to *you* to take the first step — and here's just how *not* to go about it!

AT THE DISCO

Boys are at discos to eye up the talent basically, and, if there's plenty of other female talent around, you have to be *very* careful about what you do and say. Don't dress up outrageously just to catch his eye. You'll catch his eye, all right, and he'll probably have a good laugh at how stupid you look in your leopardskin leotard and orange wig. Don't make an exhibition of yourself by jumping about like a kangaroo on hot desert sand while grinning insanely at him as you jump above the crowd. He *won't* be impressed!

On the other hand, don't stand there trying to look so cool that ice wouldn't melt in your mouth. It may be OK for Clint Eastwood to chew gum and wear shades — but you'll look out of place in down-town Barnsley. And don't stay with your friends for *every* dance — he'll be frightened to approach you! If you *must* be with your mates, don't keep getting the giggles and pointing at him as if he was some prize ape in a monkey house. If you're desperate for him to notice you, don't pretend to fall over in front of him (that's too obvious), and don't walk up and say, "Don't I know you from somewhere?" (that's even more obvious).

Suppose he actually asks you to dance. Try not to ignore him. You know how it is — you *really* fancy the guy so you look at the floor, other people, the ceiling — anywhere but at *him* while you're dancing! On the other hand, don't grin at him with a fixed smile like a finalist in Miss World, and don't for goodness' sake hang around his neck murmuring, "Oh, this means so much to me."

If he offers you a drink, ask for diluted orange, because most boys don't like expensive girls. Above all, don't try to be something you aren't or you're not going to get very far before he sees that you've tried to fool him. Remember that whatever you do he still won't think you're a patch on Hot Gossip, and if he does come over to ask you to dance, don't run to the loo first to fix your face. He won't be there when you get back!

AT SCHOOL

Either he's a new boy or he's been around for ages and is suddenly, quite gorgeously, different and grown-up. Whatever the reason, you fancy him like mad and you know you've got to do something about it. Try not to let your friends know, or they'll make your life a misery. Despite all their promises not to tell a soul, Anne'll tell Mary, who'll tell her brother, whose best mate's Jim, who lives next door to Brian — and HIS name is Brian, then your secret love's no secret any more.

If you travel on the same bus, and you get on first, don't keep the other half of your seat covered with your bag, only to whip it off and smile charmingly at him

when he gets on. Don't deliberately fall on top of him going down the bus stairs, either. He'll just wish you'd drop dead when you arrive in Ward 7 with your stupid smile and a bunch of grapes.

Don't drop your schoolbooks in front of him. He'll either step over them, or pick them up thinking what a clumsy fool you are and he's never even *likely* to fancy you. It's not a good idea to write *I love Brian* all over your bag, the desk, or the blackboard either, because besides being terribly unsubtle, *he'll* be mortified.

Don't change your whole timetable just so that you can sit next to him in Maths or Physics either — this could ruin your whole future career. Also he'll think you're a banana when you say circumference was one of the knights of the Round Table! Don't do stupid things like joining the same clubs as him if you're hopeless at badminton, shocking at swimming, or you don't know which way up to hold the cricket bat — you don't want him laughing as you crash into the net, drown, or knock yourself, rather than the cricket ball, for six!

AT THE LAUNDERETTE

Launderettes are very boring places, where a lot of deep thinking goes on — simply because there's nothing to do but watch the washing go round or fall asleep! Staring at the washing swirling around is conducive to deep thought, so there he is, thinking about tomorrow's home game, not really seeing anything.

Don't disturb him until he sighs deeply and turns to the newspaper or starts chewing his nails. This means he's done

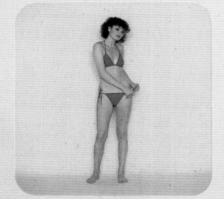

with the thinking — maybe his brain was starting to hurt. So don't start slamming things about, throwing your washing all over, crashing money into the machine, singing "I Got The Washday Blues" and generally being a noisy nuisance.

Don't take along your grottiest undies, mum's tea-towels with half a pot of soup over them and your dog's blanket. He'll think you're a slob and that the dog's blanket is actually *your* blanket.

If, or rather when, you get fed up, don't let him catch you picking at your nose, ears, etc. If you do need change for the machine or the powder dispenser, don't be so obvious as to ask him for it when the woman in charge is in front of you! He'll know straightaway that you're after him.

But don't pretend to be a big know-all about how everything works. If you're lucky, he'll show you how to put the powder in, if you're not, he'll ignore you. Don't for goodness' sake sit down next to him and say, "Nice 'ere, innit?" For one thing, you probably don't look the slightest bit like Lorraine Chase . . .!

THE BOY NEXT DOOR

There's something quite sweet about fancying the boy next door — it's sort of, well, homely, somehow, and *nice*. But unless you go about things the right way and have him fancying you, too, just think how awful it'll be for the poor bloke if he can't get away from you because his house is stuck on to yours!

Don't be too obvious. This means *not* brushing your teeth at the bathroom window every morning when he goes out to feed his rabbit, undressing behind the net curtains in your bedroom every night, or hanging over the garden fence looking for your earring every time the poor guy sets foot outside the back door.

Don't do up your bedroom window to look like a Barbara Cartland boudoir, i.e. single red roses, heart mobiles, volumes of love sonnets, or teddy bears with arms outstretched to next door's drying green — he'll just think you're a soft weedie, or a weedy softie. It's a waste of time spending every free minute gardening for your dad hoping that he'll notice you because it'll only make your hands rough, you'll get cold and fed up, and it's very likely that he'll just think you're a mad keen gardener and the two of you have nothing in common.

Playing blaring pop music, screeching along with The Skids, bellowing to The Boomtown Rats and other such raving

things might convince him that you're a raver, but he'll want you to rave off and do it elsewhere. (This could also make you unpopular with his parents.) Also, don't peer into his parents' lounge window on every one of the hundred occasions you just accidentally-on-purpose happen to be walking past every day. The family, including him, will hate you for being a nosey, gawping ninny, and they'll probably complain to your parents.

AT THE LIBRARY

It could be that you have to use the library for a school project, or even for your own amusement. So one day you stroll in, and there's this lovely guy absorbed in a book at one of the tables. So what don't you do? You *don't* make a noise — not even a discreet little cough, or you'll be *most* unpopular.

Dropping the Encyclopaedia Brittanica is a bit risky — and dangerous. He'd notice you all right, but the thing might land on your foot, and if it gets damaged you'll have to fork out (for the book, not your foot!). He'll also think you're a clumsy oaf with no respect for books (presumably he's fairly keen on the things, or he wouldn't be there).

Don't walk up to him and say, "Excuse me, but I think you have the book I want." He's bound to ask politely how long you've been into agricultural engineering or nuclear physics.

If he's obviously studying and taking notes, don't offer to sharpen his pencil, clean his glasses, turn the pages, etc. He's probably feeling quite irritable enough without your kind offers to interrupt him. If you do manage to get a seat opposite him, don't drop things on the floor just so that you can have the thrill of getting near his feet under the table! He'll soon twig to what you're doing, and you might get kicked. Likewise, don't tie his shoelaces together in the hope that he'll see the funny side of it all when he stands up and falls flat on his face. Studious types often aren't too hot on the humour.

Try not to get into a heavy situation you can't cope with. That is to say, pick books with care before you sit opposite him. It's no good getting involved in a literary discussion over the selected works of Tolstoy that you picked off the shelf, when the nearest you've ever been to "War And Peace" is fighting your kid brother for the last piece of chewing gum — and losing.

How Moody Are You?

IF you want to know what sort of mood you're in and what you should and should *not* do about it, try our special quiz and we'll tell you! It's quite simple — first of all, choose your favourite colour of the moment, and just answer the questions that appear in that colour section. Your score will direct you to a certain part of the conclusions, and that'll tell you all about you and your mood of the moment!

If you find it hard to choose one colour, not to worry! You can pick two or three colours (but not more). Then, answer ALL the questions in those sections. Divide your score by two if you used two colours, or divide it by three if you used three colours.

You can do the quiz another day, if you feel in a different mood. Choose a different colour (or colours) and you'll get a different answer, to help you with your mood of that particular moment!

IF YOUR FAVOURITE COLOUR IS RED:

You start with a score of 100 in this section. Deduct the points given.

1. Would you like to have your bedroom decorated in reds?
Would you wear an all-red outfit?
Would you fancy a meal in a café decorated all in red?
  a. Yes to all 3 — deduct 1 point.
  b. Yes to 2 — deduct 2 points.
  c. Yes to 1 or none — deduct 5 points.

2. Do you ever dream of blood?
  a. Yes. Deduct 1 point.
  b. No. Deduct 5 points.

3. Choose a word from the following group: sincere, straightforward, positive, forward, action, definite.
  a. If you chose straightforward or action, deduct 1 point.
  b. If you chose forward, deduct 2 points.

  c. If you chose positive or definite, deduct 3 points.
  d. If you chose sincere, deduct 5 points.

4. Would it put you off a boy if someone said he was aggressive, even if you hadn't met him?
  a. No. Deduct 1 point.
  b. It might put you off, but you'd still meet him and decide for yourself. Deduct 2 points.
  c. Definitely you wouldn't want to meet him. Deduct 5 points.

IF YOUR FAVOURITE COLOUR IS YELLOW:

You start with a score of 80 in this section. Deduct the points given.

1. Do you enjoy eating yellow food (cheese, butter, eggs, etc.)?
Would you wear yellow shoes with a yellow dress?
Would you like a bed with yellow sheets and covers?
  a. Yes to all 3 — deduct 1 point.
  b. Yes to 2 — deduct 2 points.
  c. Yes to 1 or none — deduct 5 points.

2. Do your problems seem less serious when the sun is shining?
  a. Not particularly. Deduct 5 points.
  b. Yes, usually. Deduct 1 point.

3. Choose a word from the following group: cheerful, bright, happy, fortunate, lucky, smile.
  a. If you chose smile, deduct 1 point.
  b. If you chose fortunate or lucky, deduct 2 points.
  c. If you chose any of the others, deduct 5 points.

4. If you spent the evening with your boyfriend and he was moody or unhappy the whole time for no reason, would you feel your romance was on its last legs?
  a. No. Deduct 1 point.
  b. Maybe — it would depend on your own mood. Deduct 2 points.
  c. Yes. Deduct 5 points.

IF YOUR FAVOURITE COLOUR IS GREEN:

You start with a score of 60 in this section. Deduct the points given.

1. Do you make a point of eating a lot of vegetables because you think they're good for you?
Do you think it's unlucky to bring certain green plants indoors — like lilac branches or hawthorn?
Do you like green as a colour but find it impossible to wear?
  a. No to all 3 — deduct 1 point.
  b. No to 2 — deduct 2 points.
  c. No to 1 or none — deduct 5 points.

2. Do you find that a room with pale-green walls has a calming effect on you?
a. Yes. Deduct 1 point.
b. No. Deduct 5 points.

3. Choose a word from the following group: belief, choice, attitude, thought, care, decide.
a. If you chose care, deduct 1 point.
b. If you chose belief or thought, deduct 2 points.
c. If you chose decide, deduct 3 points.
d. If you chose choice or attitude, deduct 5 points.

4. What do you think is the ideal length of time for an engagement?
a. It varies according to the temperaments of the couple. Deduct 1 point.
b. 18 months or less. Deduct 2 points.
c. More than 18 months. Deduct 5 points.

IF YOUR FAVOURITE COLOUR IS BLUE:

You start with a score of 40 in this section. Deduct the points given.

1. Would you like an outfit in shades of blue?
There aren't many natural blue foods — would you fancy eating ordinary food like potatoes or bread if it were coloured blue? Would you like your bedroom to be decorated in shades of blue?
a. Yes to all 3 — deduct 1 point.
b. Yes to 2 — deduct 2 points.
c. Yes to 1 or none — deduct 5 points.

2. Do you believe in the saying, "Pink makes the boys wink, blue makes the boys true"?
a. Yes. Deduct 5 points.
b. No. Deduct 1 point.

3. Choose a word from the following group: tension, argument, tiff, bicker, sulk.
a. If you chose argument, deduct 1 point.
b. If you chose bicker or tiff, deduct 2 points.
c. If you chose any other, deduct 5 points.

4. How long do you feel it would take you to get over the break-up of a relationship with a boy you've been seeing regularly for six months, and he did the breaking-up?
a. You'd never completely get over it. Deduct 5 points.
b. You'd have forgotten your sorrows in six months. Deduct 1 point.
c. It would take more than six months to forget. Deduct 2 points.

IF YOUR FAVOURITE COLOUR IS PURPLE:

You start with a score of 20 in this section. Deduct the points given.

1. Do you fancy the idea of yourself in a matching lavender nightie and negligee? When you eat coloured Smarties, do you eat the purple ones first? Do you think pansy-purple eye-shadow looks sexy?
a. Yes to all 3 — deduct 1 point.
b. Yes to 2 — deduct 2 points.
c. Yes to 1 or none — deduct 5 points.

2. Do you dream in colour?
a. Yes. Deduct 1 point.
b. Don't usually remember dreams, so can't tell. Deduct 2 points.
c. No. Deduct 5 points.

3. Choose a word from the following group: star-crossed, misfortune, fate, weird, jinx.
a. If you chose misfortune or weird, deduct 1 point.
b. If you chose fate or jinx, deduct 2 points.
c. If you chose star-crossed, deduct 5 points.

4. Do you feel that somewhere there is a boy who is exactly right for you, and it's just a matter of luck bringing you together?
a. Yes. Deduct 5 points.
b. No. Deduct 1 point.
c. You think there is more than one. Deduct 2 points.

Now count up your score (remember, if you scored for TWO COLOURS, *halve your score*, if you scored for THREE COLOURS, *divide your score by three* and turn to the conclusions.

QUIZ CONCLUSIONS

89-99 points: Steady — you could be heading for a big row or a challenge of some sort. Take a little more time to make sure that what you're going is what you really want. Did you feel like this a week ago? Then the action you're considering could be right. If not — if you just woke up today in this dashing, crazy mood — try to put off decisions until tomorrow!

80-88 points: You're in a very positive mood at the moment, and this would be a good time to be more daring and outgoing than normal. So if you have a favour to ask, a rise to seek, or want to put your foot down, now's the time. But make sure you have all your facts right, first!

69-79 points: You're a bit too casual at the moment about everything! You have lots of confidence, but are maybe a bit too impulsive for your own good. If you're thinking of spending more than one week's money on one particular purchase, think about it for at least 24 hours.

60-68 points: You're a fairly happy-go-lucky person anyway, and today is a good day for you. Things will run very smoothly so now is the right time to tackle any chores that you've been putting off! It's also a good time to think of a change in your normal routine.

49-59 points: You're entering a more serious mood than you've been in and the next 24 hours could be important. Don't be too outspoken — remember, people aren't always as good at keeping secrets as they could be. This isn't a time to make snap judgments about important things like a job, a boyfriend, or a holiday. Take time to think about it!

40-48 points: You've got everything going for you, but you must act positively to take advantage of opportunities. What you need is some friendly help, just a friend to talk things over with. It could help you a lot to take exercise, you'll find it easier to relax mentally and physically afterwards.

29-39 points: A bit ratty or edgy today then, are we? You're probably regretting something you said or did earlier. It's much better to kiss and make up than brood if it's a boyfriend. Try to put things right with a friendly word or two. It could be you are normally more easy going, but you're feeling tense at the moment and need to relax. Try to get more relaxation and a good cry to get it out of your system will probably work wonders!

20-28 points: You're going through rather an unhappy phase. You definitely need a bit of cheering up so this would be a good time to indulge yourself in your favourite treat! Don't be ashamed of feeling a bit weepy, a good cry to get it out of your system will probably work wonders!

9-19 points: Could jealousy be your big problem today? Remember, if you have a problem it's much better to do something positive about solving it, rather than just brood over it. Whatever you do, don't try to solve it in some underhand or sneaky way — that'll just make things worse!

0-8 points: You're a very emotional person, and you depend a lot on luck. If you tried to be less guided by your heart and relied more on your own brains and talent, you'd be happier and probably make more of a success of your life! And you have quite a lot of sex appeal even though you don't think you do, so don't under-rate yourself! Go out and make a splash!

WHAT LINE IS HE HANDING YOU?

Everybody has their destiny in the palm of their hands — literally! All you have to know is how to read it. In this special feature we explain how palmistry works so that you can learn all about the secrets of a boy's true romantic nature. So read on . . . then tenderly take hold of his hand . . . and all his secrets will be revealed!

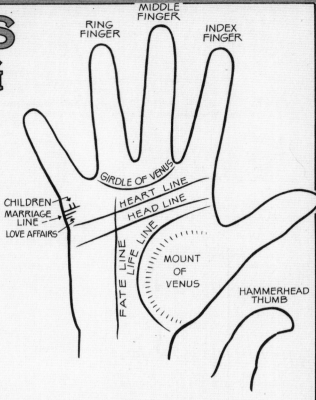

STAR ✳   ISLAND ⊸   FORK ⊰   CROSS ✚

HOW TO READ HIS HANDS

The lines on his hands show his character and what's likely to happen to him, and *you* if you're with him!

The Heart line, for instance, runs across his palm above the Head line and it reveals the secrets of his romantic feelings.

He's very romantic if his Heart line is a deep strong line that cuts well into his hand. He's a boy who's never bored with love and will always be interesting to be with.

But you'll *never* receive a love letter from a boy whose Heart line runs straight across his palm without a curve. He's definitely too direct and unromantic for such sentimentality. So if it's a romantic boy you're looking for then a boy whose Heart line swoops across his palm is the one for you!

But be on your guard! If his Heart line runs *too* far across his palm, he's a boy who only imagines he's in love. He may be in love with *love* and not with *you!*

Broken marriages break the Heart line, palmists say, but a happy marriage is in store for the boy with a Heart line beginning under his index finger and running strong and unbroken across his palm.

A boy's Heart line will also show his romantic sorrows. Each small line extending down from his Heart line and each break in the Heart line is a disappointment in love.

If you want to know how much a boy's head rules his heart, compare the Head and Heart lines. Whichever line is deeper and longer rules the other. You'll have quite a time swaying the emotions of a boy with a faint Heart line and a strong Head line.

But a boy with a strong Heart line and weak Head line is bound to be over emotional and impractical in love. So, go for a boy with lines of equal strength.

Be cautious with a boy whose Heart line curves sharply upward in a right angle towards his fingers. He tends to act impulsively in love without thinking of the consequences — and you could be the one to suffer.

IS HE SEXY?

Yes he is, if the pad called the Mount of Venus, extending from the base of his thumb into the centre of his palm is fleshy and well developed! His sexiness is also shown by the Girdle of Venus, a semicircular line running from between the index and middle finger to a space between the ring and little finger.

When this line is strong he's a boy more interested in a girl's physical attributes than her personality! He's probably a male chauvinist, so beware! If broken in several places, he's a boy who makes many physical attachments but no long-lasting emotional ties. He'll be good fun if you don't try to tie him down.

HIS ROMANCES AND MARRIAGE

*A boy who wants to keep his past from a girl should **never** let her look at the small horizontal lines on the side of his hand under his little finger. So try to take a look before he realises what it means! Each weak line is a love affair and the deeper ones represent a marriage. You may even find **yourself** in his hand. If you're romantically involved with him you'll certainly be one of the weaker lines, at least!*

A long engagement is in store for the boy whose Marriage line begins with a fork. But if it ends in a fork *this marriage will end in divorce or separation.*

HIS FAULTS

The larger the thumb the stronger the ego and ambition. Girls unwilling to do just what a boy wants should avoid boys with large, long thumbs. He'll want to keep you under *his* control. A domineering boy may also have an index finger as long as his ring finger or a thumb which curves backwards like a hammerhead. Such a boy may be overbearing and childish so you'd probably do well to avoid him.

But a boy with a weak, small thumb and short index finger will let himself be nagged by a girl — he may also sweep a girl off her feet with promises he can't keep. So you won't want *him* either!

A short thumb that does not extend to the middle joint of the index finger is a sign of lack of will-power or sense of responsibility. This type of boy may let you down. If his thumb is flexible and bends easily away from his hand, he is generous and easy going and will make a great boyfriend. If his thumb lacks flexibility and does not bend easily away from his hand, he is stubborn and probably mean over money.

So now you know *his* **destiny — if only he'll let you take a look at his hands!**

We all know what girls are scared of . . . but what are *boys* scared of? We know boys aren't supposed to be scared of anyone or anything, but we went ahead anyway and asked a handful of boys for their honest, considered opinions about the things that frighten them — and we came up with all sorts of fascinating answers, on all sorts of fascinating subjects! Here are our results — we're sure they'll change your attitudes to the boys in *your* life . . .

THINGS THAT SCARE BOYS

NOT BEING NORMAL

Sean, 19: "You wouldn't believe the hang-ups some blokes have about their bodies. I worried like mad because I didn't start shaving till I was nearly 18. What made it even worse was my best mate had a moustache growing when he was 12! I felt like a freak. The first hair on my chest was a landmark for me too — I felt dead butch, like a man at last! It sounds stupid but little things like that can give you incredible hang-ups. It's even worse for small blokes, because they can get these terrible inferiority complexes, especially where girls are concerned — I mean, it's not much fun being 5 feet nothing when the girl you're mad about is a cool 5 ft. 6 in. now, is it? It's much easier for girls than it is for boys, because girls aren't as cruel to each other, and they don't have as much to live up to . . ."

SHOWING THEIR FEELINGS

Danny, 18: "I don't think boys are all *that* different to girls when it comes to feelings — it's just when it comes to showing their feelings that most blokes completely freeze up. I'm pretty squeamish for instance, and my very first girlfriend dropped me because of it! It's funny now, but it wasn't then because I felt a complete failure. Her nose started to bleed really badly one night — so badly that I fainted in front of some of her mates just as we were going into a disco. Now, I suppose, I go over the top — go to the other extreme and act all big and tough and manly. It's not me, really, but I think that's the image most girls go for. Boys have got to hide their feelings more than girls. It's the same with girls though — they hide their feelings and pretend they're what they're not just as much as we do."

MARRIAGE

Joe, 17: "I do want to get married — one day, but not now. One of my best mates who's 18 got married about six months ago — he had to because the girl was pregnant, and even I can see it's just not going to work out between them. I feel really sorry for him because he's made such a mess of his life. He hardly ever goes out with the lads anymore and when he does, his wife — *she's* only just turned 17 — kicks up a fuss. I don't want to end up like that. I'm going to get myself a really good job, play the field and meet lots of girls then settle down when I'm about 30. Why tie yourself to a wife and baby, all that responsibility, when your life's really only just beginning? I think girls are a lot to blame. All they think about is a ring and babies. They can't see in front of their noses."

GOING TOO FAR

Sam, 15: "Sex is everywhere — on films, TV, books, magazines, and most guys do think about it a lot. I know I do. Well, it's hard not to think about it. I hate the way everything's so one-sided though — you know, guys supposed to be after *just one thing*. Well, I'm not. I know a lot of guys are but some girls just ask for it, the way they dress and behave. If they could hear the things some guys say about them behind their backs . . .! Most girls are pushovers — they go all lovey-dovey and will do anything for a guy with the right line of patter — or at least, that's what a lot of my mates say. Most of them talk a lot of hot air though, so you end up not knowing what to believe. A lot of guys are really unsure when you get down to it, though. I mean, where do you draw the line? I think everything should go a lot more slowly than it does. I mean, it's not the end of the world if you don't have sex by the time you're 15. There are too many pressures on young people today. The whole thing is so mixed-up. I don't think magazines like yours help things either." (Well!)

GIRLS

Ian, 15: "At our school there are three kinds of girls — the snobby ones who are dead flash, — flash clothes, make-up, the works, the kind who are caught up in the "who's going out with who and him — I wouldn't look at him twice he's not good enough for me" syndrome; the really nice girls who aren't loud and pushy; and the yobbos — the girls who are all tough and big-mouthed. I'd really like to get to know the nice ones. The other ones I couldn't care less about and I just wouldn't want to talk to them. But it's really hard, and a bit scary too, trying to break the ice. It's still up to the boy to talk to them first, to ask them out and generally do all the running, which isn't easy to do, especially if you haven't even been out with a girl yet. Girls are like things from another planet. I just don't understand them. A guy like me finds it really hard to break the ice — I think most blokes do at first."

Finally (whew!) we think Colin deserves the last word. He's big enough to admit that lots of things scare him . . .

Colin, 16: "What am I scared of? Well, chatting up girls in groups for a start — I hate that. It's the same asking a girl to dance when she's with her mates. One thing I dread is when a mate and I get two girls up to dance and I get the ugly one who won't go away.

"Then there's bed-wetting, at a mate's house. Being made to look a fool by her elder brother in front of her family and knowing that I can't smash him one in the face 'cos that won't do me any good. Taking a new girl to an X film and not being able to get in. Getting beaten up. Being turned down after plucking up the courage to ask a girl out. Will that do?"

Did you know that what you write in your diary gives away an awful lot about what you're *really* like? Everyone's diary is different — as you can see from the pages we've sneaked from the diaries of five very different girls. All *you* have to do is compare their scribblings to yours, decide which is nearest your style — and find out the secrets which are lurking in the pages of your diary. (A double reason for keeping it under lock and key!)

ARE YOU A WRITE GIVE~ AWAY?

WET WENDY'S DIARY

MONDAY Felt sick, but Mum said I had to go to school, worse luck. Felt worse in Biology — no wonder, we were dissecting a horrible THING. Not sure what it was exactly, because didn't dare look at it. But Theresa threw a bit of it at me so I ran out screaming and went to the medical room to lie down.

TUESDAY Still felt very shaky after yesterday. There wasn't any hot water to wash in because the switch was off. And when I cleaned my teeth, my gums bled. I expect I've got that awful disease which makes your teeth fall out.

WEDNESDAY School dentist came so hid in the toilet. At break, John Greenfield came up, got talking and asked me out on Friday. I'm sure he was just taking the mickey so I told him I had to go to my gran's.

THURSDAY Theresa says I should have one of those new haircuts. But my hair's like old rats' tails and nothing would do any good. My hands are mottled today — I wonder if I'm going down with something?

FRIDAY Had a bit of a sore throat today. Theresa says John Greenfield really fancies me — but I don't believe her. How could he fancy me? How could anybody? Looking forward to watching TV all tomorrow.

If Your Diary's Like Wendy's . . .

We all feel like Wendy from time to time — when things go wrong. But nobody's that much of a failure. Everybody's got something going for them. When a boy asks you out, don't assume he's got to be joking. He just might be serious and attracted to you — there's no accounting for tastes!

Try increasing your self-confidence. For a start, endless fretting about your health is silly — it's usually a sign that you've got nothing whatever wrong with you.

If your life consists of watching TV, just get up and go — OUT! Anywhere: for a walk, for a bike-ride. You're far too shy — and when it comes to boys you assume you have nothing to offer, so no wonder you don't get asked out anywhere! Join a few clubs, get your free time organised so you spend it with a drama group, or a photography club, or whatever, and forget about your imaginary problems and worries!

DOROTHY DREAMER

MONDAY A strange and weird day. Dark clouds — all the birds are silent. Why? Came bottom in Geography test. Spent Needlework lesson dreaming about the French assistant M. Plaque. Miss Sullivan read us a ghost story today in English. I was so scared I had to hold on to my desk. M. Plaque still away. I wonder what's wrong.

TUESDAY M. Plaque still away. If only I could be by his bedside and nurse him back to health . . . sponge his brow and brew up his hot lemon drink. I saw a flower in a hedgerow today, picked it and made a wish.

WEDNESDAY It came true! M. Plaque came back! And that rhymes! Maybe I will write a poem about it! He looks very pale but terrifically romantic.

THURSDAY I bit my ruler in half today when M. Plaque walked past the classroom window. Splinters in the gum quite painful, but for him I could bear anything.

FRIDAY M. Plaque trod on me! It was *wonderful!* He said *pardon* in his lovely French voice and looked into my eyes! I shall never wash my foot again! He *touched* me! Came bottom in History and Maths. Got run over tonight outside school, but not seriously. Was looking up at French-room windows at the time.

If Your Diary's Like Dorothy's . . .

Dreaming about things (or to be more exact, boys!) is natural. But being in such a dream about them that you're out of touch with reality is another matter. And what's more, it's a very stupid state to be in. Whilst you're dreaming about Mr Right, a real flesh-and-blood boy might be trying to catch your eye . . . and failing!

It's also pretty dangerous to get yourself into such a romantic frame of mind that you believe in things like premonitions. When you think you're being psychic or feeling that something strange is going to happen, you're probably only just indulging your moods.

As far as boys are concerned, you're too interested in them. It's natural to be interested. But not to think of nothing else. So give yourself a break, and get going with some pastimes that will extend you as a person. Languishing in a romantic dream-world is *not* the answer to life's problems!

VAIN VICKY

MONDAY Woken by golden light streaming in through my curtains. The trees are covered with blossom and I have got a huge spot on my chin. A new boy got on the bus today: tall and dark, with smouldering eyes and a sulky mouth. I turned my face away so he wouldn't see my spot.

TUESDAY Washed my hair in the new **Extract of Dogrose and Cowparsley** shampoo. Smells awful — like a goat with B.O. Today my spot was worse: like a Belisha beacon. Covered it with make-up and buried my face in my scarf.

WEDNESDAY I wish Dad wouldn't wear that awful old suit. He collected me from school today because of the bus strike, and everyone could see his lapels were the wrong shape. I could've *died*.

THURSDAY A fantastic day! I shall remember this day as long as I live! The boy on the bus sat by me! I could feel his shoulder against mine! He's got the most beautiful hands — big, and brown. What's more my spot popped yesterday so I didn't have to hide my face. If only we didn't have to wear school uniform.

FRIDAY He didn't turn up. Good job, too, 'cos there was a girl on the bus who was really fantastic looking. The cow. It's not fair. Beautiful sunset today. Washed my hair in **Extract of Barley and Groundsel**. Smells foul.

If Your Diary's Like Vicky's . . .

If you think you're a bit like Vicky, well, relax a little. It's not the end of the world if you've got a spot or a blemish.

People like Vicky who are interested in beauty are usually aware of all sorts of other beauty in the world — not just their own! This is great. You probably like looking at paintings or sculpture, or just enjoying the wonders of nature. Flowers, sea-shells, feathers — you love them all, you like to collect them.

You're much too aware of your looks when it comes to meeting boys, though. You try to stun them with your beauty, whereas most boys would feel more comfortable just talking casually with a girl to break the ice.

PRACTICAL PAULA

MONDAY Got up early. Was just about to go jogging in the park when Mum asked me to go to the corner shop for some milk 'cos of the milkmen's strike. So I jogged to the shop and back. The result? A milk-shake! (Ho ho!) Mended Steve's bike puncture this evening.

TUESDAY Overslept till 7.30. In an awful rush. Forgot to feed the hamster, didn't have time to clean my shoes or iron my skirt. (Or iron the hamster, ho ho!) Hopeless day. Couldn't do hockey because of the rain.

WEDNESDAY At youth club played Steve at table tennis. Beat him hollow. He seemed fed up. It's his birthday next week. I said I'd make him a cake. That cheered him up. He *must* ask me out soon.

THURSDAY At weight-training tonight, a bloke twisted his ankle. I gave him the old first-aid treatment, and the coach was very impressed. I hope Steve noticed, but I think he was talking to that wet girl Mandy Pillick. She always comes to watch. Never lifts a finger though. (Nor a bar-bell, ho ho!)

FRIDAY I was really enjoying myself tonight making a yoghurt machine out of a few old milk-bottles and a mousetrap, when Sheila had to come round and drag me off to the disco. She said Steve would be there. He was . . . wrapped around Mandy Pillick.

If Your Diary's Like Paula's . . .

If you feel you might be a bit like Paula, well . . . congratulations! You've certainly made the most of your talents and learned a lot of skills that'll help you get on well with people. You'll always be invaluable to any group of people. You're cheery, you crack jokes, you're great in a crisis . . .

If you haven't got a boyfriend, or have trouble keeping them, you're probably putting them off by being too good at everything, too organised. *Ask* him things instead of *telling* him. There's nothing wrong with being a tomboy, but let him know you're a real girl underneath!

SUSAN SWOT

MONDAY Great day. The maths test was everything I'd been hoping for. Had a very good talk with Mark Smith at break, about the maths test. We argued about question 6. He said the answer was $ab_2 = qrt + 2.008 + zrt = 700.000006$ but I disagreed.

TUESDAY Found a terrific old book in the second-hand bookshop: called Ferrier's **Functions of the Brain**. Great stuff. Read it secretly under the desk in the needlework lesson. Pricked myself twice. Blood is interesting. I'd like to do an experiment measuring people's clotting rates.

WEDNESDAY Smashing concert on Radio 3: a new concerto for Harp, Flute and Elastic Band by Erich Twitterguts. I wonder if Mark was listening to it. I thought of him in the slow movement.

THURSDAY Asked Mark if he'd heard the concert, but he said he'd been over at the **Hope and Anchor** in Whistley, watching a band called **The Snots**. Sometimes Mark surprises me. I wonder what his clotting rate is.

FRIDAY Results of maths test! Mark was top but he did get No. 6 wrong! I was second — but I don't mind him being top sometimes. Janice says Mark might take more notice of me if I plucked my eyebrows and maybe my nostrils as well, but I know he's above such things. Read 288 pages of **War and Peace** and fell asleep to the sound of Beetroothoven's Fifth Symphony.

If Your Diary's Like Susan's . . .

If your diary extract is a bit like Susan's, it's obvious that you're highly intelligent, and very academic. Being interested in school work isn't odd — for some people it's only natural. We can't all sit goggling at *Top Of The Pops*.

When it comes to boys, you're a bit frightening to some boys because they find clever girls are a threat to them. But you *needn't* be a threat if you're just relaxed and friendly. Bright boys like bright girls to talk to.

So if you're a bit like Susan, be patient with boys. Talk to them about everyday things as well as the problems of the universe! And don't be ashamed if you want to doll yourself up now and then. Why shouldn't you be clever *and* pretty? It's a winning combination!

SPOT THE GROT

First, check that a Grot *is* what you've got by —
HIS APPEARANCE

His appearance isn't the best guide to a Grot. Some Grots are scruffy, some are smart, some are in-between. But a too scruffy guy who obviously doesn't care what he looks like is likely not to care too much about the girls in his life, either. And that makes him a Grot.

At the other end of the scale, watch out for the *too* neat, *too* smart and *too* well-dressed guy. Ask yourself how he gets that way. All those clean shirts, the perfect creases in his trousers. You can bet he doesn't get as immaculate as that by himself. So he's already got *one* devoted slave pandering to him. Has he got you lined up as Number 2? Then he's a Grot.

THE WAY HE SPENDS HIS MONEY ON YOU

Is he generous? It's important here to separate the poor guy who's low on cash from the genuine meanie Grot. Your genuine poor-as-a-church-mouse guy will happily fork out to buy you an ice-cream. The Grot will fuss about buying you an ice-cream but he'll let you have a lick of his. Even though he could afford 100 ice-creams.

The Grot is likely to carry a purse. Men with purses are careful of the pennies. There's nothing wrong with that, but combine it with the Grot and you've got a first-class Meanie.

THE PLACES HE TAKES YOU

This is tied in with the way he spends his money on you. He's finally got round to agreeing to buy you a meal. You fancy a particular restaurant. He says *"Yeah, but there's a cheaper place just round the corner."* Maybe he's just being careful with his cash. Or maybe he doesn't think you rate a first-class restaurant. Some guys give girls what they think they deserve. So if you get dragged into a burger bar that's the level you're tagged at in his grotty mind.

THE WAY HE ACTS TOWARDS YOU WHEN YOU'RE IN COMPANY

Is he off-hand, cool? Does he leave you standing on your own while he takes off to chat with his mates? Does he talk to people he knows without bothering to introduce you? He does? Then he's a Grot for sure. He doesn't count you as important, can't even be bothered to show you off. Face the facts, the guy is taking you for granted.

Take a long, cool look at your guy. Does he stand you up, let you down, give you the runaround and leave you stranded? Is he treating you like an old bag? If he is, then the chances are, that what *you've* got is — a Grot. And what's a Grot? A guy who's not so hot and doesn't care a lot, that's what! So, if you suspect that *you're* stuck with a Grot, read on! We tell you, first of all, how to check that you *have* got landed with a genuine Grot and if (poor fool) you find that you have, don't despair — we'll tell you what to do about it!

OK. On the evidence you find you're stuck with a Grot. The next question is — what to do.

First ask yourself if you're genuinely fond of him. Would it hurt badly if you split up? Answer *no* and all you have to do is give him the push. Simple.

Answer *yes* and you've got problems. How are you going to change a guy like that? Because that's what you've got to do, for your own sake and for his. So —

★ Start with his appearance. If he's scruffy and careless about his looks, nag him into smartening up. Or turn up looking mucky and slovenly yourself and see how *he* likes it. If he doesn't, tell him that's just how *you* feel about *him*.

The too-smart guy needs some attention, too. Ask him why he needs to be so immaculate, what's he afraid of. Guys don't like suggestions that they're afraid. It might do the trick. Or if his old mum is behind the scenes slaving away you could try getting at her instead and maybe start a rebellion so he'll have to iron his own shirts in future.

★ How are you going to knock the meanness about money out of him? Not easily, that's for sure. It might pay you to start being aggressive with him. Try lines like — *"What's the matter, you don't think I'm worth spending that much on?"* It might do the trick.

A gentler way is the kindly *"Let me help"* approach. When he's reluctant about parting with his cash, act as if you know he's really very generous and say, *"Haven't you got enough? Look, why not let me make up the difference? You can pay me back later."* This'll put him in a spot.

You can use the same line when he tries to drag you to the cheaper restaurant. *"If you can't afford it,"* you can say, *"let's go Dutch. I'd just love to have a real, romantic meal with you."*

Even *he* will have to admit that there's not a lot of romance in a burger bar. If he has got a heart, this kind of approach should find it and, if you're lucky, he won't even take up your "going Dutch" offer.

★ When you're in company and he's doing his off-hand bit, you've got two lines of action. Stick around and ignore *him* the way *he's* ignoring *you*. He won't like you showing signs of independence. Don't hesitate to break into the group of people he's talking to if you feel like it and introducing yourself. *"You may not have guessed it but I'm his girl-friend."* This'll make him look like an ill-mannered yob to his friends and if he's got any sense he'll save himself future embarrassment by making sure he includes you in the action.

The second line of action is just to walk out and go home. Pretty drastic stuff, but the only way if you can't raise the nerve to do anything else. If the guy is keen on you, he's going to want to know *why* you walked out on him and you can tell him you're fed up with being ignored and treated like you're not important. (A lot of Grots don't realise just how grotty they are until it's pointed out to them.)

If he's not keen on you, then he isn't going to care why you walked out. Then you'd be better off nursing your broken heart. Don't go back to him, no matter how much it hurts not to. If you do, he's going to go on using you as a doormat.

THE important thing is to work up the nerve to be honest with the Grot. And maybe the best time, the time when least embarrassment will be caused, is when you're alone together. A heart to heart talk might do the trick. So long as the guy knows you're keen and you don't want to lose him, he's likely to listen to your list of complaints against him. Like we said, a lot of Grots don't realise how grotty they are.

*But before you start, have a think about **yourself**. While you're listing **your** complaints, is he going to be matching them with complaints about **you**? So don't start on him, unless you're sure you're not also a Grot!*

CAN *YOU* TAKE A HINT? WHEN SOMEONE'S TRYING TO TELL YOU SOMETHING BUT IS TOO SHY, POLITE OR EMBARRASSED TO COME RIGHT OUT WITH IT — DO YOU CATCH ON? OR DO SUBTLE HINTS PASS YOU BY? IF THEY DO, LIFE COULD BE A BIT AWKWARD FOR YOU — AND YOUR MATES!

Do You Know When To Take A Hint?

IF your friends start arriving at your house with clothes pegs on their noses, think twice before shouting, "Oh, is that the latest fashion? I must rush out and buy a clothes peg!" Clothes pegs on noses aren't one bit fashionable. Could it be that your friends are trying to tell you something? Is it possible you may have B.O.? (Hadn't thought of that, had you?)

When hints are being dropped, the sooner you catch on — the better. It can save an awful lot of discomfort, especially in the case of B.O., and save your friends from having to buy gas-masks in a desperate last attempt to let you know what's wrong.

Another example is when you're happy and you want to share your happiness. That's understandable. But if you've just started dating The Most Gorgeous Guy In Town, your friends are going to want to know all about him and you're certainly going to tell them.

But if you keep harping on about it, pretty soon your friends are going to get fed up with hearing about Him (especially if they haven't got boys of their own at the time).

If they start changing the subject every time you mention Him, take the hint. They'll talk about fashion, records, the possibility of life on other planets, and Einstein's Theory of Relativity. Anything except HIM.

If this happens, you should really ease up on talking about Him. Otherwise, in the end, they'll start screaming and tearing out their hair with cries of, "I can't stand any more!"

But what happens when your romance with HIM starts to fade — how is he going to let you know if you're still madly in love with him and haven't noticed him cooling off?

He could come straight out and tell you, but if he doesn't want to hurt your feelings he won't do it like that.

He'll try to be kind about it. That's when hints will start dropping like rocks.

He may leave a note for you saying, *Sorry, can't keep our date tonight. Have emigrated to North Borneo.* This should give you an inkling that he might be cooling off!

But it's more likely he'll be less obvious than that. He'll start breaking dates with weak excuses you don't really believe.

When love's flown out the window it doesn't come back. Take the hints and retire gracefully before he has to resort to more drastic measures, like putting a barbed-wire fence all round his house so you can't drop in to ask why he didn't turn up for your last date.

Don't be the Piggy in the Middle, either. Sometimes, when two girls have been close friends for a long time, one of them still expects their regular meetings to continue even though the other one's got a steady boyfriend and would really like to spend some time alone with him.

If *you're* the one who tags along, keep your eyes open for warning signs. Your friend may not mind you turning up and making a threesome from time to time.

But if you find yourself chatting away about the weather and whether the Bee Gees would look any different if they had the Osmonds' teeth, and your buddy and her guy don't seem to be paying much attention 'cos they're busy cuddling — take the hint.

Even if you ask your friend if she minds if you tag along it doesn't follow that she means no when she says no.

If she doesn't sound as if she means it — that's the hint.

Hints are very indirect. When you've set your mind on buying a particular dress and your friend says: *Are you sure it will suit you?* What she *really* means is, *I don't think it will suit you.*

When you've planned a great scheme of some kind and your enthusiasm is met with a remark like, *Well, yes, I suppose it might be a good idea,* you can be pretty sure your scheme will be a dead loss.

A remark like, *Are you sure you know what you're doing?* is very often a hint that the speaker thinks you don't. If you're a non-swimmer and you're about to jump into the deep end of the swimming pool by mistake, it could turn out to be the last hint you'll ever have a chance to ignore.

Most hints are gentle and well meaning. Some can be cruel or unkind. When you find yourself having to drop hints to let a friend know she's being a pain in the neck in some way, try to do it without hurting her feelings.

If your boyfriend is still hanging around when the lovelight has gone out of your eyes, if your best friend has B.O. or is boring you to tears, make your hints as delicate as you can.

And try to avoid such unsubtle hints as clothes pegs on your nose, barbed-wire fences round your house or running around screaming, *I can't stand any more.*

There are better ways. Anyway, barbed wire is pretty expensive stuff.

Clothes For

Clothes can say a lot about you and the sort of person you are to people who don't know you. So it's important to remember that there's a time and place for everything. Who'd go hill walking in stilettos or to a garden party in denim shorts, for example? They're extreme examples, but here are some light-hearted guidelines to knowing *what* to wear, and *when*!•

WHAT TO WEAR WHEN YOU'RE — MEETING HIS PARENTS

You've been going out with him for quite a while, then he suddenly announces, "Would you like to come to tea on Sunday?" And you think: Oh, no . . . ! It's not that you don't *want* to go, but the prospect of meeting his mum and dad is nerve-racking enough without the added problem of what to wear!

The mere fact that he's asked you home means that he likes you a lot and wants to show you off to his parents.

If you care about him in the same way, you'll want to create the right sort of impression with them at first, and let them see what a nice, sensible, attractive, smart and down-to-earth girl you are for their son.

What To Wear

It's a safe bet that you're choosing the right clothes if you go through your wardrobe and pick an outfit that you don't like but your mum has always raved about! The only problem with wearing the little petal-pink suit with the Peter Pan collar that your mum adores is that if you don't feel happy wearing it, it will undermine your confidence and make you feel pretty fed-up, which will show in your face.

So pick clothes you feel happy in. A skirt with a matching blouse or jumper, matching coloured tights (without ladders!), and a leather shoulder bag and matching sensible-looking shoes will appeal to his mum.

Alternatively, if you have one, wear a fairly demure, high-necked dress, which you can pretty up with a nice brooch or a scarf at the neck. Mums seem to like pretty brooches and neck scarves!

If you have long hair, pull it back or wear it up. Mothers in general don't like hair flopping round faces and fringes falling into eyes, tea, soup, etc.

Keep your make-up very simple — just a touch of eyeshadow, mascara and lip gloss. It's very difficult meeting your boy's mother for the first time — if you're too dressed up she may think you're flashy; if you're not dressed up enough she may think you couldn't care less!

The best thing is to play everything down a little to begin with, as far as clothes are concerned. Play up the happy, sweet, kind and friendly side of yourself, and that way it's a safe bet that his mum will stop looking at your clothes and begin to notice the real you.

What Not To Wear

Even if your boy sees you every day of the week in jeans and T-shirts and, more to the point, *loves* to see you in jeans and T-shirts,

the same clothes won't wash with his mum. Jeans, of any size, shape or form, are definitely *out* for that first meeting over the tea table!

In fact, even your brand-new, dead-expensive, straight-legged, £25-a-go, pink satin trousers are out, because mothers seem to prefer a girl to be an old-fashioned girl (with, don't forget, manners to match).

Don't, whatever you do, wear a T-shirt with a slogan like "See me, feel me . . . !" His dad may be impressed, but his better half will be horrified, unless she's a *very* liberated lady.

High, thin-heeled shoes are out, too. Anyway, they might leave holes in his mum's good Cushionfloor when you're drying the dishes.

Avoid anything that's shocking pink, bright yellow, passionate purple or pea-green. Don't wear anything strapless or see-through, or she'll soon see through *you*, and, even though you might be a dedicated punk, for goodness' sake leave the coal-mine eyes, rigor-mortis lips and vampire fingernails at home.

And finally, even if you have no chest to speak of, wear a bra . . .

WHAT TO WEAR WHEN YOU'RE — ON A FIRST DATE

So he's asked you out. Whether he's seen you around at school, or just around the town, he must fancy you already, and must really like the way you look. But even so, *everyone* gets into a flap about what to wear for a first date, and spends hours beforehand rummaging through wardrobe and drawers, finally ending up wearing what they decided they looked revolting in four hours before!

Whatever you wear, you'll think you look awful — it's all tied up with the whole first date scene — but remember, it's *you* he's

All Reasons !

interested in, and clothes aren't really all that important, though it helps if you feel that you're looking OK.

What To Wear

Unless you've met him at a party or disco, when you've been dressed to kill anyway, nine times out of ten he'll only have seen you in your school uniform or everyday clothes. Obviously, you want to knock him out on that first date, but don't go overboard. Most boys find something really appealing in the girl who's naturally fresh and pretty, so go for pretty clothes, and a hint of flowery perfume!

Wear a self-coloured silky blouse which is nice to touch, and pretty it up with lace round the collar, or a matching piece of ribbon. Choose a pretty skirt in a nice fresh cotton — no butchy tweed or cord.

Boys like dresses, the floatier and softer the better, so if you have a nice peasanty or frilly one, wear it.

Wear your flimsiest shoes or sandals to show off your pretty little feet. If they're big, wear boots, which boys find sexy, as long as they're not wellies, hob-nailed or ankle-length, sheepskin booties.

Borrow one of your mum's lacy hankies, he'll think it's really cute when you cry at the pictures (or you can use it to wipe away his tears when you tell him you don't want to see him again).

If you have long hair, wear it loose, unless you can be sure it'll all tumble down at the crucial moment, in true Hollywood Romance style.

What Not To Wear

If you were decked out at the disco like a Christmas tree when you met him he obviously likes it, so it's OK to dress the same for the first date. But dressing up in garish colours, split skirts, fish-net T-shirts, chain belt and black stockings and suspenders when he's only seen you in school uniform is guaranteed to frighten the life out of him.

The punk look is too aggressive (unless he's a punk himself). Try to avoid trousers, as all male chauvinist pigs like to see the real shape of a girl's legs (one exception here, and that's if your nickname's Tilly Treetrunk or Claire Cricketstump).

On the other hand, if you've got a great figure and look amazing in jeans, slither into them. On the right girl, they're very sexy.

Don't wear rude brooches; he may get entirely the wrong idea about you. Steer clear of military jackets, or anything vaguely masculine, which might frighten him.

Don't wear a woolly jumper or cardigan. There's nothing very soft and sexy about functional old wool.

Stay clear of stockings and suspender belts, on your first date anyway. Again, he might get the wrong idea about you and suddenly become too hot to handle. Don't wear clumpy great elephant shoes which could break his toes when he kisses you goodnight, or tights held together with nail varnish.

Don't wear anything that's not as fresh as it could be — not if you want him to get closer, anyway!

WHAT TO WEAR WHEN YOU'RE — AT THE DISCO

Now the disco's one place you can really let rip with your clothes — if you're not careful! There's absolutely no excuse for being shy and frightened about getting

dressed up for the disco. If you do feel like that, then you'd be well advised to spend your evenings in the public library instead. Discos and disco gear have never had it so good, and unless the gear's right you won't do your boogying any justice at all. You're there to let go, have a good time, and get yourself *noticed*! In all disco-goers there's a bit of the show-off, so throw caution to the wind, terrify the budgie, give your dad a seizure, and dress to kill!

What To Wear

Simply wear whatever you feel really good in, and will make you stand out from the crowd. The brighter the colour, the better — or all in white is great because it shows up well under disco lights. Silks and satins are fantastic — they glimmer in the lights and, if you've a good figure, cling to the right bits of your anatomy when you're dancing!

Choose straight-legged satin pants in any colour of the rainbow, with a skimpy little shimmery top.

The higher your heels, the better, as long as you don't keep falling over, which will ruin the image! If you're happier in a skirt, stick to the same colourful materials.

If you've a waist, nip it in with a wide, glittery or patent belt. Wear lots of jewellery, especially silver or gold to glitter under the lights.

Sprinkle matching glitter on your hair, but whatever you do, wear lashings of lip gloss which really looks good shimmering against white disco teeth!

Above all, don't be frightened to be outrageous, and remember to wear a huge smile — there's nothing worse than a miserable sea of disco faces looking as if they're only there for the beer, and even that's rotten . . .

What Not To Wear

What not to wear, basically, is anything that you wear at work or change into when you get home from school to watch the telly in. Boring everyday clothes will make you

feel boring and everyday. That means plain old jeans, deadly dull skirts and any other boring old clothes that don't turn you, or anyone else, on. Don't wear anything that you'll feel hot and uncomfortable in after half an hour.

That includes anything too tight which might look good, but leaves you terrified that you'll get soaked with sweat which might show. Or, worst of all, split from top to bottom (literally!).

Don't wear anything blatantly braless and see-through. If you're looking for a nice guy, that's the wrong way to go about it.

In the majority of cases, boys don't really like it, unless they're only after what they can get, and that sort aren't worth knowing. And, likewise, avoid skirts slit up to your bottom, or tops slashed down to your waist.

Again, this kind of gear really will put nice boys off.

Don't wear flat shoes. They look pretty silly at a disco. Don't wear boring, flesh-coloured tights either — not when there's every colour under the sun to choose from.

And don't, *please*, wear your bag on your shoulder, or put it on the floor in front of you when you're dancing. It looks too awful for words.

WHAT TO WEAR WHEN YOU'RE — OUT FOR A MEAL

Going out for dinner does *not* mean the Wimpy Bar or the sitty-down bit of the local chipper. Dinner *does* mean a bit of luxury that doesn't happen very often because boys are usually too hard up.

But suppose your boyfriend's saved up to take you out for dinner to celebrate your anniversary, or birthday.

It's worth making a very special effort to look good for, because it's costing him a pretty penny, more likely than not, and whether it's the local Reo Stakis Steakhouse or a five-star hotel, the whole eating-out

thing in a nice atmosphere is a great experience.

What To Wear

If you're being taken out for a nice evening meal, not a luxury one, that is a Chinese, Indian or Steakhouse-type place, the best thing to go for is simply a pretty dress, provided it's not very tightly fitted because you'll never get past the first few forkfuls of rice or Steakhouse French Fries!

But if this evening meal is in a five-star hotel or expensive, romantic candlelit restaurant with soft music, finger bowls and toothpicks, do him the honour of looking gorgeous! This is the one time to wear a long dress, simple and elegant if possible, to make the best of what's underneath.

Go for halter-necks or tiny shoulder straps to show off your shoulders in the candlelight and wear one very simple silver or gold chain round your neck, with a matching chain round your wrist.

If your dress is simple and self-coloured, pin a rosebud or tiny flower on it — you can even tuck a tiny flower into your hair, which, if it's long, should be swept back or up, or softly waved.

Make sure you take a little evening purse or clutch bag — your everyday takes-every-thing-but-the-kitchen-sink shoulder bag will look too clumsy. Wear lashings of lovely perfume and concentrate on making your eye make-up as pretty as possible to give that big, dewy-eyed look across the table.

Wear a pretty silk or crochet shawl around your shoulders to slip off when you sit down.

What Not To Wear

No-one ever goes out for dinner in trousers — it's just not done! Only if you own a really fabulous silk harem suit is it acceptable, and even then some high-class hotels will frown on it. Never wear anything tight, especially if you have a midriff which will begin to expand as the meal progresses. If you're a messy eater don't wear light colours, which, horror of horrors, might show anything you spill.

Don't wear anything that's too way out. Your long shocking pink Lurex tube dress may be OK at the disco, but would look quite out of place at a ritzy restaurant.

Don't wear cheap jewellery — if that's all you have, don't wear anything at all. If you have long hair, don't wear it loose and floppy — it might fall in the soup, and anyway, it looks much more sophisticated when worn off the face.

Don't spoil the whole effect by floating into the restaurant in a plastic mac, tweed knee-length coat or cardi slung over your shoulders. If you don't have a fur coat, silk or crochet shawl, go without. Don't wear boots under your dress and avoid floaty scarves round your neck. They'll float all right —into the soup.

WHAT TO WEAR WHEN YOU'RE — GOING TO AN INTERVIEW

Everyone, at some stage in their lives, has to face the dreaded interview. Interviews are horrible, no-one likes them, but first impressions are what interviews are all about. No prospective employer is going to be impressed with a girl who obviously hasn't made the slightest effort to look her best; that attitude will reflect on her work as far as the prospective employer is concerned, i.e. lazy, careless and untidy.

No matter whether you're trying to get a job

as a dishwasher or a personal secretary, be as smart as possible, to create an image of efficiency.

What To Wear

The golden rule to remember is that everything must look clean and well cared for. Even if you can't afford a new outfit, make sure it looks neat and tidy. The best thing to wear for an interview is a smart suit, with a well-cut jacket and skirt, but, unfortunately, they don't come cheap, as most interviewers realise these days, so you just have to make do with the next best thing.

Choose a plain blouse and skirt in sober colours, for example, a cream blouse (or jumper) with an unfussy dark or matching skirt. If you feel drab like that, wear a little floral brooch or pin at the neck of the blouse, which must be fastened to a decent height.

Your skirt should be calf length, with dark or flesh-coloured tights, and smart shoes with a matching bag. If you want a touch of luxury, try a silky scarf round your neck.

Polish your shoes like mad, check tights for holes or ladders, and see that your hands and fingernails are spotless.

Wear simple make-up, and if you want to look the cool, efficient secretary type, take a notepad and pen in your bag to jot down notes, because the interviewer will expect you to ask questions.

Make sure you have a clean hankie (blowing your nose is a great diversion when you're stuck for something to say!).

What Not To Wear

Again trousers are out, even in these days of Women's Lib.and sexual equality.You have to be sensible about this. You may know you look great in trousers, but prospective employers will not be impressed. Even the smooth, camel, stay-press slacks should be given a miss (anyway, who'd want to wear them?). Dungarees aren't acceptable, either.

If you're a punk avoid anything even faintly to do with your private punk life — this includes safety-pin-style brooches, tiny silver razor-blade necklaces, even plastic banana badges. You won't get taken on for fear that you'll be more efficient at smashing filing cabinets and hurling tea urns through windows than typing.

Don't wear anything remotely slinky or sexy — you won't get the job if they think you'll spend your time climbing into the filing cabinet with the office messenger boy.

Finally, don't try to make yourself look amazingly good, because, if you get the job, it'll take all your pay packets to keep up the image!

WHAT TO WEAR WHEN YOU'RE — AT A FOOTBALL MATCH

It would be interesting to know what percentage of the male population are footie freaks. If you're going out with one of the minority, then you're dead lucky; if you're going out with one of the majority, then hard luck. Unless, of course, you're one of those strange females who actually enjoys watching fellas mindlessly chasing a ball round a field! The day will dawn when you'll have to spend the best part of a precious Saturday shivering on the sidelines, but the right gear can make the whole boring experience more bearable.

What To Wear

Well, as football is, basically, a winter sport, you'd look pretty silly in a summer dress — you'd also freeze. Yes, at last, this is where jeans come to the fore. Trousers of any shape or size are a must, but if you want to please the boy who's dragged you along, your jeans, or, even better, tracksuit bottoms, should be in the boyfriend's team colours (this is really so that the other side's fans can single you out and kick you in the bottom when you bend over to retrieve your rattle).

Wear the brightest, biggest, baggiest sweater you can find, with four other jumpers underneath, and thermal underwear underneath them. You may look like a Michelin man, but at least you'll be warm.

Knit yourself a bobble hat, scarf and mitts in the right colours, and buy one of those awful rattles — not specifically to cheer the team on, but the physical effort of swinging the thing keeps you warm.

Don't forget your dad's socks under your boots (preferably hob-nailed for defence!). Duffel coats are useful — they're warm, you can twiddle the toggles around when it gets boring, and hide under the hood when you want to fall asleep.

What Not To Wear

Don't wear a dress. That's really stupid, because it's much more draughty than trousers. Don't wear tights, you'll tear them to shreds on the wooden seats and boards, and don't wear heeled shoes. After the game you'll fall flat on your face trying to walk away — the heels will have sunk into the turf.

It's no good trying to do the model look at a football match, play up the sporty theme instead. It's simpler to avoid anything that looks pretty and feminine, because it'll get ruined with the flying mud, rain-drenched pink Andrex, flying pork-pie missiles and the liquid contents of assorted cans.

Don't wear pink lipstick, it might turn blue with the cold. Avoid red fingernails, too, they clash with blue mottled fingers.

And lastly, for very obvious reasons, don't wear the wrong colours . . .

Don't Monkey Around with The Wrong Boy!

IF you haven't already heard, this is the Year of the Monkey, as dictated by the Chinese calendar. Certain boys are *really* going to come into their own this year and it's only fair, we feel, that we give you a few tips on what to look for, because there are a lot of MCM's about — Male Chauvinist Monkeys — and you *don't* want to end up monkeying around with the wrong boy, do you?

ALEC APE

STARTING with . . . Alec Ape. He's the life and soul of the party, the centre of attention, and the source of most of that annoying noise when you enter the room.

This is because he lives up to his name and is a mimic. He can "ape" or imitate anybody from famous comedians to yourself, and we all know how annoying bad Elvis Costello imitations have become these days. So Mr Ape's first annoying trait is that he can be a *bore*.

He'll very rarely notice if *you're* feeling bored stiff, because he's so absorbed with his own fabulously aggravating imitations of Mike Yarwood imitating somebody else.

Unless you enjoy being constantly amused, give Alec Ape a *wide* berth.

BRIAN BABOON

BRIAN BABOON is a much more serious proposition. He's the fiercely possessive type. Baboons are notoriously fierce and will guard their ladies and their territory against anybody in the most *vicious* fashion.

At the same time they have a strong sense of humour and propriety. If you're easy-going, like people and enjoy dancing with lots of boys at parties and not being answerable for your whereabouts *24* hours a day, Brian is NOT your sort.

He'll drive you *mad* with his possessiveness; embarrass you in pubs or at parties by socking boys who so much as talk to you; and bore you silly with his regular routines and love of going to the same well-tried places.

If you feel a bit insecure and would like a permanent chap for the Year of the Monkey, then Brian Baboon will love, cherish and care for you, for ever, and ever, and . . .

CHARLIE CHIMPANZEE

CHARLIE CHIMPANZEE, on the other hand, can be *very* lovable indeed. Just think of those endearing tea-drinking chimps on telly, and you know how lovable a chimp *can* be.

Bear in mind though, as your heart begins to melt towards sweet, funny, handsome Charlie, that he can be very, very mischievous. This can take various forms.

He's quite oblivious of the fact that he's been seen two-timing you with that HORRIBLE girl from round the corner, and can't understand what all the fuss is about.

He's also the sort who thinks it's funny to miss the last bus, or get stranded without an umbrella in a rainstorm, or hide round the corner from where he's supposed to meet you and jump out and scare you silly.

If you can stand all this . . . then Charlie's your darling for sure!

GARY GIBBON

NO peace exists for anybody attracted to Gary Gibbon. Gibbons are the smallest, fastest and most agile of the monkey family and are exhausting company. Remember that Goodies song about "Doing The Funky Gibbon" — well it's all that and *worse.*

Gibbons can be found in squash clubs, rugger clubs, swimming pools, gymnasiums and, of *course,* every disco in the land, where they jump about and gyrate all night long, making a very elegant spectacle of themselves with hardly a bead of sweat in sight. Not fair, is it?

They also eat like pigs and stay like sticks. A trip to the cinema with one (a harrowing experience because they don't like sitting still) is accompanied by a mound of yummy chocolate which has you out in spots by Wednesday and leaves not a pimple on old Gary.

And a word of warning — they love heights, so beware of hill-walking, mountain-climbing or tree-climbing suggestions.

GRAHAM GORILLA

GRAHAM GORILLA is a misleading sort of guy. He's the boy you've been watching for a long time and silently hating, thinking he's stuck up, stand-offish, haughty and aggressive.

Then one evening at a party you see him approaching — horror of horrors! And you find he's *totally* different from how you'd imagined.

His fierce manner hides quite a strong vein of shyness and sensitivity, he's got a terrific sense of humour and is very con - siderate.

He's probably the biggest challenge of 1980 and worth the effort because he's full of surprises — most of them nice ones!

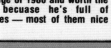

ABC OF LIFE,

APPEARANCE

This is one of the most important aspects of making the most of yourself. It's the very first thing people notice about you and the last thing they'll forget!

It's all very well avidly reading the beauty tips in magazines and wishing that you looked like a model, when you've got to be hoisted out of your armchair even to answer the phone! Don't convince yourself that it's expensive to look good — because that's just not true.

Simple, in this case, is best. When you're neat, clean and tidy, you can't help looking good, and even someone in the most fashionable clothes and make-up can sometimes look slovenly!

Take time over your appearance, because if you're feeling good then you'll radiate good looks as well!

BORROWING

It's all very well saying *never* borrow anything, but as long as you're not a consistent borrower, it often saves you buying something that you'd only use once.

But if you borrow something, make sure you return it promptly and in good condition, and if you have damaged it in any way, then tell the owner. It all depends on the situation but it's often best to buy something new if that happens. Just put yourself in their position, try imagining how *you'd* react, and you should be OK.

CRITICISM

It's easy to be critical of friends and boyfriends. Certain things about your nearest-and-dearest are bound to irritate you, but you should only criticise them rarely, and when you do, try to make your criticisms as constructive as possible.

If, for example, you think your friend treats her boyfriend really badly without knowing it, and you know that he's fed up with it, then it's obvious that a discreet word from you might work wonders. Remember, criticism is always most effective when it comes rarely and when it suggests improvements.

DATES

Dating means, simply, going out with a boy, whether once or quite regularly. The most important thing to remember about dates is that they're *not* the most important thing in the world. All they are, in fact, is just two people spending an evening together and finding out a bit more about each other. So *don't* get it out of all proportion, and you'll find that life can be really good fun.

EDUCATION

We all agree that at times, school can be very, very hard, and it can seem as though you'll *never* do anything right or understand *anything!* But another side of school is that it's the place where most of your friends are, where you can have a great laugh and join in all sorts of hobbies.

Schooldays and college days, of course, are just about the most important days of your life — and if you try your very best, then you'll never have anything to regret.

But even outside school, you're learning all the time — about relationships, about your own feelings, your strengths and weaknesses, about the way other people behave. So if you have a bad experience of any sort, just remember it'll have taught you a lot and strengthened you. It's all education for life!

FLIRTING

If you're unattached and so is he, then great! But if you're not — beware!

GOSSIP

It's hard to resist having a good old gossip, especially when there's a bit of spicy news around.

But in fact gossip never does anyone any good, and it can do real harm. So if you really want to make the most of yourself, get a reputation as the girl who **never** gossips!

HELP

Everybody, at sometime in their life, needs a little help, and it's always nice to try your best to help someone. Friends, especially, deserve some of your time when they're worried or in trouble, and even though sometimes you can't do anything, it's often just a friendly ear they need.

There's also such a thing as helping yourself, though. Whenever *you* need help, don't ever feel too proud to ask — because a problem shared isn't always just a problem halved, it can be solved as well!

INVITATIONS

Invitations are always nice to receive, proof that your company is wanted and that people like being with you.

However, don't always leave invitations to others. It's nice to have friends round now and again, and, of course that goes for boys, too. Don't always leave it to *them* to do the inviting, though, try it out for yourself.

JEALOUSY

This is one of the strongest emotions you can feel, and it never does *anything* for you. But it's also one of the most common emotions and hard to keep down. Really, jealousy isn't feeling envious of what someone else has got, it's all about what *you* haven't got — so only *you* can change that. Anyway, after reading this, you'll be well on your way — won't you!

LOVE AND YOU!

Are you really making the most of yourself, as a friend, as a girlfriend, as a daughter — as yourself, in fact? To get the best out of yourself you've got to work at it. If you sit back, and expect your life to flow happily and smoothly all the time, then you're in for quite a shock! Everybody needs to improve themselves a little, and we've got together a whole alphabet of things for you to polish up on. Go on, read it if you dare . . .!

K ISSING
Many girls have a fear of kissing. They feel nervous and anxious before they've ever kissed a boy, thinking: I don't know how to do it! He'll think I'm a baby!

There's only one golden rule to kissing: kiss when you want to, and you'll find that you just *know* how to do it — it comes naturally!

L OVE
Love is wonderful, love is everything they say it is — *when* it's real, because it's so easy to fall in love with the idea of love! So just take time and don't try to convince yourself that you're in love with a boy *too* quickly — because you can get very hurt.

There are also many other kinds of love: love for your parents, your friends — love for anyone in fact whom you care for, and if you love people, then you're definitely making the most of yourself!

M ONEY
Everybody would like to have money — and lots of it, but when you haven't got any it can really cause problems. Magazines often tell you to do odd jobs, etc., and if you try it you'll find that the money really does mount up. So use your imagination to get money *and* use your imagination when you haven't got any. Have some fun for free!

N AGGING
Are you a nag? If something about your friend or boyfriend irritates you, and you badly want to change it, the chances are that you mention it quite a lot.

It's always hard to get people to change their ways, and nagging certainly *isn't* the way to do it. So all we can say is, if you have the tendency to nag — button up.

O RGANISATION
There are so many groups, classes and clubs that are just crying out for members, that you've got no excuse for feeling bored. Pop along to your local library and find out all about all of the organisations in your area.

Learn new things, meet new people and thoroughly enjoy yourself into the bargain!

P ARENTS
Your parents know you better than anyone else. They've cared for you through the years and have given you all they could, so it's only right that you should do the same for them.

Many girls find that when they become teenagers they don't really get on with their families as well as they used to, but you've got to realise that they *don't* want to hurt you, and they *don't* want to be nasty — they worry because they love you so much.

Q UESTIONS
Questions are a vital part of life. With boyfriends especially it's always nice to show an interest in them, and it's a great way of finding out about each other and building up a relationship.

Get into the habit of asking *yourself* questions, too, about your work, feelings and ideas. That way, you're bound to keep an open mind about things.

R ISKS
All we can say here is, *don't take them!* Whether it's risks with a boy, your friends or parents, it's always better to think really carefully about the worst possible outcome — and especially with boys. If they want to take risks and you don't — just tell them, and *never* do anything against your will.

S UCCESS
Success for you is what you make it. Your friend's idea of success might be being chosen to represent the school in a quiz, whereas yours might be something completely different. Success has got to be worked for, though, and being successful *proves* you've been making the most of yourself!

T RUTH
The truth sometimes hurts. And a good friend will know the right time for the whole truth, and when it's kinder to say nothing.

For instance, you might know that your friend is being two-timed. If she seems anxious and unsure, and often asks for your opinion, chances are she wants to hear the truth and it would be a relief.

But if she's immensely happy, then you run a great risk if you destroy her happiness by telling her something that will probably wreck it.

U S
It's so easy to think of yourself *all* the time, that you can forget about other people's feelings. "Me, me, me" — if that's how you sound when you talk, then you're bound to appear a bit boring. Try to think of others a little bit more, and they're bound to think a little bit more of *you!*

V ENOM
Hate is a terrible thing to feel for anyone. And when you're young, it's not an emotion that you should be feeling too frequently! It doesn't make you look big to cause a scene or have public arguments, it's much better to live and let live! So the next time someone does something that really annoys you, then think to yourself: Does that person really mean it the way I've taken it or am I just imagining it? It may not work *all* the time, but you never know!

W ORRY
Everybody has worries, and everybody, at one time or another, can see no way out of their problem. When you're young, everybody tells you that you shouldn't worry, that you're too young to worry — but that never helps.

What you *shouldn't* do is bottle up your worries — tell someone! Even better, try not to get yourself into worrying situations!

X -TRA SPECIAL
This is what you are! Everybody on this earth is a totally unique person — and that's quite a thought!

Y OURSELF
There's really not a lot we can say except — take care, and always look after yourself well.

Z EST
You should be feeling full of zest after reading this, because now you're going to start to make the most of yourself! Turn over a new leaf and try really hard to be a nice person — it may sound corny, but it'll work!

SOMETHING OLD...

It's always fun to look back on what's been happening on the music scene at this time of the year.

We've taken a light-hearted look at 1981 and selected some famous faces you're sure to recognise. For some of them it's been business as usual as they produce hit after hit, there's also some bright new talent around, some stars who have cheated a little and "borrowed" ideas from other performers, and some who sadly haven't made it at all this year.

See if you agree!

STATUS QUO. Not one golden oldie here, but four! And really they don't look at all that different now than when they exploded onto the charts with a song called "Pictures Of Matchstick Men" in 1968.

So, Status Quo not only have the privilege of being among the top hit-making bands, but also one of the longest running. Francis Rossi and Alan Lancaster have been playing together since 1962, but it wasn't till Rick Parfitt joined the group six years later that things really started to happen for them.

Perhaps this was just a coincidence . . .

CLIFF RICHARD. None of you, or none of us for that matter, are old enough to remember Cliff when he had his first hit in 1958 with a song called "Move It!" It got to number 3 in the charts and stayed around for eleven weeks.

The rest, as they say, is history and not a year goes by without Cliff hitting the headlines.

No-one would deny him the success he's achieved and you can't help but admire the way his music appeals to all age groups.

What we'd like to know is, how he manages to stay so young-looking. Does he know something we don't know?

PAUL McCARTNEY. Most people are well informed about Paul's vastly famous career from the Beatles' first hit "Love Me Do" in 1962 right up to this day with his super group Wings.

Paul seems to have the Midas touch and like Cliff Richard he seems to get even better looking as he gets older!

Apart from being a brilliant singer/songwriter, he's a great solo performer, businessman and, according to his family, a really super dad.

Some people have all the luck!

DIANA ROSS. For a lady who has an almost grown-up family, Diana isn't doing too badly. Apart from a short spell when she didn't reign "supreme," she's been topping the charts consistently since her first hit with the Supremes in 1967 with a song called "Reflections."

When she realised that disco music was making some people very rich, Diana claimed that she could, "Do that stuff with my eyes shut." She did, and proved that there's still a lot to come from this super singer.

SOMETHING NEW...

ORCHESTRAL MANOEUVRES IN THE DARK.
Paul and Andy of OMITD have succeeded in bringing synth music to the fore as an intelligent, lyrical, real form of music.

They've taken care to ensure that it's their music people associate with them and not some clockwork dummy image. So far they've experimented far and beyond other performers working in this field, a move that will guarantee that OMITD will be around for a lot longer than other less creative musicians.

PAULINE MURRAY.
Pauline is a lady who's taking on the music scene on her terms. She's successfully created a niche in the market to suit her music and, though her emergence as a solo performer may not have been as explosive as others, she's quietly and confidently built up a strong following.

Her sense of humour is another asset that should stand her in good stead — not many people are zany enough to play with a band called the Invisible Girls who are all males!

STRAY CATS.
The runaway success of the crazy-quiffed trio has been quite phenomenal. Long before the band had a hit record or even a recording contract there was an incredible buzz amongst talent scouts, the music press and fellow musicians, about their exciting brand of music.

But they held out till someone offered them a contract with enough money behind it and also one that gave them the opportunity to do things the way they wanted.

The three Americans may not be your idea of the perfect guy but their music is definitely a hit. It's given rockabilly music a whole new sound that isn't steeped in the past but new and very exciting.

ADAM ANT.
Adam Ant was just what the doctor ordered last year when he burst on to the pop scene.

Although Adam had been working for a couple of years it wasn't till the original Ants left to join Bow Wow Wow and he formed a new band that he had his first hit with "Dog Eat Dog."

Adam is really a modern-day hero with the looks, talent and image to take the Ants to the top and keep them there. The 80's will surely go down in music history as the years of the Ant!

Now turn to page 90 for Something Borrowed and Something Blue!

SOMETHING BORROWED...

SHAKIN' STEVENS.
Elvis Presley lives on — in the shape of Shakin' Stevens.

How Presley's fans feel about the man, we're not too sure, but Shakin' is certainly cashing in on the King's recipe for success. Not only does the slick-haired singer copy Elvis's clothes, he sounds like him and even has Elvis's gyrations duplicated jerk for jerk.

His dark looks have made him a hit with male and female fans alike, and we suppose that as long as there's a market for the Presley-style sound there will be people like Shakin' popping up in the charts.

TOYAH.
We bet a lot of you had forgotten all about Lene Lovich till Toyah came along. She sounds so like the Lene, who had super hits with "Lucky Number" and "Say When," that's it's uncanny.

Toyah definitely doesn't *look* like Lene, but listen to her vocals and we're sure you'll find more than a passing resemblance to Lene's style of performing. Something else the two ladies have in common is that they've both been the subject of TV documentaries — an honour reserved for the chosen few.

After Lene's was screened however, the lady just didn't seem able to top her initial success. Toyah, take note!

GARY NUMAN.
Listening to some of Gary's music is like hearing David Bowie on an "off" day. But, let's be fair to Gary. At least, unlike some artistes, Gary admits that he's been greatly influenced by Bowie. Though we think it goes a bit deeper than that.

It's a pity, however, that Gary has been unable to take a leaf from David's book on learning to cope with success. Perhaps then he'd still be touring and letting his fans hear his music first hand — after all, there's no substitute for the real thing.

BRYAN FERRY.
Among the things Bryan has "borrowed" from other performers is a repertoire of classic, standard hits to which he's added his magical touch.

Perhaps the most famous tunes that have the Ferry treatment are Bob Dylan's "A Hard Rain's A-Gonna Fall" and "Smoke Gets In Your Eyes" that was first a hit for The Platters in 1959!

But we don't mind what he pinches because he does everything so well we bet he could make the National Anthem into a top ten hit!

SOMETHING BLUE

LES McKEOWN.
When Les released his album "All Washed Up," he said he'd chosen the title to prove to his critics that he wasn't! The album however didn't do all that well and Les took to ligging around on the other side of the Atlantic with Britt Ekland. So, what's the star, who was once part of The Bay City Rollers, been up to?

Well, things just haven't worked out for Les without the rest of the band. They're all living it up in America and enjoying some success with the American teen market — they always were a few years behind their British counterparts.

Meanwhile, though, Les certainly looks as though he's well and truly — washed up . . .

SMOKEY.
Though the band still seem to be popular in Germany, things don't seem to be happening for them in Britain.

Smokey have, however, had their fair share of success since their first hit "If You Think You Know How To Love Me" back in 1975.

Perhaps the punk movement was in some way responsible for the band's demise. Certainly it shook up the record industry and gave it a much-needed spring clean, and since then the band seem to have disappeared in a puff of smoke . . .

THE OSMONDS.
The Osmonds have just one thing going for them — their teeth — because they help the incredibly rich performers to keep smiling despite the fact that they're no longer teeny idols.

The Osmonds success seems to have waned since the boys started to get married. Not that we're blaming their wives for the decline, but it now looks as though the family are much too content sitting around at home to go out on the road.

Maybe they're busy working on a second generation group — what a thought!

LEIF GARRETT.
Leif is one of those unfortunate people who's been made into a star for no apparent reason. He fits in with the American picture of the good-looking, young blond-haired guy they go wild for. Leif unfortunately doesn't seem to have the talent to go with all the hype.

We're not denying that Leif is a really nice guy — he is — but apart from good looks and nice personality he has nothing. His main ambition is to be taken seriously as a rock singer, but so far all his records have flopped dismally.

The best advice we can give him is to hang on to his skateboard — maybe someone will remember him for that!

EARS TO IT!

You don't have to spend pounds on earrings — with a bit of imagination you only need to spend a few pence — if you make your own!

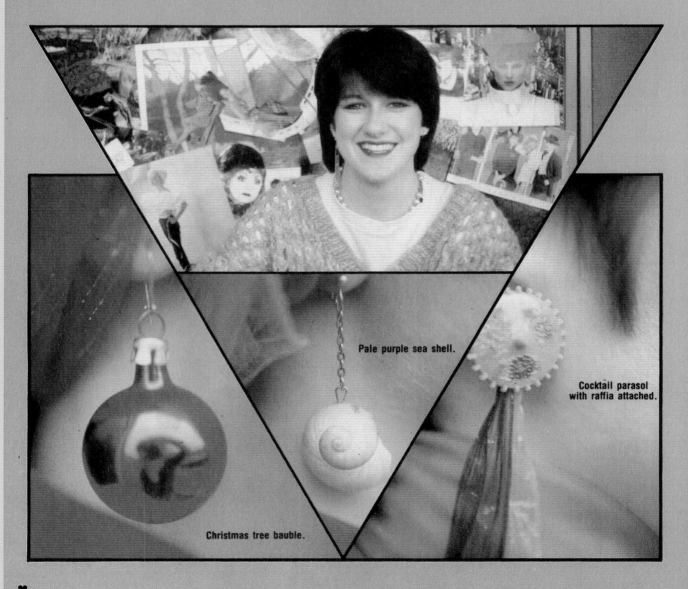

Pale purple sea shell.

Cocktail parasol with raffia attached.

Christmas tree bauble.

Earrings are very popular just now, with more and more people getting their ears pierced – often two or three times.

The jewellery stands in shops offer an enormous range of sparkly, brightly coloured things to hang from your lobes – many of which seem to be a bit too expensive for what they are, especially if you're prone to losing them!

This year, we've seen a lot of huge, brassy dangling earrings around, which have an ethnic African or Egyptian influence – but anything goes – as long as it's large!

It's very easy and cheap to make your own earrings and the great thing about it is that they'll be unique – you're not likely to see everyone else wearing a pair exactly the same as yours, which is another problem with shop-bought earrings.

Once you start thinking about making your own earrings – the possibilities are endless!

Curtain rings, old necklaces, wooden beads, toys, buttons, are just a few of the things you could use. Even those tiny plastic toys you get inside crackers would make great earrings.

Have a look round the house – there are bound to be hundreds of things you could use!

The earrings shown here were all made from collected objects with the help of a strong glue and the odd coating of enamel paint. They're the handiwork of Deborah Allison, a first year fashion student at Ravensbourne College of Art and Design.

"I started to make earrings because a lot of the ones on the market were too expensive and not individual enough," Deborah told us. "At one time I had as many as fifty different earrings, made from anything I could get my hands on – like marbles, coloured paper clips,

and fuses in different colours.

"The good thing about them is that they're just for fun and they don't cost anything, so it doesn't matter if you lose them, as earrings do tend to drop off very easily."

Earring Aids:
If you're interested in making yourself some earrings, the clips can be bought from craft shops, bead shops and street market stalls, or you could send for them. Creative Bead Craft Ltd., Unit 26, Chiltern Trading Estate, Earl Howe Road, Holmer Green, High Wycombe, Bucks., do a small order service, and have a wide selection of beads and earrings clips. Write to them for details, enclosing a stamped addressed envelope.

Remember – don't wear anything too large, heavy or breakable on your ears!

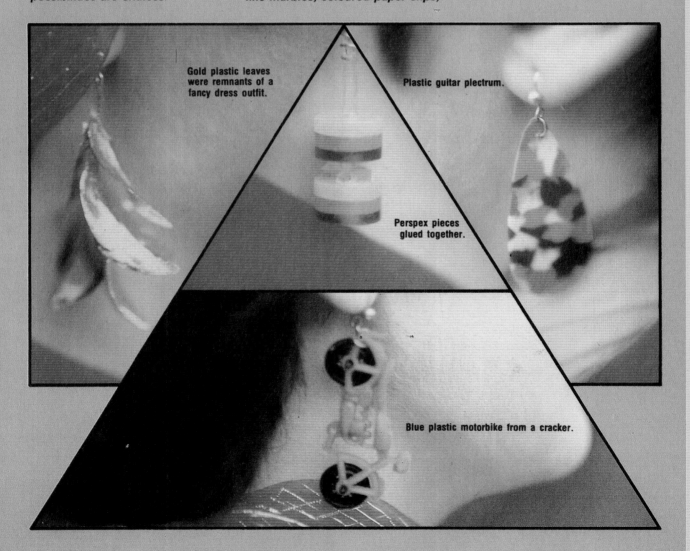

Gold plastic leaves were remnants of a fancy dress outfit.

Plastic guitar plectrum.

Perspex pieces glued together.

Blue plastic motorbike from a cracker.

New Looks

TARTAN TRENDS . . .

Tartan never seems to go out of fashion — it looked good on Bonnie Prince Charlie and looks just as good 1982 style! Mix your tartans and tweeds for a really original look — add knickerbockers, waistcoats and a huge scarf slung over your shoulder — and you'll be all set for your own Highland fashion fling!

. . . or are they? If you get the feeling you've seen the new 1982 fashions before – you probably have – in your history books! This year, the designers have gone as far afield as places like Turkey and Lapland to bring you clothes with an ethnic, peasant flavour – and as far back in time as Bonnie Prince Charlie for the colourful tartans we'll be seeing a lot of. The Pirate styles are still as exciting as they were in Errol Flynn's day – and the romantics can look forward to an even frillier new year!

SWASHBUCKLING STYLE

Pirate styles are still very much part of the picture for 1982 fashion — in true Errol Flynn tradition! Look out for swashbuckling touches like sashes, billowing pants, puffy sleeves, lace-up tunics, thick gold bangles right down to fall-down socks. It all adds up to one of the most adventurous, exciting looks around!

FOLKLORE FASHION
The ethnic influence! Smocks, dirndl skirts, boleros, embroidered blouses, gaucho pants and jacquard socks are all coming back in style! Pile on the layers — not just to keep you warm! Use your imagination and mix different prints together for a really colourful peasant look!

New Looks

ROMANTIC RUFFLES

Take a chance on romance! Go for pretty, softer new styles — ruffled blouses, black velvet bows — with lots of frills and lace. The new romantic styles include knickerbockers, breeches and capes — in old-fashioned fabrics like velvet, satin and taffeta. So take a trip back in time to discover a brand-new way of romantic dressing!

THE

All the things you'll find hardest to understand about your boyfriend, and the things he's most worried about, are all here. If you want to know exactly what makes him tick, just read on!

APPEARANCE

Girls aren't the only ones who are obsessed by their appearance — boys are, too! As they reach adolescence, boys are only too aware of the way they look.

They worry about whether they're muscular or puny, whether they've got anything resembling a beard or not, and whether their voices have broken or not. Even in these days of equality, there's still a lot of pressure on boys to be big and strong and "manly."

So stop and think how sensitive and anxious a boy is likely to be if he's small, or skinny, or a late developer. It might help you understand him a bit better!

BRAGGING

Most boys boast a lot — they can't help it. They boast about their bikes, motor bikes, stereos and girls. Boys together have a bad influence on one another — well, they certainly often feel pressurised by their mates into pretending that they're doing things that they're actually miles away from experiencing.

So beware if you hear a boy boasting about his success with girls. Don't jump to the conclusion that a girl's "easy" just because you overhear a boy saying so (especially if you hear a boy saying so!).

COMMITMENT

Many boys are afraid of having a really deep relationship with a girl. Younger boys want to go out with their mates and they usually only want to see a girl now and then (while still being able to boast that they've got a girlfriend). Older

boys like to play the field. There are some boys who aren't afraid of committing themselves, but they're unusual.

DOUBLE STANDARDS

For hundreds of years the Double Standard has ruled — and ruined —

women's lives. It means that men feel it's all right for them to have lots of girls, but not for girls to have a lot of boyfriends. They also want one special girlfriend or wife — and if *she* goes around with other men, that's unforgivable!

This crazy (and unfair) notion is dying out, but there are still boys around who demand faithfulness from their girlfriends whilst happily two-timing them themselves.

FIGHTING

When boys are little, fighting is never taken seriously. Sometimes, mothers and fathers encourage it! But when boys grow up they fight because it's difficult to control their anger at a time when all their emotions are much stronger than before. Also, a lot of boys fight because it makes them look big — or at least they *think* it does.

GANGS

Most boys want to be in some sort of gang. When they are in a gang, there's a lot of pressure on each individual to behave only in ways which are acceptable to the gang. This might include aggro at football matches, boasting about their sexual experiences, or getting drunk. Most boys won't like doing a lot of the things that the gang says he must, but it takes a really strong character to stand out against it and refuse to take part.

IMMATURITY

Most girls find that boys their own age are a bit immature. This is because girls mature, physically and emotionally, a couple of years earlier than boys. A girl of thirteen or fourteen, for example, will find that boys her own age are not only pretty childish but actually more physically immature than her as well.

Most girls therefore tend to go for older boys, until the late teens, when things tend to even out.

KISSING

Everybody's interested in kissing. In general, though, boys don't have the same kind of approach to it as girls do. A girl's likely to get interested in a boy first and *then* want to kiss him. A boy is more likely to want to kiss a girl — *any* girl — just to see what it's like.

A kiss may mean very different things to the two people involved. You might be crazy about him, but he may be just experimenting. So beware!

BOY FACTS!

LOVE

People need to feel loved to be happy and secure, but boys especially are often scared of admitting this. They feel that if they say they love their girlfriends, they'll be trapped. The last thing they want is for their mates to think that they're under a girl's thumb. So even a boy who does love you may not admit it — even to himself.

OPENNESS

Complete honesty in relationships is worth working for, but with boys you really will have to work for it. For a start, most boys are afraid of hurting girls so they tell them what they think they want to hear, not what's really true.

Your boyfriend might tell you you look great even when you know your new dress doesn't suit you. And he'll tell you he never looks at other girls when you know he does.

Total honesty really is the best basis for a relationship, though — then, you're likely to stay friends whatever happens!

PUBS

Drinking is one thing boys all seem to think is masculine. Lots of boys get drunk at parties and go to pubs when they're under-age just to prove how tough they are. Unfortunately, there's nothing that looks worse or less appealing than a drunk!

If your guy shows signs of thinking that drinking is something big, tell him in no uncertain terms just how stupid you think drunks are — boring and unsexy. Then, maybe he'll think twice before trying to prove himself in such a daft way!

QUESTIONS

He doesn't know much about you and you don't know much about him, right? Well, it makes sense for you to ask each other questions, especially about sex, love and marriage and your attitudes to them.

ROMANCE

Romance is all about the excitement which surrounds getting to know some-one of the opposite sex, being attracted to them and becoming fascinated by them.

The thing to remember, though, is that a boy will enjoy things in private with you that he'd never, ever dream of admitting to when he's with his mates. So show some tact and don't remind him of romantic things he's done and said, especially when he's with a gang of his toughest mates!

TENDERNESS

Most girls need tenderness from their boyfriends, but some boys are reluc-tant to give it. It's not that they don't feel it: they get embarrassed and shy.

You may have to teach your boy-friend to be affectionate, but don't despair — it *can* be done!

UGLY HABITS

Lots of boys act in some pretty terrible (disgusting!) ways when they're with other boys. Some of them think it impresses girls. Things like dirty talk, filthy jokes and constant swearing aren't a sign that your boyfriend is a yob, though.

It might just be that he's trying to impress you. If it doesn't impress you (and it shouldn't!) tell him so.

WOLFS

Sooner or later, you're going to meet a *wolf* — a boy with wandering hands. If he's a stranger and you're enjoying a slow dance with him at the disco when he suddenly starts to grope you, then you should just break away from him. You don't have to make a big scene about it — just be firm.

If your steady boyfriend starts to get a bit much, though, that's different: he's probably getting carried away by his feelings for you as well as seeing how far he can get! Now is the time to have a serious talk about where to draw the line. Make sure you draw the line where *you* want it.

YOUNGER BOYS

Don't write off younger boys (that is, boys of your own age) as possible boy-friends. They may be smaller than you and more immature, but the nice thing about them is that they're likely to be mates with you first, and then, as they grow up, change into something more.

Younger boys are more likely to treat you with the respect you deserve than some older boys who like to prove how grown-up and powerful they are by treating you like a child.

ZZZzzz . . .

A lot of boys are boring and are more likely to send you to sleep than to set your heart racing. Unfortunately, a lot of girls put up with boys like this because they think having a boyfriend (even a boring one) is better than not having a boyfriend at all.

Well, that's rubbish — and one sure way of putting you off other boyfriends for life!

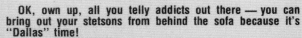

THE OTHER DALLAS STARS...

OK, own up, all you telly addicts out there — you can bring out your stetsons from behind the sofa because it's "Dallas" time!

Don't you ever feel life is boring when you're not engrossed in the Ewing exploits?

Well, wakey, wakey, because here we have the Southfork superstars on this very page, with of course some lesser-known stars as addicted to the series as we are. We asked some of our favourite people who *their* favourite was, and here's what they told us . . . Read on and find out that everybody loves a Ewing . . .

STEVE STRANGE
Sue Ellen must have the most mobile mouth ever. It can go in twenty different directions at once! She's equal with Pam who must have the most mobile **eyes** ever — they can go in twenty different directions at once.

ROB HALFORD — Judas Priest
The best character isn't even in it now, it's Kirstin. She was so scheming and would stop at nothing to get what she wanted. She was one lady with absolutely no scruples.

THERESE BAZAR — Dollar
Miss Ellie drives me up the wall. She's so tolerant and such a martyr . . . I shudder when she gives her all-forgiving smile — and that's about fifteen times a minute!

BOB GELDOF
I don't really have much time to watch "Dallas" now because I'm usually so busy, but for sheer star appeal you can't beat Pam. She wobbles a bit, too. I wonder if you've got to have a wobble to get a part?

PHIL LYNOTT
It's got to be J.R., the evil one himself. It's wonderful that when he does something really nasty, he always manages that sly smile.

SHEENA EASTON
Oh, Sue Ellen's my favourite because it would give me great pleasure to see her get throttled. I'd really enjoy *that* episode.

HOW TO HANDLE HIM...

The first time you meet him, you'll think he's *great*, no faults, no nasty habits — in short, you'll think he's just perfect. Once you get to know him better, and you're seeing him on a regular basis, though, you're bound to uncover a few not so nice things about him. Next time his bossiness, his moodiness or his wandering hands act get too much for you to bear, don't hurl your handbag at him — instead, read on and find out how to handle him!

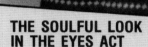

THE WANDERING HANDS ACT

Every boyfriend from time to time gets carried away by his feelings and this can pose problems for his girlfriend.

There's only one way to react if your boyfriend tries to go too far physically (too far being quite simply what *you* regard as too far) and that's to stop him at once.

The best thing to do is to change the mood abruptly. Break away, say, ''Stop that '' sharply and get out of his clutches. Make it clear you're annoyed, and make it clear right *then* that you have limits, and tell him exactly what they are. A serious talk will cool him off *wonderfully*.

THE SOULFUL LOOK IN THE EYES ACT

If he's really nuts about you, you might begin to feel pressurised to spend all your time with him and to reassure him constantly that you really care.

If this is the case, it's very important to break away from his clutches *before* you begin to find him a drag and all the good things about your relationship fade into the past.

Tell him straight that you don't want to get too serious too soon.

Make a point of going out without him (with girl-friends maybe) at least a couple of times a week. If he moans and complains about it — well, you might even have to start thinking about ending the relationship.

THE I WANT TO BE FREE ACT

Some boys get attacks of restlessness. He might be fed up with his job or his school, or horror of horrors, he may be feeling a bit cooped up in his relationship with *you*.

His restlessness might show itself in depression, or in attacks of rather weird aggressive behaviour: playing around and doing stupid things, maybe even getting into trouble of some sort. If he's generally restless — that is, he's just fed up with life in general — all you can do is try to get him to talk about it in order to sort out some practical action.

If he's restless about his relationship with you, however, you can do more. Don't cling on for dear life, however panicked you are.

If you desperately want to keep him, the natural reaction is to say how much you love him and to beg and plead with him not to give you up. But the best thing to do is actually the opposite.

Play it *cool.* Go out without him sometimes. Don't keep ringing him up. Give the impression that you're having a great time and that you certainly don't depend on *him.*

That'll give him a chance to feel free and unhassled — and the chances are that he'll then realise how much he does like you!

THE I DON'T CARE ABOUT YOU ACT

Carelessness can show in many ways. Maybe he says he'll phone you at a certain time and then doesn't bother or forgets? Or he borrows money from you and that's the last you hear of it? Or he's careless with things that belong to you?

The best way to treat this nasty situation is to give him a short, sharp talking-to: Tell him you're fed up being taken for granted, that he's getting so don't-care in his attitude that you're sure it's best to pack it all in and finish with each other.

There's just the *chance* that he'll say ''OK!'' But if he does, he wasn't worth keeping anyway!

More likely, though, he'll realise how important you are to him and start taking care again.

So . . . whatever moods your boyfriend gets into, you ought to be able to handle them now!

Who's A Pretty Boy?

Long, long ago, the last thing on a boy's mind was how to attract a girl. He just dotted her one on the head with his trusty club and hauled her off to his cave.

Today, though, life's a lot more complicated, and relationships are a lot more subtle. The me-Tarzan-you-Jane approach doesn't work now that there are more fellas around than girls (what a nice arrangement!) and boys are thinking more and more about the image they project.

We spoke to some boys and asked them how they saw themselves in the attractiveness stakes and jokingly asked how they'd rate themselves on a scale of 1-10. Here's what we came up with . . .

Steven, who's eighteen, works in a bank.

"I'm pretty average really; average height and build so I'd guess I'd rate a five. I'm just not the sort of bloke who could pull birds by sheer looks alone. If you put me in a shop window, there'd be no queues!

"I've had a couple of nice girl-friends, who were really special, and luckily they got to know the real me first – I can't say it was my looks really. My present girlfriend thinks I'm fantastic, so who am I to argue?

"I'm still living at home, which is a bit restrictive. I suppose I dream of branching out, getting a flat and changing my image completely. I'd love to be someone like Sting. I can't help feeling that I'm missing out on some things. Maybe I should be more outrageous and daring in my life – but even if the chances came along I don't know how I'd react."

Steven sounds like a pretty honest, reliable guy, a boy to trust — but is that the type the girls really go for? Here's Paul, and he's just the opposite. He's good looking *and* he knows it.

"Ten I'd rate – sure, why not! I have no bother attracting girls. I suppose I look the part. I'm pleased with the way I look. Life must be a lot less interesting if you're ugly. Knowing girls fancy you gives you confidence.

"I'm never short of dates but if it's too easy I lose interest and cool off. I enjoy the chatting-up bit. Mind you, I never crawl. But if a girl plays a little bit hard to get, she's got me interested.

"Sometimes I do get the feeling I'm putting on an act all the time, trying to impress. I hear myself trotting out the same old lines with a new girl. Sometimes I don't like myself much and I get fed up playing the scene, but I couldn't see myself sticking to one girl. What a waste!"

Paul certainly knows what he wants, and a lot of girls find that attractive. Bob, on the other hand, hasn't got any confidence at all. He's still at school.

"I don't rate at all. I'm sixteen and I look about thirteen, and I don't know one girl who isn't put off by that. They all go for the big guys, the guys who look older than they do, so that means I'd have to get someone at primary school!

"I think girls go for looks first and foremost. I mean at a disco, if you ask a girl to dance she gives you the once over and if you don't match up she'll turn you down. It's pretty unfair.

"Maybe I'm not meeting the right girls but the ones I meet, especially at school, are pretty hard. Although everyone says it's personality that counts, they want a fella with looks and a bit of cash to spend on them – and I don't have either."

Are we really that bad? Tony is a guy who has the looks but he hasn't got a girlfriend at the moment. He's an assistant in a photographic shop.

"I'd rate five on a good day! I've never gone out with a girl for longer than two months and it's been ages since I asked a girl out because I get more and more scared of being

turned down. It gets worse as you get older, I think. You tend to take things more seriously.

"It's rotten being a bloke, having to be pushy, having to chat up a girl when you're just not sure whether she's interested or not.

"There have been a couple of times I've met a girl and well, kind of backed off at the last minute. Afterwards, I go over what she's said in my head and half the time I realise that it was all my fault. I should have been more positive – asked to see her home, asked her out, at least asked for her phone number, but I always lose my nerve **and** the girl.

"It's just a basic lack of confidence in myself. It even extends to my work – if I was more pushy I'd get a great job as a photographer on a paper maybe instead of wasting my time here."

Are girls so frightening, then? Are they only after guys with looks? Next we asked a few of the monsters themselves — the girls — for their opinions of boys, and they weren't shy to tell us what they thought!

Julie is a girl who has strong feelings and surprisingly, the boys she doesn't like are the nice ones . . .

"Nice guys are boring. I don't even like handsome types – I like interesting types. Somehow I'm always more attracted to boys who treat me badly – who don't phone when they say they

Then?

will, who stand me up, or two-time me. It's much more exciting!

"Sure, I shed a lot of tears but I'd hate to be stuck in the safe 'two nights a week and every weekend' routine some of my friends are in."

That's quite a surprising attitude and one probably not many girls share, but it takes all kinds. Karen is good looking and she freely admits to judging a bloke by his looks.

"I'm lucky because I can pick and choose the type of guy I want. I go weak at the knees for skinny blokes who've got good dress sense. If a guy doesn't make the effort with how he looks then I'm not interested.

"I know I couldn't go out with someone who wasn't good looking, because every time we went out I'd feel embarrassed with him and I'd be wishing I was with someone else."

So what about the ideal imaginary muscle man? The truth is, he just doesn't exist. So next time you feel you've got no chance with a boy just stop and think that he's probably feeling as terrified as *you*!

The thing to remember is that when you're looking through the eyes of love, *everybody's* gorgeous!

GETTING FRUITY! Something For (Almost) Nothing

Make yourself a bag that's roomy enough to hold schoolbooks, shopping and all your junk — it couldn't be easier! All you need to make the kind of bag shown here is a piece of denim or canvas, any old leftover paint lying around the house and one or two fruits or vegetables.

The sort of material you use to make the bag is really up to you, but it should be strong and fairly light in colour. Off-white denim or canvas is ideal and a piece 50 cms. by 115 cms., which is the amount you need, shouldn't cost much more than £1.

Once you've got hold of the material, the first thing you have to do to make your bag is to print a design on it. Take one of the fruits or vegetables which you've chosen — an apple, for instance — and cut it in half.

Now lay your piece of material out flat on a table, or on the floor. Using a small brush, coat the cut side of your fruit with a thin coat of paint and then print this on to your fabric.

Repeat this procedure all over the material, printing either at random or building up a pattern. You can, of course, use different fruits and print them in various colours. For instance, we used an apple printed in orange, red and black.

You can use any type of household paint to decorate your bag although the easiest to apply is non-drip emulsion — don't try to use water colours as these will wash out.

Most fruits and vegetables will print well as long as they aren't *too* juicy. You can't, for instance, print a plum very easily as it'll squash. If you decide to use an onion, leave it in a warm place for a few hours after cutting it in half, because this will make the rings stand out more and give a better print.

Once you've printed your material, hang it up and leave it to dry for about 12 hours.

WHEN the pattern is dry, cut two strips, each about 8 cms. wide, from one of the shorter edges of the material — these are to make the handles. Take one of these strips and fold it in half lengthways with the pattern inside. Now sew the strip along one short edge and one long edge to make a tube. Using a knitting needle, blunt end first, push the closed edge down the tube, thus turning the handle the right way out and revealing the pattern. Do this with both handles.

Next, take the large piece of material and fold in a strip about 1 cm. wide along each short edge. Stitch these and then attach the handles to them by sewing their

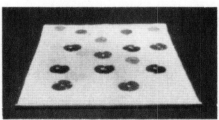

The material with the fruit prints on it.

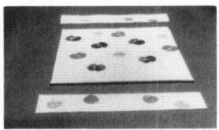

Cut two strips off the material. These are used to make the handles.

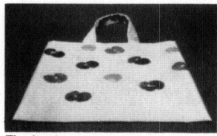

The bag!

ends to these hems, leaving a gap of about 20 cms. between each end.

You should now have a large, flat piece of material with a handle at each end. Now fold this in half, with the pattern on the inside, and sew along the edges, leaving you with an inside out bag. Finally, iron the seams open and turn the bag inside out to reveal the pattern.

With a little care, and about two hours work, you'll have made yourself a shopping bag, one that's pretty unique and totally different from anything you could buy in the shops!

I Saw Him First!

A Jackie short story specially written by Winnie Czulinski.

HIS name was Paul and he was gorgeous. Everyone thought so — especially me. Naturally, I fancied him like mad — everyone did! — but just for once, I seemed to have the advantage over all my giggling rivals.

I had discovered, by means of a great deal of effort and a bit of very unsubtle detective work, that Paul lived just three streets away from me and that we went to the same school, although he was in a different form. There was, however, a Snag.

Martine. Actually, she was (occasionally) my friend, but not so's you'd notice. Not that you could help noticing Martine, with her glossy black hair, glossy red lips and glossy-magazine clothes.

She also lived near Paul and went to the same school, and I lived in constant fear of the moment that he would notice her and be helplessly dazzled.

I would never, ever have wanted Paul to know that I was chasing him, of course — a girl has her pride. But I certainly wasn't going to let that female piranha have him without putting up a bit of a fight . . .

So, on a rather nice, crisp winter morning, I decided to begin "Operation Paul." I knew (because of all the time I'd spent snooping around) exactly when he was due to walk past the end of my street, so I dawdled along as slowly as I could, praying that Martine wouldn't arrive at the same time.

About five minutes later, after I'd looked at everything I could possibly look at, then examined it in minute detail again, Paul appeared.

I pretended to be very interested in

she breathed, "but of course, it was twice as nice meeting you and Ron there . . ."

What you might term a faint glimmer of hope began to flicker through my deepest, darkest despair. She and Paul hadn't met on purpose and they hadn't been alone . . .

". . . he did suggest that we should get Rona to make up a four one night," She paused for effect. "Could be fun," she purred, batting her eyelashes.

Paul looked up, rather enthusiastically, I thought. "I said. "I sort of suspected you were quite keen on Ron! And if Rona'll come with me, we can definitely get something organised!"

BY the end of the day, of course, I had recovered a bit, and decided to have another go. Maybe I wasn't as devastating as Martine, but I wasn't half bad. Mum was always telling me I was quite pretty.

It did bother me a bit, though, that mothers tend to say that even if their child has a face that would frighten a horse . . . But I put that disturbing thought to the back of my mind and decided to walk home by way of Paul's house.

He'd be almost bound to catch me up, I thought, so I wandered along quite slowly.

He didn't, of course, and I was back in the dumps again before I got to my own front door. Martine must have caught him, I thought miserably, and he's so besotted, he hasn't the strength to resist.

Next morning, though, he was hanging around on my street corner, just for a change. As I walked towards him, trying to look cool and unconcerned, he smiled straight at me and I felt myself flush scarlet all over.

He looked so gorgeous that it took me a few minutes to realise he was actually speaking to me.

". . . Adam and the Ants con-

Paul just gaped after her and I sagged inwardly. I was no competition at all after that little display.

"Well," I said, with a light laugh. "Back to the grind!"

"Mmm . . ." said Paul, in a very absent-minded voice. I gave up. He would never be mine.

"Thanks," she said, stiffly. "I'll think about it and let you know.",

She smiled as if the effort would kill her and stalked off as soon as we got to the school gates.

Once we were alone, I heard Paul take a deep breath and say, "Great girl, Martine. She must've known that I've been wanting to get to know you for ages. It was nice of her to arrange all this.

"Mind you —", He looked at the ground, and coughed slightly. "She can be a bit overpowering, can't she?"

I choked, and he had to slap me on the back before I recovered enough to walk into class. What a good thing, I thought, as he put his arm round me, that some of us were more — subtle about things . . .

THE world spun round and Martine — seemed to disappear. When the world stopped spinning round, she appeared again, looking red and angry and deflated and blazing mad! She didn't make a fool of herself by explaining that he'd got it all wrong, though.

She was far too sophisticated and cool for that and she wasn't going to ruin her image, even for Paul.

I became vaguely aware that Paul was speaking to me. "That is, if you don't mind, Rona?"

I hesitated exactly two seconds. "It sounds smashing to me!" I said, grinning all over my face.

He moved a little closer. Not so close that it made much difference, but still . . .

I turned to Martine and said,

I'd fancied Paul for ages — but so had Martine. And what chance did I have against Westdale School's answer to Debbie Harry . . .?

two horrible little boys having a snow-ball fight on the other side of the road and waited until he called out to me before I looked round.

"Rona! Rona, wait a minute!"

Gratified, I turned and watched him squelch up to me. His voice made my blood run sort of hot and cold at the same time, but, of course, I wasn't going to let him know that.

"Hello," I said, as calmly as I could.

"Hello, Paul," said Martine, appearing as if by magic from a side-street.

PAUL turned. "Oh – Martine! I didn't expect to see you this early."

"No," I said, gritting my teeth. "Nor did I!"

She ignored me. "You're looking good this morning, Paul," she murmured, batting her eyelashes, Paul blushed.

"Er – thanks, Martine. Why don't you walk along with us?," he said, like the gentleman he is.

Why he had to choose that particular moment to be a gentleman, I don't know, but we walked along together – in total silence. I thought the sultry looks Martine was casting at Paul would melt the snow and I spent the rest of the walk dreaming up terrible things that could happen to her between here and the school gates.

"Well," she breathed as we reached the playground, "simply must dash to – biology!" She ran her eyes over Paul as if she would have just loved to experiment on him and wiggled off.

cert . . .", he was saying. "I was thinking –",

"Yes?" said Martine, sidling up from somewhere behind him and planting herself very deliberately between us.

I closed my eyes and thought very uncharitable thoughts, about how many years I'd get in jail for strangling some-one with their own scarf. When I opened them, she had put her arm through Paul's. She smiled at me, smugly.

"Paul was telling you about the wonderful time we had last night, was he? I can't remember when I enjoyed myself so much!"

I FELT my mouth open and I shut it sharpish, feeling more of a fool than I could bear. What wonderful time? When? Where? I thought desperately. To add insult to injury, I also dropped all my books (from shock) and had to get down on my hands and knees to gather all the bits and pieces together.

I must have looked really awkward, scrambling about in the snow while the immaculate Martine looked on, sneer-ing, faintly.

"Here, Rona," Paul was saying. "Let me give you a hand."

I collected my books and what remained of my dignity, thanked Paul as graciously as I could, and the three of us walked along together.

At least, Paul and Martine were together – I was relegated to the iciest area on the out-side of the pavement.

Paul was looking a bit pink for some reason and he didn't seem to want to look at Martine. It was so obvious he was really keen on her – boys are like that . . .

She didn't give me a look in, of course – she kept talking all the way along the road.

"I always did like the coffee bar,"

innocently, "Where do you think Ron would like to go? All this was your idea, so it's only fair that you should choose!"

We all have to go on first dates at some point in our lives and they're not always successful. But why? Read on to find out how to avoid those first-date disasters!

FIRST DATE PITFALLS

YOU'VE got yourself a brand-new boy and you're about to meet him for your first real date. Everything looks lovely. It'll be wonderful. Nothing can possibly go wrong . . .

Except *First-Date Pitfalls*—and that's the end of another promising romance. They're the mistakes that make the first-date girl clutch her brow and moan, "I shouldn't have done *that*!" as her new guy hares off up the road in a cloud of dust!

Here are just a few:

I SHOULDN'T HAVE . . . got his name wrong. His name's Bill and he reckons he's made such a good impression on you that you'll remember him for ever. Or even longer. But you turn up for that first date and say, "Hi, Sid, . . . er, Frank . . . er, Arthur?" This gives him the impression that he's not quite as memorable as he thought he was and he's likely to go right off you immediately.

But forgetting his name isn't as bad as forgetting what he looks like and walking right past him as he stands at the meeting place with a welcoming smile.

I SHOULDN'T HAVE . . . eaten garlic. Chomping through a garlic-riddled meal before going on that first date isn't a good idea. It'll put him right off the idea of kissing you, and if you've really overdone the garlic flavouring he may even wear a gas mask, which will make conversation difficult. Don't kid yourself that you've had a lucky escape and the garlic has scared him off 'cos he's a vampire. He probably isn't.

I SHOULDN'T HAVE . . . introduced him to my best friend. Not if your best friend is a beautiful man-eater, you shouldn't. It's no fun turning up at the disco to show off your fabulous new boyfriend and then having to walk home on your own, mumbling tearfully, while your dishy best friend waltzes off with him. Keep him to yourself for a while, until you get used to each other. Once he's really got to know you he's not so likely to be snatched. Unless you're incredibly bad-tempered and spotty and horrible. Which you're not, are you? Well, not all three.

I SHOULDN'T HAVE . . . turned up late. Remember the guy doesn't know you all that well. All he knows is that you agreed to a date and you've had a whole night and a day to change your mind. So he's a bit scared of being made a fool of and isn't going to spend too long waiting for a girl who may not turn up at all. If you do turn up late and are lucky enough to find him still standing there like a lemon, have a good excuse. Something to soften him up, like: "I had to stop to rescue a drowning puppy from the lake." Or: "I was caught in a rainstorm and had to go back home to change." If you're very late and he's looking a little tight around the mouth, make it two puppies (or even four), or a freak hurricane.

I SHOULDN'T HAVE . . . taken him home. Dragging the guy home to meet the folks on the first date is a bad idea. The guy has used up most of his available nerve in asking you for a date in the first place. Having to be stared at critically by Mum, Dad, Gran, Aunt Ethel, the budgie and the cat will put him under more strain than the human mind can stand. So don't take him home until he's relaxed enough to cope with it. This could take months, especially if your Aunt Ethel is anything like everybody else's Aunt Ethel.

I SHOULDN'T HAVE . . . arrived for the date in the wrong clothes. It's a good idea to find out roughly what he's got planned for that first date. It won't help much if you turn up in your dolliest dress to find him standing with his greasy motor bike, all dressed up in leathers and ready to bomb off to a grass-track meeting. Or if you arrive in your scruffiest gear expecting to bomb off on his bike while he's immaculate in his best suit and has booked a table for two at the Ritz.

I SHOULDN'T HAVE . . . mentioned my last boyfriend. Keep your last guy out of it. If you say nice things about him, like what a great dancer he was, or how he used to throw his jacket over puddles for you to walk on, your new guy will be worried about how he's going to match up to such a wonderful person. He'll also be wondering how you lost Mr Wonderful. Is there something about you he doesn't know?

And if you try to make the new guy feel good by saying rotten things about your last boy, that won't work either. New guy will have the uneasy feeling that you'll be saying nasty things about him when you move on to your next fella.

. SHOULDN'T HAVE . . . insisted on going to the pictures. He's going to be doing his best to please on that first date, but when he says, "Where do you fancy going?" don't pick on something expensive, just in case he's flat broke. It can be embarrassing watching a poor guy blushing hotly as he sorts through a collection of small change, shirt buttons and dead moths, trying to get enough cash together for two seats in the stalls. Offering to go dutch is fine, but paying the whole lot yourself isn't going to make him feel much better. So settle for a walk on that first date and a couple of Cokes in a café. He'll appreciate it and it'll prove you're not the kind of girl who's trying to rip him off. Of course, once you've discovered that he's *incredibly* rich . . . that's different.

So think hard before going on that first date. Avoid the *First-Date Pitfalls* and have a great time. That way you won't crawl miserably home, minus your new guy, moaning, "*I shouldn't have . . .*"

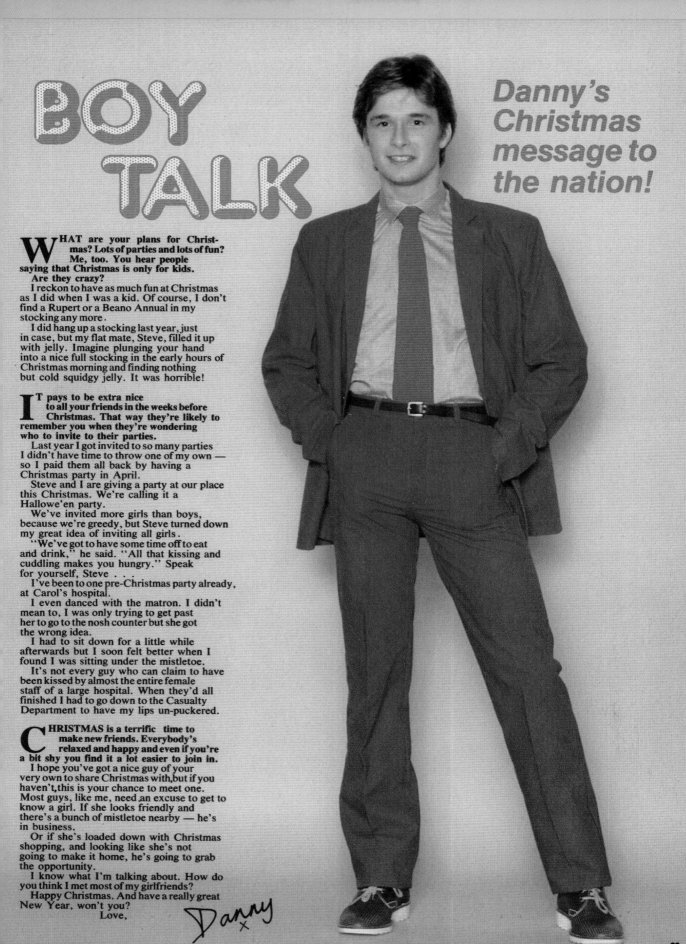

BOY TALK

Danny's Christmas message to the nation!

WHAT are your plans for Christmas? Lots of parties and lots of fun? Me, too. You hear people saying that Christmas is only for kids. Are they crazy?

I reckon to have as much fun at Christmas as I did when I was a kid. Of course, I don't find a Rupert or a Beano Annual in my stocking any more.

I did hang up a stocking last year, just in case, but my flat mate, Steve, filled it up with jelly. Imagine plunging your hand into a nice full stocking in the early hours of Christmas morning and finding nothing but cold squidgy jelly. It was horrible!

IT pays to be extra nice to all your friends in the weeks before Christmas. That way they're likely to remember you when they're wondering who to invite to their parties.

Last year I got invited to so many parties I didn't have time to throw one of my own — so I paid them all back by having a Christmas party in April.

Steve and I are giving a party at our place this Christmas. We're calling it a Hallowe'en party.

We've invited more girls than boys, because we're greedy, but Steve turned down my great idea of inviting all girls.

"We've got to have some time off to eat and drink," he said. "All that kissing and cuddling makes you hungry." Speak for yourself, Steve . . .

I've been to one pre-Christmas party already, at Carol's hospital.

I even danced with the matron. I didn't mean to, I was only trying to get past her to go to the nosh counter but she got the wrong idea.

I had to sit down for a little while afterwards but I soon felt better when I found I was sitting under the mistletoe.

It's not every guy who can claim to have been kissed by almost the entire female staff of a large hospital. When they'd all finished I had to go down to the Casualty Department to have my lips un-puckered.

CHRISTMAS is a terrific time to make new friends. Everybody's relaxed and happy and even if you're a bit shy you find it a lot easier to join in.

I hope you've got a nice guy of your very own to share Christmas with, but if you haven't, this is your chance to meet one. Most guys, like me, need an excuse to get to know a girl. If she looks friendly and there's a bunch of mistletoe nearby — he's in business.

Or if she's loaded down with Christmas shopping, and looking like she's not going to make it home, he's going to grab the opportunity.

I know what I'm talking about. How do you think I met most of my girlfriends?

Happy Christmas. And have a really great New Year, won't you?

Love,

Danny
x

ARIES

At your best, you're full of energy, honest, brave and strong. But at your worst, you can be quick-tempered, impatient, selfish and bossy. You have to be first in everything—the lunch queue, exams, work, relationships. You want everything now and you barge through life making sure you get it. You can be courageous and adventurous, but you can also be just plain aggressive and bad-tempered. You never think before you speak and for this reason you are not the ideal person to trust with secrets!

TAURUS

You can be practical, reliable and warm-hearted. But you can also be stodgy and self-centred and so stuck in a rut that it's difficult to see your way out of it. At your worst, you hate change and are stubborn enough to stick to your opinions no matter what. (You still think there should only be one television channel.) As far as boys are concerned, you're faithful, warm-hearted—and possessive. If your boyfriend so much as glances in another girl's direction, you'll be in a bad mood for a fortnight!

GEMINI

You're so lively, witty and attractive that you just can't help being a two-timing flirt as well! And you get away with it because you're so cunning and convincing. You can be caught entwined with your boyfriend's best mate and still manage to convince them both that you were only testing out your theory that your boyfriend kisses better than any other boy you know. You find it difficult to stick with anything. Once something new appears on the horizon—a new hobby, a new friend, a new boy—you drop all your old interests.

CANCER

Basically, you're kind, sensitive and sympathetic. But if things aren't going right for you, you can be over-emotional, touchy and moody. You're also an expert at harbouring grudges. People can go for months trying to figure out what it is they've done to offend you. You'll never tell them, though, because you think they should instinctively know what's wrong. And it could well be you've taken offence because they've told you you should tidy up your desk/room/handbag, because you do have the reputation for being one of the most untidy signs of the zodiac!

HORROR

Your star sign can tell you a lot about your character and personality—and that means your bad points as well as your good points. Each sign of the zodiac has its nasty side, so if you want to find out what yours is, just read on for some astro facts you <u>don't</u> want to know!

LEO

You're attractive and popular and everybody's sunshine girl—and don't you know it! You just want to spread happiness wherever you go. The trouble is, if other people don't want to fall in with your plans for them, you feel it's your duty to step in and organise their dull, boring little lives for them. You can't help being popular, but you might be a bit more popular if you stopped thinking you were doing people a favour by talking to them. And hard though it might be for you, you <u>could</u> step out of the spotlight once or twice— even if it's only for a few moments!

VIRGO

You're the modest, hard-working, helpful sign of the zodiac. The trouble is, if you're not careful, you can end up being picky, fussy and over-critical. You have to remember that cleaning the cooker and tidying out the hall cupboard isn't everyone's idea of a fun evening. You also tend to worry too much. You worry about your clothes, your hair, your health, other people's health, and if you can't find anything to worry about, you worry about not worrying. You'll never admit to any of this, though, because Virgos love to pretend they're perfect!

LIBRA

You're the nicest, sweetest, most tactful person around. The trouble is, you're so tactful and so anxious not to give offence, you end up being totally ignored. You take so many sides in a quarrel, no-one's got a clue what you actually do think. And after a while, you don't either. You tend to put off making decisions, too, and end up having them made for you. You rely on friends to tell you what to wear, where to go and who to go there with. If you ever do decide you want something, though, you usually end up getting it, one way or another!

SCORPIO

You have powerful feelings and emotions and unfortunately, one of the most powerful is your jealousy. Scorpios are Jealous. You're jealous if your friend gets better exam marks than you; you're jealous if your sister gets a bigger slice of cake than you; you're even jealous if the cat gets to sleep in your chair. And if your boyfriend dares to talk to another girl, they'll both feel the sting of your sharp Scorpio personality. You're stubborn, secretive and suspicious, but you're fascinating and there will always be something exciting going on when you're around!

SAGITTARIUS

You love freedom and adventure and you're in your element striding fearlessly into unknown dangers. Unfortunately, you can end up striding fearlessly into other people's lives. You're one of the most tactless signs of the zodiac and if anyone's going to tell their best friend her new haircut makes her look like Worzel Gummidge, it's going to be you. You tend to exaggerate, too, and you can make deciding between having your chips with or without vinegar seem as difficult as trying to decide which outfit to wear to a Royal Garden party.

CAPRICORN

You see yourself as reliable, careful and self-disciplined. But other people may just think you're being over-practical and disapproving. You can be a bit self-righteous and at your worst, will lecture your friends about what they should be doing with their lives instead of— horrors—enjoying themselves. Just because you think it's your duty to sit at home of an evening sorting out your parents' gas bill, it doesn't mean your friends are complete wastrels because they'd rather go to the movies. It's actually fun to do something mad and daft once in a while. Try it!

AQUARIUS

If there's a cause to be fought for or a wrong to be righted, you'll be the first to lend a hand, so long as there's no emotional commitment. You'd rather be working to Save the Whale than working on your relationships. You also always hate and disapprove of what the majority of people like to do. This means that you can spend many lonely evenings making Save the Whale T-shirts out of recycled string while your frinds are all enjoying themselves at the disco. Of course if everyone were to start making string T-shirts, you'd be off to the disco like a shot!

PISCES

You're sympathetic, sweet and kind. You just hate being nasty to anyone, and this means that you spend your time being nice to the nastiest, weediest people around. You're so busy being nice to other people, in fact, you forget how to run your own life and end up becoming totally dependent. If you don't get total emotional support from friends and boyfriends, you can whine on and on until you do. In fact, at your very worst, you can end up being a real drag. Try being genuinely, honestly, nasty once in a while. You'll be a nicer person for it!

Who Do You View?

Are you crazy about "Coronation Street," daft about "Dallas" and sold on "Superman"? If so, try our special TV and film quiz!

Cop That!

How much do you know about TV cops and robbers? Well, here's your chance to find out!

1. On which island does Jim Bergerac fight crime?

2. OK, so everyone knows they're called Cagney and Lacey. But what're their first names? Are they:
   a. Chris and Maggie,
   b. Maggie and Beth,
   c. Chris and Mary-Beth?

3. Which American police series does Tom Reilly star in?

4. General Lee is a bit of a fast character who is always being chased by the police. What show does he star in?

5. Lee Horsley stars as this Texas millionaire turned private eye. Can you name him?

6. Bodie and Doyle worked for C.I.5. in "The Professionals". What do these letters stand for?

Your Starter For Ten

Find out if you're our special "Mastermind" in this section on TV quizzes.

1. Dusty Bin stars in which quiz show?
2. Mike Read hosts which quiz show?
3. A computer called Mr Babbidge helps in this quiz show. Can you name it?

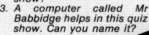

4. Which show does this describe: "contestants team up with star guests and use their skill to remember where they heard it and who they heard it from"?
5. In which quiz show do contestants shout "Higher" or "Lower"?
6. Willie Carson and Bill Beaumont are team captains in which quiz show?

Series Stuff

See how much you know about your favourite TV series.

1. Where do Petra Taylor, Gordon Collins and Roger Huntingdon all live?
2. Krystle, Fallon and Alexis star in which American series?
3. OK, "Fame" fans – everyone knows this is Carlo Imperato, but can you give us the full name of the character he plays in the series and what career he's aiming for?

4. He left school, where he had a reputation for being a real tearaway, and tried hard to get a job – who are we talking about?

5. Name the high-powered series this gorgeous guy appears in.
6. Name the dishy actor who stars as Brian Tilsley in "Coronation Street."

Music While You Watch

If you're a pop fan — then you're bound to do well with these questions on TV music programmes.

1. D.J. Peter Powell hosted this BBC 2 music show. Can you name it?
2. It began on January 1, 1964, and is Britain's longest-running pop programme. Name that show!
3. Lisa Stansfield jumped for joy when she was asked to present this mad-cap Tyne Tees show. What's it called?
4. This likely-looking lot starred in Channel 4's first Friday evening music show. Do you remember what it was called?
5. Unscramble these letters to discover a BBC 2 arts and music programme. VIREEDRSI
6. Name the show which combines a live pop concert with a simultaneous broadcast on Radio One.

2. This hunky heart-throb starred as Zak Mayo in a romantic movie. Two points if you can tell us the actor's name and also name the movie.
3. Which famous pop star played the lead role in "Merry Christmas, Mr Lawrence"?

Screen Test

Are you a film fan? Then try these movie questions for size!
1. What's the connection between Michael Jackson and E.T.? (No, it isn't that they're both out of this world!)

4. Can you name Cannon and Ball's crazy comedy film?
5. What's special about "Jaws III"?
6. "Local Hero" was set in what part of Britain?
   a. Scotland.
   b. Wales.
   c. Northern Ireland.
7. OK, all you science-fiction fans. Name the third "Star Wars" movie.

A Commercial Break

'Ad enough yet? No? Well try these questions!
1. What's "the best drink of the day"?
2. Barbara Woodhouse tells you to do what?
3. What's "tasty, tasty, very very tasty"?
4. What can you make someone happy with?
5. "If the name fits – wear it." What's the name?
6. "Bite it, crunch it, chew it." What are we talking about?

ANSWERS

Score one point for each correct answer.

Cop That!
1. Jersey 2. (c) 3. "C.H.i.P.s" 4. "The Dukes Of Hazzard" 5. "Matt Houston" 6. "Criminal Intelligence".

Your Starter For Ten
1. "3, 2, 1" 2. "Pop Quiz" 3. "Family Fortunes" 4. "Punchlines" 5. "Play Your Cards Right" 6. "A Question Of Sport".

Series Stuff
1. "Brookside" 2. "Dynasty" 3. Danny Amatullo — a comedian 4. Tucker Jenkins, alias actor Todd Carty 5. "Falcon Crest" 6. Christopher Quinten.

Screen Test
1. Michael collaborated on the "E.T. Storybook" album 2. Richard Gere — "An Officer And A Gentleman" 3. David Bowie 4. "Boys In Blue" 5. It's in 3-D 6. (a) 7. "Return Of The Jedi".

Music While You Watch
1. "The Oxford Road Show" 2. "Top Of The Pops" 3. "Razzmatazz" 4. "The Tube" 5. "Riverside" 6. "Sight And Sound In Concert".

A Commercial Break
1. Tea 2. "Go smash an egg!" 3. Kelloggs Bran Flakes 4. A phone call 5. Levi's 6. Lion Bar.

CONCLUSIONS

30-37 — Award yourself a pat on the back — you're definitely our media mastermind! There's not much you don't know about the world of TV and films. In fact, ignore everyone calling you "Square Eyes." We think they suit you!

20-29 — You're not exactly hooked on television and films but you have quite a good knowledge of them. You'll never threaten Barry Norman on "Film 83" or Barry Took on "Points Of View" but you're a normal Jackie TV and film fan.

19 and under — Mmm! D'you actually know what a TV is? It's that square thing that sits in the corner of your living-room — no, we're not speaking about your dad, stupid! As for the cinema, well, you probably don't even realise that the local flicks is now a bingo hall!

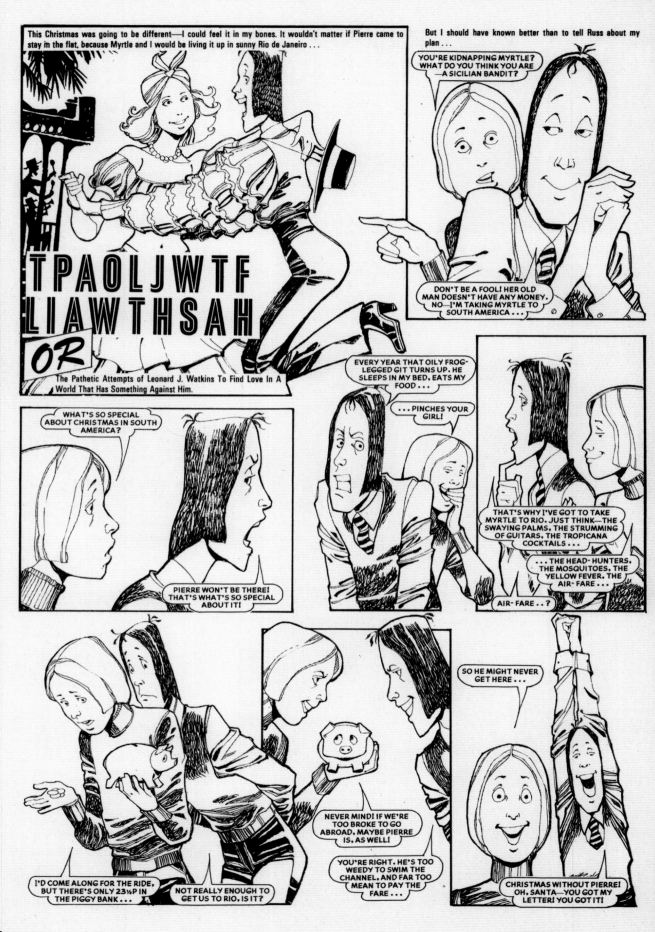

HAIR'S HEALTH!

Here's how to keep your hair happy!

● *Hair grows at ½ inch a month and no amount of pulling and stretching will speed this rate up. However, your hair does grow slightly quicker in warm weather so be prepared to visit your hairdresser more in summer.*

● Every day you lose about 50 hairs — so don't panic every time one falls out! If a hair is yanked out instead of falling out naturally, it can take up to 3 months to regrow.

● *Each hair has a lifespan of anything from a few months to several years. The part of the hair we can see is actually dead!*

● To make sure your hair is shiny and healthy, eat the proper things — lean meat, liver, seafood and fresh fruit and vegetables.

● *Brush your hair thoroughly before you wash it. This releases dust and grease, giving a better finished product.*

● Wash your hair in *warm* water. Water that's too hot not only hurts your head — it encourages grease in your hair.

● *You can tell a good shampoo if it goes through your hair easily and rinses out quickly.*

● Normal hair can be washed with most shampoos — but don't let this tempt you into resorting to the very cheap and nasty kind.

● *Dry hair needs a moisturising shampoo, preferably with a built-in conditioner. Special ingredients to look out for include rosemary, camomile and Vitamin C.*

● When blow-drying your hair, don't let the hairdryer touch your hair, and don't concentrate the blast on one spot for very long as the heat will damage your hair.

● If you suffer from dandruff, use a good dandruff shampoo. After the dandruff has cleared up, go back to your normal shampoo.

Pic by courtesy of Henara.

● Oily hair needs an oil-free shampoo. Don't be tempted by brands which promise to 'cut through the grease' — they'll take away all those essential oils your hair needs along with the grease it could do without.

● *Rinsing your hair should take much longer than the actual shampooing and is just as important.*

● Rinse your hair in *cool* water for the final rinse. You could also add vinegar to the water, if you've got dark hair; or lemon juice, if you're fair haired. This will make your hair really shiny.

● *Don't leave conditioner on for longer than it says on the bottle — it will have stopped working by then.*

● Always rinse conditioner off thoroughly or it will leave a dull covering on your hair.

● *Don't be surprised if your hair seems much longer when it's wet — good condition hair stretches by up to ⅓ of its length after it's been in water.*

● Hair is at its weakest when it's wet so be extra careful with it. *Never* brush wet hair.

● *After washing, wrap your hair in a towel to blot the moisture. Then comb it out very gently with a wide-toothed comb.*

● If you have to wash your hair every day, use a mild shampoo.

● *Never blow dry your hair bone dry. It will stay in much better condition if it's left with a touch of moisture to dry off naturally and be absorbed into the hair.*

● Remember to wash your hairbrush when you wash your hair.

● *If you want a really strong hold on your hair, use gel and hairspray together and then style your hair.*

● Brushing your hair upside down gives it bounce and helps circulation, giving healthy hair.

● *Don't overbrush. Forget all about brushing your hair 100 times before you go to bed. It breaks your hair and make it look greasy. Around 25 strokes is more than enough for even the longest hair.*

● If you back comb your hair, remember to brush it out — carefully.

● *When you are sunbathing put a little conditioner through your hair to protect it from the sun's harmful rays. Remember to rinse it out afterwards, though.*

● And finally . . . standing on your head does wonders for your hair! Try it and see!

Most boys are nice most of the time. No boy is perfect, but some boys are just plain *bad* and if you're unlucky enough to get involved with a bad boy, you're right in line to find out why so many love songs are sad songs.

Think you're too smart to fall for a bad boy? Think again! A bad boy's greatest asset is that he can attract girls the way a spider attracts flies. And he's just as deadly. So don't get caught in his trap. Learn to spot a bad boy before he gets the chance to capture — and break — your heart.

WARNING! These Boys Are Dangerous!

DANGER!

The Bad Boy who won't take No for an answer.

This bad boy is probably the most dangerous of all. He's charming, tender and romantic, but his one aim with girls is to go a lot further than just kissing and cuddling. And if you say "No," he's got a whole arsenal of speeches already prepared and all guaranteed to break down your defences.

He'll tell you you're not a couple of kids any more . . . he'll tell you that for him this is the real thing . . . he'll let you know there have been other girls in his life — girls who weren't afraid like you . . .

And if you like him, which you most probably will, since this type of boy is usually popular and attractive, you'll listen to him.

Even though you know all about his reputation, you'll persuade yourself, with a little help from him, that you're different from all those other girls. You'll think this really is the real thing for him and that he really is in love with you, so what harm can it do?

The answer is an awful lot.

And if you think he really does love you, ask yourself why he's trying to push you to take decisions you feel are wrong for you.

Any boy who tries to cash in on emotional blackmail like this is bad news. If he won't listen to your opinions, respect your ideas and trust you to know what's right for *you*, he's a candidate for our bad boys line-up.

Beware of the boy who pushes you too far, who threatens to drop you "unless." A boy who cares about you will want decisions about the physical side of your relationship to be mutual ones.

But the bad boy doesn't care about you at all. He's out to get his own way and he'll threaten to walk out on you if he doesn't. And if, against your better judgment, you're silly enough to give in to him, he'll walk out on you anyway.

To a bad boy like this, a relationship means proving himself. Proving he can get any girl he wants. And once the challenge is gone — he is, too.

The Bad Boy who wants to take over your life.

He walks into your life and everything is suddenly beautiful. He really loves you. He's fascinated by everything about you — your hair, your clothes, the new shoes you bought . . .

He takes so much interest in you, in fact, that pretty soon he's suggesting what you ought to wear when he takes you out. He's also considerate enough to point out all the little faults you have.

So you wear the clothes he likes you to wear, you go to the places he wants you to go, you think the way he wants you to think, and you end up being completely dominated by him.

And when the dominating bad boy

does tell you it's over, you spend a long time wondering why. Didn't you try to be everything he wanted in a girl? Didn't you dress the way he liked and talk the way he liked and think the way he liked?

Yes, you did — and that was your mistake.

Beware of the boy who tries to do all your thinking for you and tries to turn you into someone else. If a relationship founders on the colour of a dress or the kind of records you like listening to, it isn't much of a relationship. And if a boy is attracted enough to ask you out in the first place why would he want to change you?

The boy who does is more than likely a little bit selfish and insecure and isn't ready for a relationship based on mutual give and take.

So don't make the mistake of allowing some boy to tell you what to think and how to dress. Nice boys will accept you as you are and won't try to change you. Bad boys won't.

> Falling for a genuine bad boy can be a heartbreaking experience and it can take a long time to recover.
>
> Remember, though, the good guys really do outnumber the bad guys and chances are you'll be a whole lot luckier second time around!

DANGER!

The Bad Boy who'll two, three and even four-time you.

This particular bad boy finds it easy — too easy — to attract girls, and he finds them impossible to resist. He just adores being adored.

And the trouble is, he's just so easy to fall in love with. He'll tell you he really loves you back, too, and while he's saying it he probably means it. And he probably means it when he whispers exactly the same thing to Karen, Lucy, Annette or Hazel . . .

The two-timer is superb. When you eventually catch him out, it's more likely to be because he wanted you to. Then, you see, he doesn't have to go through all the trouble involved in breaking off a relationship when he's tired of it.

All he has to do is let himself be caught out a few times and, what do you know, *you* do all the work for him! You send him packing.

Then, of course, you spend the next few weeks wondering why it was you packed up a boy you were crazy about. Maybe you should have forgiven him . . . maybe there's still time . . . maybe you should be more broad minded about these things . . . maybe he's really nice underneath it all . . .

Well, he's not! He's attractive and fun and great to be with, but he's also a grade one Bad Boy.

DANGER!

The Bad Boy who pretends you don't exist.

Unlike the two-timer, this bad boy needs, and wants, just one steady girlfriend. He likes having a steady girlfriend in the background. The trouble is, in the background is strictly where you'll stay.

When he takes you out, he'll be attentive, concerned about you, and generally a pretty nice person to be with. Then you meet one or two of his friends and suddenly your nice boyfriend becomes a prime candidate for the bad boy stakes.

He doesn't introduce you to anyone, he completely ignores you, he leaves you sitting on your own while he chats to his mates and he generally behaves as if you just don't exist.

He likes to feel free to chat up other girls at parties, to talk to his mates and generally to feel that he can do as he likes. At the same time, though, he likes the security of having a steady girlfriend. It's a classic case of the person who wants the best of both worlds.

The one thing in this bad boy's favour is that he won't actually two-time you and he'll be attentive and loving when you're on your own. It's when other people are around that you'll suddenly become part of the wallpaper as far as he's concerned.

The last thing this boy wants is to be free. But he likes to play at being free. It's all a game, you see, and if you get entangled with this bad boy, you could end up the loser.

DON'T LOOK NOW – IT'S

SUPERYAWN!

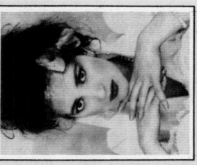

You know the feeling — you're halfway through a detailed description of Granny's birthday party when suddenly you notice your mate's glazed expression as her eyelids begin to droop. In other words, she's BORED — and you're BORING! So how d'you beat the boring blues? Read on, discover your own brand of bore, and you'll never have to face another yawn!

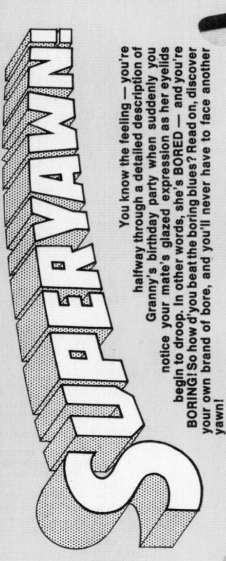

CONDITION: THE GRUMBLE-BORE
REMEDY:

Only the boring are bored, as the saying goes, and it's true, too! It stands to reason that those among us who slither out of bed amid grumbles and groans, slouch to school with a face of thunder and fester the evening away in front of the telly aren't the most dynamic or exciting of people. If life bores you, it's impossible to summon up the slightest scrap of enthusiasm for any goings-on, and with a sullen expression, you'll spend life with a constant chip on your shoulder. In other words, you're a Grumble-Bore — of the very worst kind!

Think about it, and if you suspect you're boring, analyse your attitude to life in general. There's nothing more irritating than having a Grumble-Bore around — someone who's totally fed-up and lives under a huge, grey cloud, constantly reminding everyone of the fact. The first step in breaking out of the super-yawn trap is to banish your boredom, so work up a little more enthusiasm for life — whether it's the countryside you love or a gorgeous sunrise — and you'll be a whole lot more fun to have around!

CONDITION: THE SELF-BORE
REMEDY:

We're all guilty of looking after number one, flattering ourselves and guarding our own interests. It's when this feeling of self-importance gets out of hand that you're well on the way to becoming a self-bore!

You'll have heard people rambling on about their talents and achievements — boring all in sight — and the tragedy is that Self-Bores just don't seem to notice their audience of stifled yawns. Are you a Self-Bore? If you suspect that, yes, you do ramble on about number one, take stock of yourself and resolve to keep your tongue under control in future.

Self-Bores, surprisingly, aren't as confident as they may seem. In fact, as well as trying to convince everyone in sight that they're amazingly talented and interesting, they're trying just as hard to prove to *themselves* that they're worthwhile. Perhaps you've admitted that you do go on rather a lot and you've realised that although people are interested in your new fella — and are dying to hear about your first date — they only want to hear about the man of your dreams once. By the third telling, the tale's lost its attraction — so instead of boosting your ego and boring all around you, show an interest in your friends. Ask questions, be willing to listen as well as chatter, and when you hear yourself begin, "You know what I did at the weekend . . ." — bite your

CONDITION: THE HOBBY-BORE

REMEDY:

One sure way to banish the grumble-bores, perk up your life and become a more interesting person into the bargain, is to pack your spare time with special hobbies — whether it's sketching, swimming, sewing, singing or squash!

School goings-on needn't be boring — and they're usually free — so why not give the gymnastics club/drama meeting a try? You're not only broadening your interests, but meeting a whole new crowd, too — and when you meet up with your mates, you're sure to have more to talk about.

One word of warning, though — rabbiting on can be bad for your health! Quite simply, make sure you don't become a Hobby-Bore. Everyone knows at least one — they're the people who drone on and on about golf/football/dancing, so lost in enthusiasm for their particular interest that they don't notice the sea of glazed expressions and collection of stifled yawns. In controlled doses, friends will find your new-found hobby fascinating — it's when you don't know when to stop that you're in danger of catching the Hobby-Bore condition. Think as you speak, imagine how you sound and what you'd be thinking if you were listening in!

CONDITION: THE BOY-BORE

REMEDY:

Of all bores, the Boy-Bore's the most common, because to a certain extent, we're all guilty of being boy-mad. Fellas? We love 'em!

Boy-Bores, however, let this obsession take over their lives. They drool over fellas in class and on the bus — the paper-boy, the fella next door, their mate's brother — anyone, in fact, as long as they're male! You can hear clusters of Boy-Bores — usually, they stick together — gossiping about their conquests and fellas they fancy, fellas they know, fellas they don't know . . . yawn! In short, it's boring!

Are boys the most important thing in your life? Tackle the problem now, as you're not only missing out on a whole lot of fun, but just think — if you spend twenty-four hours a day rambling on about fellas, when you actually go out with a guy, what on earth will you talk about?

It's a sad fact that Boy-Bores aren't very popular with the boys themselves. So, instead of thinking fellas, forget about them for a while. Switch your attentions instead to your mates and plan days out, evenings at each other's houses and lunchtime trips round the shops. Friends are just as valuable as fellas, you know — even more so, perhaps, as they're sure to stick around for longer!

A DICTIONARY OF SUPER-BORES!

We've only scratched the surface of bore-types, giving only a handful of suggestions on avoiding the bore-syndrome yourself. Bores come in all shapes and sizes — and here's a collection of conditions to avoid like the plague!

* **The I-Feel-Sick-Bore** — we've all met 'em. We've all suffered their involved descriptions of bunions, rashes and other niceties, too. Get well soon, I-Feel-Sick-Bores!

* **The Calorie-Bore** — also a mathematical genius, who tots up calories, works out whether you can afford to eat that biccie and makes you sink into a guilt-ridden sulk when you've polished off a pizza. She's a sure appetite depressant, is our friend the Calorie-Bore!

* **The Gossip-Bore** — yes, we were interested in Ethel-Next-Door's escapades, but after the fiftieth rendition, the story's lost its sparkle. Mind your own business, Gossip-Bore!

* **The Music-Bore** — yes, she knows exactly why The Jam split up, precisely where Duran Duran live . . . in fact she's had tea with them . . . no, she's gone on holiday with them!

Let's hope we've helped you beat the boring blues and become more interesting, popular and fun . . . let's hope we've helped you beat the boredom blues, too, with our Jackie Annual! You can't possibly be boring after our fun features, beauty and fashion hints, super stories, great quizzes . . . yawn . . . zzzzzz.

WHAT DO BOYS

Your reaction to each of the scenes below can tell you an awful lot about your attitude to boys—and can also reveal what *they* think about *you*. Just pick which sentence you think best fits each scene, add up your score and then turn to the conclusions to find out just what you and boys think about each other!

1. This couple have just met at a lively, fun party. Is he saying to her—
a) " OK, I give up. If that's not a jelly-baby hanging from your ear, then what is it?"
b) " Just a bit higher and you'll feel my heart beating."
c) " You must go to the same dentist as me. I can tell by your fillings."

3. She's just opened the door to this boy. What do you think he's saying to her?
a) " Is your sister in?"
b) " Remember me? We got engaged last night!"
c) " If your mum's in, I've come about the gas leak. If she's not, what are you doing tonight?"

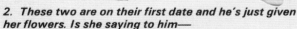

2. These two are on their first date and he's just given her flowers. Is she saying to him—
a) " Very nice. Why have you given them to me?"
b) " They're lovely. No-one's ever given me flowers before."
c) " Thanks very much. But just *what* am I going to do with flowers in a *disco?*"

4. This couple have just finished a fun game of tennis. Is he saying to her—
a) " I don't care who won. As far as I'm concerned, it's love all."
b) " Never mind. You might win next time."
c) " You may not be very good at tennis, but at least you're game for a laugh!"

THINK OF YOU?

5. *These two are out for a romantic walk in the country. Is she saying to him—*
a) " If youre going to kiss me, do it quick before this wind blows us both away!"
b) " I never noticed before, but now I can see your eyes aren't really blue at all."
c) " I don't care what the view's like from up here. I only have eyes for you."

6. *This couple are out for a walk in the park. Is he saying to her—*
a) " Look! There goes Concorde!"
b) " We'll have a place like this one day."
c) "You and that duck have a lot in common. Neither of you are very good swimmers!"

7. *These two are fooling about with a camera. Is she saying to him—*
a) " Make sure you get in *all* my fillings, won't you!"
b) " Do you know we'll get cramp standing like this?"
c) " This photo will always remind you of me."

8. *This couple are in a disco and for a dare, she's just ripped his shirt off. Is he now saying to her—*
a) " Careful! My mum wahed that this morning!"
b) " Thanks! I neeed that! It's really hot in here!"
c) " Hey! Don't be daft! That girl *was* my cousin, you know!"

Now count up your score and turn to the conclusions.

1. a)11 b)9 c)7.   5. a)11 b)7 c)9.
2. a)7 b)9 c)11.   6. a)7 b)9 c)11.
3. a)7 b)9 c)11.   7. a)11 b)7 c)9.
4. a)9 b)7 c)11.   8. a)7 b)11 c)9.

CONCLUSIONS

IF YOU SCORED: BETWEEN 56 AND 64

You're extremely practical and down-to-earth, but as far as boys are concerned, you're inclined to take everything they say with two pinches of salt! Maybe you've been badly hurt in the past, which would account for you being almost deliberately unromantic most of the time. This attitude does tend to scare boys off a bit because they think you don't like them. The truth is, though, you do like them—it's just that you're scared to show your feelings in case you get hurt. Maybe you should try relaxing more. Not all boys are as bad as you think. In fact, quite a few of them are very nice, if only you'll give them the chance to prove it!

IF YOU SCORED: BETWEEN 64 and 72

Aah! You're nothing but a big soppy romantic who wants everybody to take care of her. You're ready to fall for any boy who says two nice words to you (like, " Hi there!") and after three dates you're dreaming about engagement rings and wedding bells. Fortunately, you've got a good sense of humour which saves you taking yourself too seriously. Boys find you warm and easy to get on with, and you'll never be short of dates and admirers. Try not to see every boy you meet as the Great Love of Your Life, though. If you do, boys will get scared off by your attitude and the next time you mention weddings or engagements, you won't see them for dust!

IF YOU SCORED: BETWEEN 72 AND 88

You're warm, friendly and a bundle of laughs and you refuse to take anyone, far less boys, seriously. At the moment, you don't want to be tied down to one particular person. Boys like you because they feel they can talk to you easily and have a few laughs without it all getting too heavy. When you do find your particular person, though, it'll be a case of " till death us do part," because underneath all that bouncy humour, you're very loyal and sincere. Watch you don't miss out on the right boy for you, though, by being too jokey. If you are, he may think you don't care enough about him. You can be romantic and serious when you want, so give it a try sometimes!

123

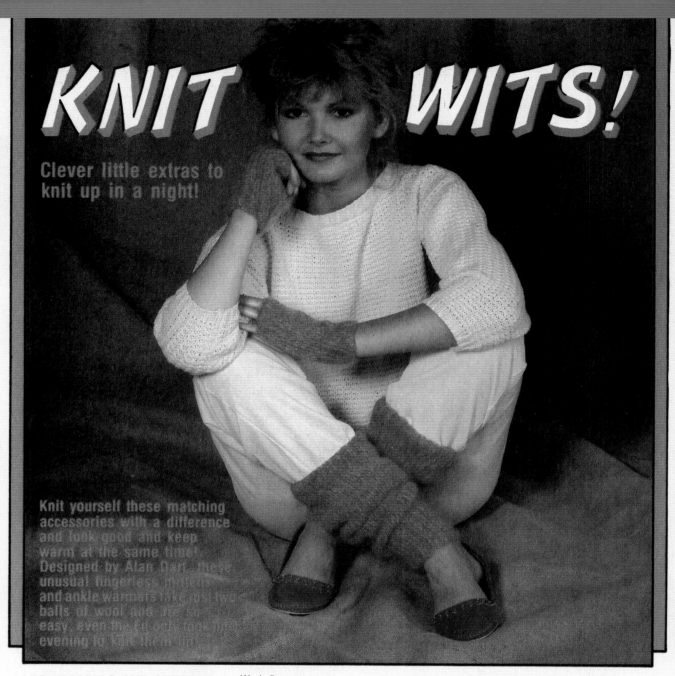

KNIT WITS!

Clever little extras to knit up in a night!

Knit yourself these matching accessories with a difference and look good and keep warm at the same time! Designed by Alan Dart, these unusual fingerless mittens and ankle warmers take just two balls of wool and are so easy, even the EG only took one evening to knit them up!

LEGWARMERS AND MITTENS

YARN — Two x 100 g balls of Sirdar Gemini Brushed Chunky.

NEEDLES — A pair each of 5½ mm and 6½ mm, and a stitch holder.

TENSION — 13½ sts and 19 rows to 10 cm square, measured over stocking-stitch on 6½ mm needles.

ABBREVIATIONS — K — knit, P — purl, st(s) — stitch(es), cont — continue, comm — commencing, st-st — stocking-stitch, one row knit, one row purl, inc — increase, beg — beginning.

LEGWARMERS

With 5½ mm needles cast on 32 sts and work 14 rows K1, P1 rib.
Change to 6½ mm needles and cont in st-st comm with a K row.

Work 5 rows.
Inc (by working into front and back of st) 1 st at beg and end of next and every following 5th row until there are 46 sts on the needle.
Cont without shaping for 10 rows, ending with a P row.
Change to 5½ mm needles and work 8 rows K1, P1 rib.
Cast off in rib.

MITTENS

With 5½ mm needles cast on 26 sts and work 10 rows K1, P1 rib.
Change to 6½ mm needles and cont in st-st comm with a K row.
Row 1 — K.
Row 2 and all alternate rows — P.
Row 3 — K13, inc (by working into horizontal thread before next st), K13.
Row 5 — K13, inc, K1, inc, K13.
Row 7 — K13, inc, K3, inc, K13.

Row 9 — K13, inc, K5, inc, K13.
Row 11 — K13, inc, K7, inc, K13.
Row 12 — P.
Next row — K13, slip these sts on to a stitch holder, with 5½ mm needles work 9 sts in K1, P1 rib, slip remaining 13 sts on to a stitch holder.
Work 3 rows P1, K1 rib on these 9 sts.
Cast off loosely in rib.
Slip the first set of held sts on to a 6½ mm needle, rejoin yarn to the remaining held sts, and with 6½ mm needles K to end (26 sts).
Next row — P.
Change to 5½ mm needles and work 4 rows K1, P1 rib.
Cast off loosely in rib.

TO MAKE UP

Do not press work. Join seams on leg-warmers. Darn in yarn at base of thumbs. Join thumb seams. Join seams of mittens.

What did he mean by that?

When it comes to dealing with boys, one of the things to remember is that they don't always say what they mean. It can take a lot of time and practice to break through the language barrier and find out what they're really thinking, so to speed things up a bit, here's our fun look at some of the things a boy might say to you—and what he really means . . .

YOUR FIRST DATE

What he says
" It's a great evening. Fancy walking to the disco?"
What he means
" I know it's freezing and about to rain, but I could only get £5 off my dad and the bus fare's 50p each into town."
Or he could say
" Aren't you taking a bag or something?"
And what he means is
" If you're not taking a bag, that means you're not taking a purse and that means you're not taking any money. And I've only got a fiver."

AT THE DISCO

He says
" Let's sit in the corner. It's far quieter over there."
What he means is
" It's really dark in the corner. Let's go and have a necking session."
Or, if you're very unlucky, he could mean
" It's really dark in the corner. With any luck my mates won't see me with you over there."
When he wants to impress, he'll say
" Great record, huh? I know that group pretty well."
What he means is
" I once sent them a song I'd written and they sent it back asking me to try again in five years' time."

WHEN YOU'VE BEEN SEEING EACH OTHER FOR A WHILE

He'll say
" I phoned you last night and you weren't in."

What he means is,
" Someone told me you went out with Steve Smith last night. Did you?"
Or he'll say
" Me? Go out with Brenda Jones? Don't be silly! Who told you that?"
What he means is
" How did you find out about me and Brenda? I bet it was that so-called mate of mine. Was it him?"

WHEN HE WANTS TO DROP YOU IN FAVOUR OF BRENDA JONES

He'll say
" I think we should stop seeing each other for a week or two. That'll give us a chance to find out what we really feel about each other."
What he means is
" I want to go out with Brenda Jones. But just in case things don't work out, I want to make sure you'll still be around."
Or he'll say
" I like you too much to lie to you."
What he means is
" I'm too much of a coward to tell you the truth, so there's no way I'm going to mention Brenda Jones. I

wonder if you'll believe me if I tell you I'm going to join the Foreign Legion?"
Or he could say
" I think we're getting too involved, too soon."
And what he'll mean is,
" I want to go out with Brenda Jones."

WHEN HE WANTS YOU TO BE HIS GIRL

He'll say
" My brother's coming home in four months. You'll like him."
What he means is
" I want you to know I'd still like to be going out with you in four months. And besides that, I want you to meet my family."
Or he'll say
" I really like you a lot. More than I've ever liked any girl."
What he means is
" I think I love you."
Or he could say,
" I love you."
And what he'll more than likely mean is
" I love you!"

How To Cope When He Says Goodbye

IT'S finally happened. He's told you he doesn't want to see you any more. Your whole world's collapsed and you can't imagine how you're going to get through life without him. But you can — and you will. What's more, you can almost chart your progress through a break-up. Your timing and your speed will depend on you as an individual, but you can be sure you'll go through all the normal stages of crying over him, missing him, remembering all the good times and, unbelievable as it seems at the moment, getting over him.

The first thing you'll do is cry for him

So go ahead and cry. Lock your bedroom door and cry all you want to. Stare at his picture. Torture yourself with the thought that you'll never see him again. Imagine him kissing his new girl. And cry some more.

Then you'll think it was all your fault

This is when that awful phrase, *"If only"* creeps into your thoughts. You think, *"If only I'd been more understanding about that other girl,"* or, *"If only I'd been more interested in snooker,"* or you could even think, if you've got it badly enough, *"If only I was prettier he wouldn't have chucked me."* Well — forget it!

Chuck out all the if-onlys and might-have-beens and start to shift the blame a little. Instead of feeling it's all your fault, think about how awful **he** was. Think about how creepy he was to go out with that other girl; think about how selfish he was to expect you to put up with him playing snooker five nights a week; think about how you're actually **too** pretty for a toad like him.

Think anything you like so long as you start to feel good and **angry** with him.

Then it's time to face the truth

Now you finally admit it's over. You stop hoping, stop waiting for the phone to ring and stop dreaming about the big reunion scene.

Now's the time to keep your tears for when you're alone. Now's the time to resist the temptation to blurt everything out to anyone who'll listen.

And while you're facing the truth, ring all your mutual friends and tell them you've split. It's easier to get this out of the way quickly and you'll be relieved once everyone knows.

You'll find that quite a few mutual friends will prove to be less mutual, so be prepared for this.

Be prepared, too, for everyone to ask, "Where's Bert/Steve/Harry?" as if you were permanently glued together — which you were, of course.

Trouble is, you've been two

for so long, you've forgotten how to be alone. But it can be fun!

Now's the time to go crazy and be adventurous. Make yourself over, take up new interests. Don't play safe with flower-pressing or cookery classes — try tap-dancing, self-defence classes or a drama group.

Now's the time to face up to yourself

Use the break-up positively. Take decisions you've always put off and do things you've always wanted to do. If you've always wanted to go Youth Hostelling, or take dance classes, or try your hand at motor cycle maintenance but always put it off because of him, now's the time to strike out.

You've no-one else to think about now, so you can be as selfish and independent as you like.

You're almost cured now

It won't all be plain sailing, of course. Just when you think you're beginning to get over him, some little incident will set you off again. This is when you start to think you'd give it all up, if only

you could have those times back.

But that feeling doesn't last long and you're now halfway towards being able to remember the special things about your relationship without pain. Now, too, you're well on the way to remembering what you loved about him without necessarily wanting him back.

Now you can start again

Now you're ready to face the world again. Your cousin's twenty-first party may not sound like fun — but go anyway. You'll be meeting people, and that's what counts.

Try not to compare new experiences with the way things used to be. What you had was very special — and that kind of relationship doesn't happen every day, or with every boy.

Complete recovery — The test

You see him again — and everything you've worked for hangs in the balance. Resist the temptation to ignore him.

Face him. Smile at him. The sheer satisfaction of knowing you look good, knowing you've survived,

will be worth the willpower it takes to smile and chat to him for a minute or two.

Chances are you'll think he's changed and you may wonder how you could have spent so much time and trouble getting over someone who's so — well — *ordinary.*

Getting over a break up, starting all over again, isn't a case of slamming a door on one part of your life and opening a new one. It's much slower than that and a much more complicated process. It's a bit like wandering along corridors when you're not too sure of the way.

The most important factor in your recovery is time. Gradually, instead of only acting as if you're over the heartbreak, you'll find it's true.

You'll admit you wouldn't have missed out on the relationship, even though it made you more miserable than you've ever been. You've been in love — and out of love. It's a crazy merry-go-round and you're getting ready to jump on all over again . . .

Curls, Curls, Curls !

Try out the following ideas and you'll never be bored with your hair again!

PIPE DREAMS!

To achieve a wrinkly, pre-Raphaelite cascade of curls, try this pipe cleaner method. You'll need about two packets of pipe cleaners if your hair is fairly long; they're quite cheap and available from newsagents and tobacconists or your dad, if he's a pipe smoker. (He won't need them once you've nagged him into giving up his pipe on account of his health!)

Bend each pipe cleaner in half, like a hoop, and plait two strands of hair round it, one strand to each leg of the loop (see photo). Twist the pipe cleaner round to secure the hair and repeat until you've plaited your whole head of hair. Leave to dry for a few hours or overnight before unpleating each pipe cleaner again. If you want your curls to last, spray them with a fine mist of hair spray and don't comb or brush your hair.

You'll achieve a similar effect without pipe cleaners if you make lots of little plaits all over your hair. Tie the ends of the plaits with wool to keep them in, but don't use elastic bands as they damage your hair. However, you'll probably find the pipe cleaner method is less fiddly.

RAG DOLLY!

Binding up damp hair with rags has been done by generations of girls — ask your mum or granny! It takes several attempts before you discover the best way to wrap and tie your own particular hair for the end result you want, so practise plenty before you attempt to stun at a special occasion!

The way the girl in the photo has bound her hair will result in a full, bouncy head of hair rather than tight curls, because she's only tied up about half the length of each strand. So, if your shoulder-length or even jaw-length hair is looking rather lank and droopy, try this idea to put back its natural bounce.

First rip up some old soft cotton items of clothing to make your rags. You can sleep quite comfortably with your hair in rags but, if you tied your hair with attractive patterned cotton or rags, you could actually keep them in as you gb about your business in the daytime — at weekends or holiday time, anyway!

To give the end result extra body, grab a section of wet hair and pull it in the opposite direction to the way you want it to lie and tie one knot or two in your rag as you tie it round. Carry on until all your hair is wrapped up.

Wait until your hair is dry then untie the rags and brush or comb your hair into the style you want.

127

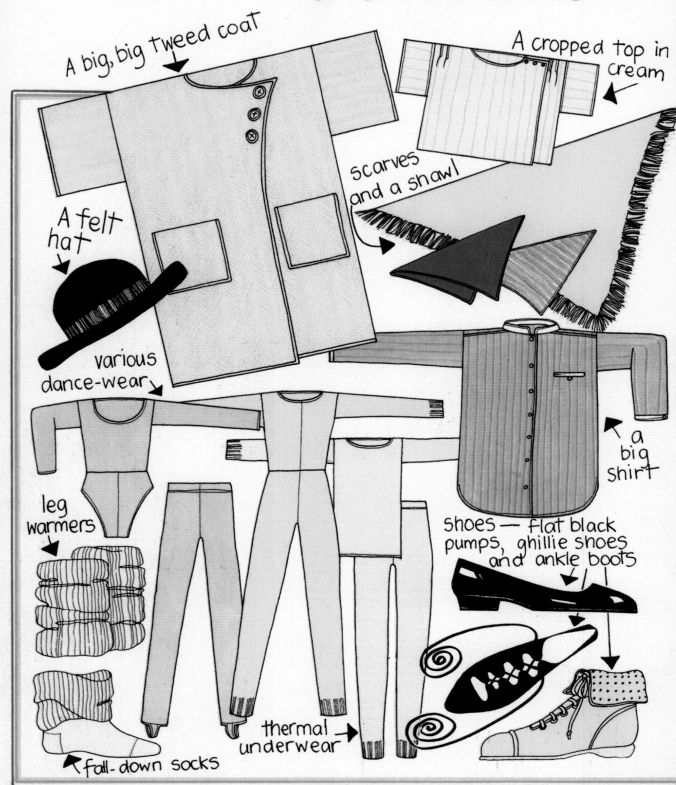

Swap skirts for shawls for trousers for tops — and come up with a look that's all your own!

Winter

A big, big tweed coat

A cropped top in cream

A felt hat

scarves and a shawl

various dance-wear

a big shirt

leg warmers

shoes — flat black pumps, ghillie shoes and ankle boots

thermal underwear

fall-down socks

Wardrobe!

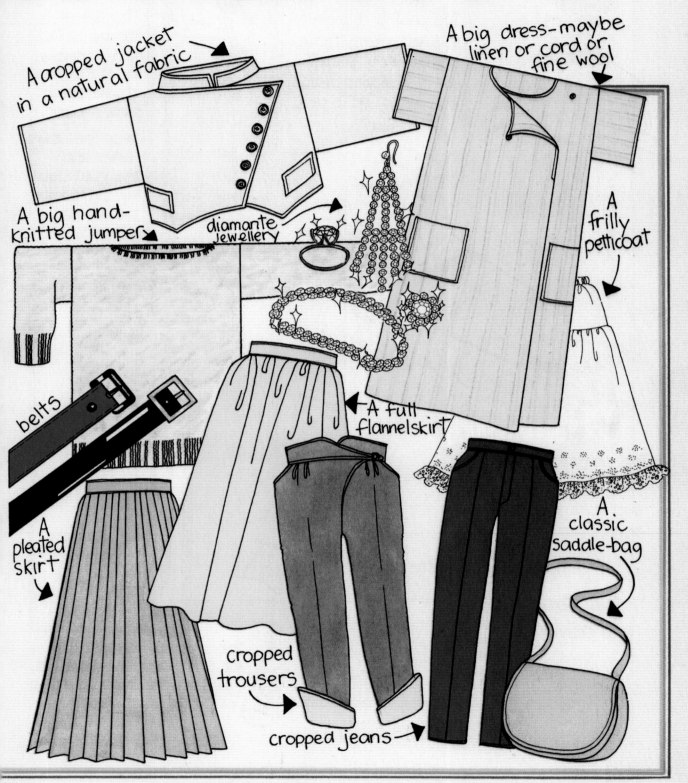

A cropped jacket in a natural fabric

A big dress—maybe linen or cord or fine wool

A big hand-knitted jumper

diamante jewellery

A frilly petticoat

belts

A full flannel skirt

A pleated skirt

A classic saddle-bag

cropped trousers

cropped jeans

Putting the look together —

The coat is big - wear it over everything — don't worry about skirts hanging below the coat — it's a nice look!

The dress can be belted and worn over the skirts or trousers and dance-wear.

Wear fall-down socks and the hat and the petticoat-pile on the layers.

The cropped jacket goes over every-thing too.

Don't forget your diamante!

The cropped top with the skirt and the shawl as a belt on the hips — roll a scarf for your neck.

YOU SAID IT!
YOU SAID IT!
YOU SAID IT!
YOU SAID IT!
YOU SAID IT!
YOU SAID

Boy George has said some daft things, some funny things and some downright weird things in his time. Here's just a few he's come out with in the past couple of years. And remember — he said it . . .

Boy George on Beauty:

"I used to go out with a green face, or a blue face and a red neck. I used to look like one of the ugly sisters."

"I make the best of what I've got. Anyway, I'm not interested in that 'isn't he pretty' crowd."

"I don't care if people think I'm a girl."

"I don't want to be a sex symbol, I don't want to be a freak or a clown. I want to be a bit more interesting."

Boy George on Hong Kong:

"It was weird going 17,000 miles and still getting mobbed when I got off the plane. It was 7.30 in the morning and I had no make-up on. I looked like a potato. And the papers said I was heavily made-up. I looked like a pig. In fact I looked like two pigs."

Boy George on Himself:

"My mum and dad know that underneath all this make-up I'm pretty normal. Well, I think I am."

"I'm game for anything really."

"When I first started experimenting with clothes, my mum tried to keep me indoors."

"I think I look better if I don't smile. I'd look like a clown if I did."

"It's easy to get attention."

"Sometimes I look at myself in the mirror and think — you prat. It does you good to laugh at yourself."

"I've got a lot more in common with Norman Wisdom than Simon le Bon."

"I think I've got a really good voice, I'm really pleased with it."

"I don't think I'm any better than anyone else just because I dress up."

Boy George on The Band:

"I think one of the good things about this band is that we really don't know what we are."

Boy George on other people:

"I hate people who think they're really risqué and daring."

"I like reality, old women with Mr Spock eyebrows. I like character . . . that's art."

Boy George on Marilyn:

"Marilyn was a little soul boy when I met him, I remember I thought he was a right wally."

room mates!

Let your bedroom reflect your personality, with some of these great ideas for giving it style!

PRETTY FEMININE

So you're the romantic type? In that case, how about a very pretty feminine style like the one shown here? Our reversible quilt has clouds on one side and hearts on the other. It costs £16.99 and the pillow cases are £7.50. This look depends on lots of little knick-knacks like the little wooden boxes (shown on the floor), the heart shaped cushion, framed photographs on the dressing-table and pretty pot plants.

The fans shown here can be found at various small gift stores. The two paper ones left and right were only 59p and the feather one 69p. The pink lamp shade costs around £4.99 (available from Debenhams stores).

PRIMARY POINTS

If you want to completely transform your room and you're lucky enough to be getting a helping hand from Mum and Dad money-wise, here's a style you may like.

Everything is in primary colours, which keeps the room bright and cheerful and makes it look more like a bedsit than a bedroom!

The quilt cover is a design called Shooting Star and it's shown here with matching reversible pillow cases. The single quilt costs £16.99 and pillow cases are £7.50 per pair. The red cotton piped cushion is £3.99. Copy our idea and hang belts and beads on a bright coathanger. You can get a pack of 3 coathangers in yellow, green, red or white for 75p. All of these items are available from Lifestyle departments in branches of House of Fraser stores.

Plastic kitchenware comes in great colours and is very useful for holding clothes rather than vegetables and kitchen tools as intended. Shown here are a large yellow Spacemaker bin (£2.99), a small red bin (£1.99), and a yellow vegetable rack by Addis (£2.85). On the small table (smallest of a set of three from MFI stores, price £10.99) are a red Crayonne kitchen utensil holder, (£1.69), a small racing car jelly mould (49p), and a red lampshade (£4.99). All these items are available from Debenhams stores. The blue curly lead and plug are available from electrical stores at approximately £3.49 in various colours.

50 ways to

1. COME ALIVE AT NIGHT! Make up that's perfect in daylight can look pallid at night so use twice as much blusher, dark brown or black mascara and eye-liner, rich coloured lipsticks and plenty of gloss and iridescent highlighters!

Night is the right time to experiment, too — try wearing gold apricot eyeshadow on your eye-lids and cheeks, or colour your eyebrows the same shade as your eyeliner pencil, even if it's green!

2. MORE LUCK WHEN YOU PLUCK! Plucking your eyebrows into shape can make quite a difference to your appearance, so make the process painless by holding a hot flannel over your eyebrows for a few minutes before you begin and always pluck in the direction of growth with a close-headed pair of tweezers.

3. OPEN UP YOUR EYES by brushing your eyebrows upwards after you've plucked them — keep them up with a little Vaseline!

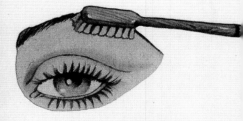

4. BALANCE A BIG NOSE OR WIDE MOUTH by sweeping and shaping your eyebrows upwards and outwards — this also helps space out narrow eyes.

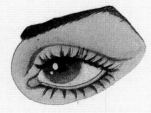

5. FOR A ROUND FACE pluck your eyebrows into an angular shape.

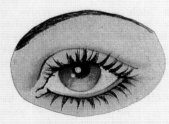

look fantastic

6. SHOW OFF YOUR EYES and a good forehead with nicely rounded brows.

7. OVERPLUCKED? Use a sharp eyebrow pencil to sketch in individual lashes.

8. FOR A QUICK REFRESH in the middle of the day make your own face-cleansing pads by soaking squares of cottonwool or lint in your favourite cleanser or toner and packing them in a small tin or soap box.

9. POWDER should go on after foundation but before any other make-up.

10. UNEVEN LIPS can be balanced up if you cover your lips with foundation, blot with a powder puff then draw in the correct shape with a lip pencil and fill in with lipstick.

11. MAKE LIPSTICK LAST LONGER by applying, blotting with a tissue and reapplying.

12. CONTROL GREASY SKIN with a water-based foundation like Rimmel's Oil Free Foundation for greasy skin.

13. MATCH FOUNDATION TO YOUR SKIN TONE by trying some on your face. Don't go by the shade it looks in the bottle!

14. IF YOU'VE PICKED THE WRONG SHADE don't panic, buy your next supply now but in a shade lighter or darker so you can mix the two together till you get the exact shade. The darker colour will also come in useful as shader.

15. WARM FOUNDATION in your hand first for smoother application.

16. APPLY FOUNDATION ANY WAY YOU LIKE — in dots all over face and blended on with fingertips or on a damp sponge — but try to apply it as quickly as possible.

17. LIGHTEN THE TEXTURE of your foundation in summer by mixing it with equal quantities of moisturiser.

18. FRESHEN UP YOUR MAKE-UP by patting a pad of damp cotton wool all over your face.

19. USE EVERY LAST DROP OF FOUNDATION by leaving the bottle upside down between uses, dropping some moisturiser into the bottle and mixing it up, or using a long-handled brush, or a cotton bud, to get every last drop out.

20. DISGUISE RED CHEEKS with green tinted moisturiser (Boots No. 7) or colour corrective powder like Bourjois' Jade.

21. DUST OFF EXCESS POWDER in a downward and outward direction using a big, babysoft face brush or a ball of cotton wool.

22. IN AN EMERGENCY use talcum powder lightly dusted over face instead of face powder.

23. FOR A PERFECT EYESHADOW BASE cover your entire eyelid with foundation.

24. BLUE EYESHADOW and eye pencils accentuate the whites of the eyes.

25. BEFORE YOU THROW AWAY any finished make-up in tubes cut open the tubes to extract the last few dregs.

26. IF YOU'VE GOT A FULL FACE avoid wearing pure white near the face as it throws up the light and places extra emphasis on the jaw and chin area.

27. AVOID IRRITATING EYES when removing make-up with cotton wool by slightly dampening it first.

28. ALWAYS REMOVE EYE MAKE-UP wiping from inner corner of eyes outwards.

29. ALWAYS USE ELECTRIC TONGS and curlers on dry hair. If the hair's wet or damp the high heat produced can scald.

30. INVENT HIGH CHEEKBONES, if you haven't got them, by using shader in a sideways low triangle at edge of cheeks (see drawing) and lots of glossy, cream-coloured highlighter above, where cheekbones should be. Blend both shader and highlighter well in and apply on top of foundation.

31. PLACE BLUSHER in the right position for your face shape. If your cheeks are slightly sunken apply blusher high on cheek. Widen a narrow face by applying blusher towards the edge of the face and if your face is plump put it more towards the centre of the face (see illustration).

32. PICK SHADE OF BLUSHER by matching it to the colour of your cheeks when you pinch them.

33. USE BLUSHER WITH MORE IMPACT by blending it with your eyeshadow and merging the two colours between cheek and eye area. Or use your lipstick as blusher for a perfect colour match.

34. GLOW ALL OVER YOUR FACE by adding touches of blusher to brow-bone, chin and earlobes.

35. BE DIFFERENT! Line around eyes with two different colours, or one colour along the top lid and another along the bottom.

36. IF YOU'VE GOT SMALL EYES, never line the inside of lids with dark kohl eyeliner — it makes them look smaller.

37. LINE DROOPY EYES with a line that grows thicker towards outer edges of eyes.

38. LINE INSIDE OF LIDS more easily by gently pulling eyelid down (or up) a bit first. If eyes are at all sensitive line with eye pencil outside lashes and smudge a little for a subtle effect.

39. NO EYELINER? Use a wet brush and powder eyeshadow.

40. CREATE NEW COLOURS by mixing different eyeshadows together in a tin lid.

41. ALWAYS CURL LASHES before applying mascara.

42. IF LASHES ARE VERY PALE consider dyeing them with a home kit (about £3) or at a salon (£4-£5) — it won't last for ever but you'll save on mascara.

43. IF LASHES ARE VERY SHORT add to them with extra single false lashes just stuck on at the outer edge of the eyes. Dab eyelash adhesive onto eyelid with an orange stick for a neater finish.

44. CHANGE CHARACTER entirely for special occasions by trying a stark, no-colour make-up as here. Create a pale, matte base by blocking out all natural colour with green powder under very pale foundation or even white theatrical powder. Hollow cheeks with brown shader (don't use blusher or highlighter). Leave lips just foundation covered but outline with a brown eye pencil. Use black eyeliner only on eyes, swinging it upwards at outer edges to create a slightly Oriental-eyed look.

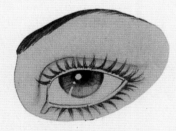

45. MAKE SMALL EYES BIG by outlining with white or pale-coloured eye pencils.

46. WHEN APPLYING MASCARA to bottom lashes hold a folded tissue underneath lashes to prevent mascara marking cheeks.

47. STOP CLOGGED LASHES by wiping mascara wand on the side of the container before applying, or by combing through lashes with an old, washed mascara wand immediately after applying mascara. Or use Maybelline's Dial A Lash mascara which allows you to control the amount of mascara that gets onto the brush.

48. SPACE OUT CLOSE-SET EYES by using highlighter on the whole area from the side of the nose up to the centre of the eyelid. Keep brows light and wing them outwards and upwards. Smudge eyeshadow on the outer area of the eyelid only. Also only mascara lashes at the outer edges of the eyes.

49. DISGUISE A DOUBLE CHIN by covering the whole area with a darker foundation than that used on your face but be sure to blend the edges well in.

50. SHOW OFF CUPID LIPS with a dot of highlighter just under the centre of your nose.

HOW LIBERATED ARE YOU?

How liberated are YOU? Come on now . . .think about it! When was the last time you chained yourself to the school railings? Can't remember . . .eh? Well, there was that time you arranged a 'sit-in' in the common room when they wouldn't let you play football for the school team! JUST COZ YOU WERE A GIRL! What a cheek!

So if you want to find out how you stand as a defender of female rights . . .eyes down, and complete our quiz below.

1. *You've managed to get yourself a little Saturday job at the local supermarket, but you discover that a boy working with you is getting a whole 10p. an hour more than you. Do you . . .*

a) Keep giving him evil looks and try to trip him up every time he walks by carrying a pile of cans?

b) Immediately march off to the manager and demand equal pay?

c) Think nothing of it! After all, he's got to lift those heavy crisp packets all day . . . which is really man's work, isn't it?

2. *Your favourite football team is playing in your home town. You try to persuade your big brother to take you with him, but he declines, saying it's no place for a girl. What do you do?*

a) Puncture his best football?

b) Go, with a mate! Who needs brothers anyway?

c) Stay at home and watch the match on the telly?

3. *You've fancied that gorgeous guy in the sixth form for ages. And he must like you too, coz he always smiles, but he never gets round to asking you out. Drat it! What are you going to do?*

a) Try bumping into him at every opportunity, murmuring . . . "We can't go on meeting like this . . ." and hoping he'll take the hint?

b) Ask him out yourself! Well, why not? What have you got to lose? Go on . . . the shock won't kill him!

c) Worship him . . . from a distance?

4. *If you went away to stay with friends for the weekend, and forgot your make-up, what would you do when you found out?*

a) Panic? Not even the cat's allowed to see you without your mascara!

b) You couldn't care less! It's what's underneath that counts as far as you're concerned. And your hosts will just have to like it or lump it!

c) Wear dark glasses all weekend, and keep apologising to everyone for looking so hideous?

5. *Your latest fella is getting a bit on the possessive side. And he detests you going out with your mates without him. Do you . . .*

a) Get crafty? Tell him you're going to see your Maths teacher about extra lessons; and then sneak out to meet your friends?

b) Make no bones about the fact that you're not his personal property, and you think it's good for both of you to have your own friends, as well as each other?

c) Put up with it? You'd sooner be with him than your mates anyway!

6. *You'd love to see that latest David Bowie film, but you don't want to go on your own. And you know your fella can't afford it. Do you . . .*

a) Keep dropping massive hints, until the poor guy's driven either to cadging the money off his Dad, or robbing his little brother's piggy bank?

b) Tell him you've been dying to see the film, and you want to treat him for Christmas/Easter/his birthday/passing his 'O' Levels . . . whichever applies?

c) Say nothing, and wait till the video's released?

7. *And finally: Do you think that fellas should still open doors and give up their seat on the bus for you?*

a) Absolutely . . . Yes! You'd expect to be given preferential treatment all the time.

b) Not really. You think people should be considered more by age and circumstance, than by their sex?

c) You'd be flattered if they did, but you wouldn't really expect it.

Right now . . . let's see how you scored! Score 2 points for every a) you ticked. 3 points for a b). And 1 point for a c).

17-21 points
What a truly liberated female you are! And being a girl's never going to stop YOU getting where you want to go. But in spite of your feminist point of view, you're fair minded and considerate, and smart enough to know the right way to tackle a problem. Fellas will admire your independent ways, and appreciate your willingness to share responsibilities and not look on them as a free meal ticket!

10-16 points
Well, you've certainly got some strong views on the subject, but we can't help feeling it's the boys that need liberating in your case! You want it all your own way, and you're not averse to using all the feminine tricks at your disposal to get what you want! Come on . . . play by the rules. Don't sneak about making catty comments—come out in the open and say what you think. Not all guys are budding chauvinists . . . at least give them a chance to prove it!

Under 10 points
Oh dear, you really don't want to be liberated, do you? You're quite happy letting him play Tarzan, while you just stay at home and play Jane. You'd cook his meals and wash his socks until you were worn to a shadow. Come on . . . get wise! Don't be pushed around. Stand up for what you want, and fellas will respect you more for it!

Happy with your score? Or feeling a bit peeved coz you always fancied yourself as an ardent women's libber and you've just found out you're not? Well, it's all up to you really! If you're happy playing second fiddle to the guy in your life, who are we to tell you you're wrong! At least now you have a choice . . . and that's something that's entirely up to you!

BODY TALK!

You may not be able to read his mind, but his body is a different matter. We all give away feelings we think we've hidden by the way we sit, stand, walk and react to others — so to find out how receptive you are, see if you can read the story behind the pictures!

Q. WHICH GIRL REALLY TURNS HIM ON?

A. The girl in the blue top. The other girl has spoken to him, so he's turned towards her to reply. But look at his body – his legs remain crossed towards the girl he likes better, and his hands, pointing in the same direction, underline his feelings.

Q. DOES HE LIKE HER?

A. He is unsettled and bored. His hands are already making the first move to get up. They're clutching the edge of his chair, and he's full of tension – not at all relaxed. His head is also turned slightly away. The girl hasn't really noticed his situation – she's outstretched and relaxed, but she's not making much effort to interest him.

Q. IS HE REALLY A TOUGH GUY?

A. He's only acting big, though he may even have fooled himself that he can take anyone on. But the real character inside feels threatened. He uses the wall for moral as well as physical support, and the way he's crossed his arms and legs shows that he's really shut in against others.

Q. IS HE TELLING THE TRUTH?

A. What he's telling you may be what you want to hear, but look closely and his body will give him away. We each have our own tell-tale movements, and as well as not being able to look you in the eye, he's shuffling his feet, playing with his hands, and looking very awkward.

Try watching yourself for a day or so, and you'll become aware of how you sit, stand, and move when you're with your friends. You can learn from the signs and movements you make when you're feeling shy or interested in someone, and then you'll know what to look for in your friends' behaviour.

YOU'RE IN HIS THOUGHTS WHEN:

1. You're across the room talking to someone else and you catch him looking at you – he's keen to know what you're doing.
2. He sees you walk into the room and tells a "big" story that bit louder than he needs to – he's trying to impress you.
3. He takes up the "big guy" pose against a handy wall or chair whenever other boys come to speak to you when you're with him – he feels threatened.

START LOOKING FOR SOME-ONE ELSE WHEN:

1. You meet him and his mouth smiles but his eyes don't – he's not being honest.
2. You suggest a date and he starts combing his hair and looking the other way – he's trying to get out of it.
3. He talks to you with his arms folded, legs crossed, and his gaze fixed firmly on the floor – he's already built a barrier between you.

GIANT POP

Well here it is at last, just what you've all been waiting for — a giant, month-by-month quiz of th[e]
point for each correct answer, then add up your score and turn to the conclusions to find out

JANUARY

1. "Imagine" by John Lennon reached number one in January '81. In what year was it first released as a single?

2. Bucks Fizz were number one in January '82 with "Land Of Make Believe," but what was the name of the song they won the Eurovision song contest with?

3. David Soul had a hit with "Don't Give Up On Us" in January '77. What was the name of the famous police show he starred in on television?

4. The Pretenders had a January hit with "Brass In Pocket." What were the names of the original Pretenders?

5. What was Shakin' Stevens' real name, which he adopted by deed poll, when he had a hit with "Oh Julie" in January '82.

6. Can you identify this song by the lyrics? —
   "I light a candle to our love
   In love our problems
   *   disappear*
   But all in all we soon discover
   That one and one is all we
   *   long to hear."*

7. In January 1979 Village People had a number one hit with YMCA. Which "village" did the group represent?

FEBRUARY

1. "Don't Cry For Me; Argentina" was a number one hit for Julie Covington in February 1977. Which successful musical was it taken from?

2. The Chrysalis label scored their first number one hit with "When I Need You." Who sang it?

3. Joe Dolce had a hit with "Shaddup You Face" in February '81, but do you know what he called the "character" he played while singing it?

4. The Jam's second single to go straight in at number one was "A Town Called Malice/Precious" in February '82. What was their first single to do this?

5. What was the name of the album that John Lennon's "Woman" came from?

6. Michael Jackson had a hit in February '83 with "Billie-Jean." Lydia Murdock sang a follow up single — what was it called?

7. Kajagoogoo had a hit with "Too Shy" before they sacked their lead singer. What was his name?

MARCH

1. Kate Bush had a smash hit with "Wuthering Heights," but who wrote the classic novel by the same name?

2. In March '79 the Bee Gees had a hit single called "Tragedy." Shortly before this they made a smash with the soundtrack of a film. This was the best selling album of all time until it was knocked off its pedestal by Thriller. What was it called?

3. In March 1981, Roxy Music were number one with "Jealous Guy." The only words printed on the sleeve of this single were the title, the artist, and the phrase "a tribute." Who was it a tribute to?

4. Tight Fit had a hit in March '82 with a cover version. It is the only number one to have as many as six names on the writing credits. What is it called?

5. The Goombay Dance Band had a hit with "Seven Tears," in '82. What, apart from singing, is their front man Oliver Brendt famous for?

6. Which album did the Thompson Twins' single "Love On Your Side" come from?

RIVIA QUIZ

...s from the past few years. Answer the questions (they're dead easy — honest), award yourself one
...'re a pop egghead, Miss Average, or just plain dumb . . .

APRIL

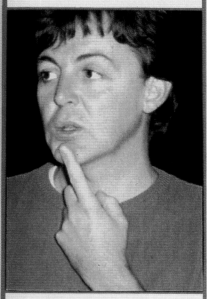

1. In April 1982 Paul McCartney had a hit single with Stevie Wonder. What was it called?

2. The Detroit Spinners had a number one with "Working My Way Back To You" in April '82. What were they originally called?

3. Mike Batt wrote Art Garfunkel's "Bright Eyes." Who had he previously written songs for?

4. Which famous person was the song "Matchstalk Men And Matchstalk Cats And Dogs" written about?

5. The Bay City Rollers had a number one hit in April '74 with "Bye Bye Baby." Can you name the only other number one hit they had?

MAY

1. Boney M had a hit in May '78 with "Rivers Of Babylon." What was the name of the B side of this record which was also a big hit for them?

2. This song was a major hit in May '83. Can you recognise it and the singer by these lyrics?
   "If you say run I'll run with you,
   And if you say hide we'll hide.
   Because my love for you
      would break my heart in two,
   If you should fall into my arms
      and tremble like a flower."

3. The first ever number one to include a day of the week in the title was by Blondie in May '79. Can you name it?

4. Dexy's Midnight Runners had their first hit with "Geno." Who was this song a tribute to?

5. Adam and The Ants had a hit in May' 81 with "Stand and Deliver" but do you know what Adam Ant's real name is?

JUNE

1. In June '83 Big Country announced the dates for their tour. Can you name their lead singer and the band he was formerly in?

2. In June '83 "The Tube" did a five-hour summer spectacular. Paula Yates was then a co-presenter of the programme. She once brought out a book of photographs called —
   a) Rock Stars In Their Underpants,
   b) Rock Stars In Their Socks,
   c) Rock Stars In The Flesh.

3. "Are Friends Electric?" was a hit for Tubeway Army in June '79. What is odd about this?

4. What was the name of the group who had a hit with "Candy Girl"?

5. The Wurzels had a hit with "Combine Harvester (Brand New Key)." What year was it released in?

GIANT POP TRIVIA QUIZ

JULY

1. John Travolta and Olivia Newton-John had a hit with "You're The One That I Want." What other track sung by them from the film "Grease" reached number one?

2. A bizarre story heard over the radio prompted a young man to write a song. A teenage Californian had shot at her playground playmates causing death and injury. What is the name of the song and what band sang it?

3. The Specials reached number one in July '81 with "Ghost Town." Subsequently they split up. What band was formed by three member of the Specials?

4. Can you name the band and its members who had a hit with "Bad Boys" in July '83.

5. "Every move you make,
Every step you take,
Every claim you stake,
I'll be watching you."
Can you name this song and who sang it?

AUGUST

1. A Scottish folk singer, Mary Sandeman, had a one-off hit in August '81 with "Japanese Boy." What was the name she used instead of her own when she recorded the record?

2. David Bowie continued the story of Major Tom in August 1980 with "Ashes To Ashes." It was not a great hit in the U.S., however, but Bowie scored an even more important triumph when he took over the title role in what Broadway production?

3. Twenty years and 25 days after his first number one hit, Cliff Richard did it again in August '79. What was the name of the record?

4. Can you name the singer and song by these lyrics. It was a hit in August '83.
"By the look in your eyes
I can tell you're gonna cry,
Is it over me?
If it is save your tears,
'Cos I'm not worth it,
you'll see."

5. This one's the same — name the group, the song and the album it came from.
"I was thirty-seven,
You were seventeen,
You were half my age,
The youth I'd never seen.
Unlikely strangers meeting in a dream,
Heaven only knows the way it should have been."

SEPTEMBER

1. In September '78 there was another hit in the charts from the film "Grease." But do you know which characters Olivia Newton-John and John Travolta played?

2. Which single by The Police followed up their "Message In A Bottle" hit?

3. A young girl from Paisley in Scotland went to number one with her first single, "Feels Like I'm In Love" in September 1980. What was she called?

4. Soft Cell reached number one in September '83 with "Tainted Love." Which record label did they record it with?

5. Who was the "fairy godmother" in the video for Adam And The Ants' "Prince Charming" single?

OCTOBER

1. Lesley Gore sang "It's My Party" in 1963. Who was it a hit for in October '81?

2. Can you name the L.P. which Culture Club's "Karma Chameleon" came from?

3. Unravel this hit by the Police in October 1980. Me cons sold toes to Dan.

4. Rod Stewart had his biggest ever hit in October '71. It sold even more than "Sailing" — what was it called?

5. "Video Killed The Radio Star" was a hit for which group in 1979?

NOVEMBER

1. Name the song and the group from these lyrics:
   *"I wanna be your number one, number one.
   I'm not the kind of girl who gives up just like that."*

2. Which band did David Bowie have a number one hit with in November '81 called "Under Pressure"?

3. Dr Hook had a number one with "When You're In Love With A Beautiful Woman" one November but in what year?

4. What nationality were the band who had a hit with "Rat Trap" in November '78 and who are they?

5. What kind of girl did Billy Joel sing about in November '83?

DECEMBER

1. Which well-known heavy metal group had a Christmas number one in 1973 with "Merry Christmas Everybody"?

2. The Flying Pickets had a Christmas hit with a cover version of "Only You." Which band first sang this?

3. Tina Turner made an amazing comeback in December '83. Who was the other half of the famous duo she sang with several years before that?

4. What was the name of Showaddywaddy's smash hit in December '76?

5. Paul Young re-released his single "Love Of The Common People" at Christmas time in 1983. It reached number 3. What were his backing singers called?

6. Who had a hit with "There's No-One Quite Like Grandma"?

7. The Police had their second chart topper with "Walking On The Moon" in December '79. Which album was it taken from?

8. Pink Floyd had a huge hit with an anti-education anthem. What was it called?

9. The only single that sold a million copies in '81 was by the Human League. What was it?

10. "Mull Of Kintyre" was number one during December '77. What was the single on the other side called?

CONCLUSIONS

. . . into Barry Manilow realise you were still years? Oh sorry, didn't you been hiding for the past few **Under 15:** Aw, c'mon. Where have never — Once a year? Oh, I see — to the radio? Once a month? How often do you listen **15-29:** This isn't so hot, is it? for half the answers. up your book of hit singles but we bet you had to look **30-54:** Not bad, not bad at all. cheated, didn't you? you might as well admit it now — you **55-70:** All right, Smarty-Pants,

STAR STYLES

1. "I must admit I've been wearing some rather weird and wonderful designs on T.V. recently," laughed Kim Wilde when we spoke to her, "but I think when you appear on the television, you have to be very much larger than life! However, when I'm out socialising, I don't wear things that do so much damage to the eyeballs!"

Has Kim got fed up with the simpler jeans and jacket look she wore at the beginning of her career?

"Before I became a singer, I was an

Art-school student, and my friends and I used to experiment with some pretty outrageous outfits and colour combinations. We'd phone up each other the night before and plan our colour schemes for the next day! I think though that you have to be in the right mood to wear certain clothes, and I often felt great in just a simple T-shirt and jeans, so I suppose it was just natural for me to carry that through when I started singing. It wasn't a planned image really, it was just what I liked to wear at the time. At the moment I suppose I'm getting interested in bolder colours, like this gypsy blouse, which is definitely one of my current faves!"

2. "Another thing people are always asking me about are these gloves," giggled Kim, "they were a birthday present from a good friend, so I can truthfully say, I have no idea where they came from, but I tell you one thing — they really do come in handy!" (Groan!)

3. "I really like diamante jewellery because it is cheap to buy and adds a bit of sparkle to your outfits. The brooch came from Miss Selfridge and I picked up the necklace at a funny little Market Stall at Camden Lock in London. I've always liked things that

shine . . . I think in a previous life I must have been a magpie!"

4. "I also love men's waistcoats, in fact any men's clothes! When I was young I was a bit of a tomboy. I was always borrowing my father's and brother's clothes, much to their annoyance, but these days they make me go out and buy my own!"

5. "This leather jacket is absolutely the favourite item of clothing I possess. It is an old friend that's travelled all over the world with me. I picked it up at a flea-market in Carnaby Street for £18. Once again it's a man's jacket, but because it was such a small size, they couldn't sell it, hence the cheap price-tag!"

6. "I only possess two badges, but they are both very special to me. One is of Billy Fury, who was a great singer and a friend of my father. The other badge is of Elvis Costello. He's got a reputation for being very hard to get on with, although I found him to be very charming as well as being a great singer and song-writer.

"And finally my message to Jackie readers is to keep your peepers peeled, because you never know what bargain you may find . . . just around the corner."

The Sound Of Soul

ONE of the most exciting things to happen on the pop scene in 1975 was the new popularity of soul music. Suddenly, everyone seemed to be listening to the likes of Barry White, Stevie Wonder and The Three Degrees.

And it's easy to see why. Soul music is great to dance to, to sing along with, or just to sit and listen to, if that's how you feel. In fact, no matter what your mood is, the soul sound fits it perfectly!

Soul isn't a new kind of music — it's been around for years now. As far back as the early 1960's, everybody was raving about groups like the Four Tops, The Temptations and the Supremes. They were all part of the Tamla Motown sound, which originated from the city of Detroit, in Michigan.

And most of these people are still around today. Diana Ross, for instance, who in those days was a member of the Supremes, an all girl group, is of course a big solo star nowadays, and it was Diana who first discovered one of Tamla's newest star groups — the Jackson Five!

Back in the 60's, Tamla had another upcoming star — a very talented singer and songwriter called Little Stevie Wonder. The "Little" in his name was because at that time, Stevie was barely into his teens!

Nowadays, Stevie's become one of the world's best known and most brilliant soul artistes. He's no longer little — in fact, he's well over six feet tall! And over the years, his musical ability has grown and developed with him!

But although Tamla still has lots of big stars, it's no longer the only label around that's got soul. Recently, it seems that new soul groups have been appearing from all directions!

From America have come a whole host of names like The Tymes, The Stylistics, George McCrae, Al Green, and amongst the ladies, Gloria Gaynor, Betty Wright and that stunning group Labelle. But maybe the most popular of all are Barry White and The Three Degrees.

Barry, of course, is that very large (21 stone!) guy from Texas who makes really smooth, smoochy records — like his LP's, "Can't Get Enough" and "Just Another Way To Say I Love You." Definitely the kind of records to listen to when you're having a quiet, romantic evening by the fireside with someone you'd like to get to know better!

The Three Degrees on the other hand, are a group of ladies whose music is best for dancing to! Fayette Pinkney, Sheila Ferguson and Valerie Holiday, the three girls who make up the group, have had a string of hits in the last year. And not only do they sound great — they also look fantastic!

But America doesn't have the monopoly in soul music. Britain's been doing its bit too, turning out soul groups like Sweet Sensation and the Average White Band.

Sweet Sensation are an eight-piece.

Manchester group who got their first break when they appeared on the TV show 'New Faces.' Shortly after, they released their first single 'Sad, Sweet Dreamer,' and since then, they've just never looked back!

One of the things that gives Sweet Sensation their distinctive sound is the fact that they have four lead singers-one of whom, 17-year-old Marcel King, is quite a star in his own right!

Since they first made it, the group have toured all over Britain, and they've become a very popular live act.

The Average White Band are also a popular live group, both here and over in America, where they're very successful indeed. But the thing that makes this group unique is not so much their music — it's more that they're the only Scottish soul group in the world!

But listening to the authentic "black" sound that the boys achieve, you'd never guess that they come from Dundee and Perth instead of Detroit and Philadelphia!

So you see, soul really isn't one kind of music at all. Under the general title of soul, there are lots of different groups, all with their own individual sounds.

But whether you like going down to the local discotheque and dancing to the music of the Average White Band, or whether you prefer dreaming the night away with Barry White, the important thing is just to enjoy yourself, in your own way! ∎

Three Degrees

Average White Band

Barry White with his backing group, Love Unlimited

145

MY THREE THRILLING DAYS WITH DAVID

AND IT WAS WORTH EVERY BLISTER!

HOW would you like to meet David Cassidy? (Need we ask!)

For most of us, meeting David is just something to think about when we're alone with our dreams. But, for one "Jackie" reader, 1974 was the year her dream came true!

Sixteen-year-old Nicole Mutch was one of three lucky girls who won a trip to Los Angeles to meet David as first prize in a competition which involved doing a 12-mile sponsored walk around London.

Nicole says she was so determined to win that competition that she spent days going round from door to door in her home town of Ruislip in Middlesex, trying to persuade people to sponsor her on her walk.

And her tactics worked—because, altogether, she managed to get 1000 sponsors, which meant that not only did she win her prize, but she also earned £221 to aid people suffering from muscular dystrophy.

"I was absolutely thrilled when I heard I'd won," Nicole told me. "I've been a fan of David's for over three and a half years, and I have all his records. My bedroom's completely covered with pictures of him—at the last count I had 5640 different photos of him!

"I was keen to meet him because I wanted to find out what he's really like. He's always made out to be so perfect, such a goody-goody—and I wanted to find out if that was true or not. Now I know he isn't like that at all!"

Along with the two other prize-winners—Paula Howe, who comes from Barry in Glamorgan, and Nicky Price from Iver Heath in Buckinghamshire—Nicole was flown over to Hollywood, where the girls stayed in a hotel called the Chancellor, on Wiltshire Boulevard in Los Angeles.

The day after they arrived, the girls spent the morning being interviewed for the local radio station, and then, in the afternoon, they were taken on to the set of "The Partridge Family" where David was busy rehearsing for his last series with the show.

"When we got there, he was busily learning his lines for the next scene, so we waited till he was finished, and he came over to see us.

"At first, he seemed even more nervous than we were! He said, 'Hi,' and then paused, as though he didn't know quite what to expect—but after a few moments he was chatting to us as though we'd known him for years.

"At that time, I wasn't sure if I'd have the chance to see him again, so I gave him a toy dog I'd brought over from England as a present for him. He seemed pleased with it!"

Next morning, Nicole went to Disneyland for the day.

"It was fantastic! There's a place called 'The Haunted House' which is like a really scary ghost train. At one stage a ghost gets into the car with you and you can feel its clammy hand touching yours!"

Then it was back to their hotel for dinner, before going to bed and lying awake, looking forward to the next day!

"Next morning, we went to the head offices of David's record company, and met everyone there," said Nicole. "And in the afternoon, we were allowed to watch David at work in the recording studio!

"He took time off to show us all round the studio himself, and he explained how he records songs, how the different instruments are recorded on separate tracks, and how the final masters are produced."

But the three girls unanimously agreed that the next day—the last of their trip—was the best one of all!

"His record company laid on a chauffeur-driven Cadillac for us," Nicole told me. "We were taken on a guided tour of all the film stars' homes in the Hollywood hills, and we visited David's manager, Ruth Aarons, at her home—and, best of all, we went to David's house, where he showed us round!

"When we first went up to the house, we had to ask for him by name before the electronic gates would open. Because of the number of people who try the gates, he has special code names which he changes every week. When we went, we had to ask for William A. Bong! (Billabong, get it?)

"The house has about eleven rooms, and is E-shaped with a guest house at the back, where his mother sometimes stays. In the lounge there was a Union Jack painted on one wall, and I asked him why —and David said it had been there when he moved in so he had left it there.

"His bedroom is huge, and he also uses it as a studio—as well as his bed he has a large grand piano in there, four guitars, and a set of drums. It has built-in cupboards, mustard carpets and white curtains.

"His lounge is furnished very plainly with a striped suite, and a white-painted dining-room table and black chairs, with fluorescent lights, and all his gold discs, twelve of them, were framed and hanging in the hall.

"He had two bathrooms, both done out in blue and I had the impression that he seems to like cleanliness, but he's not too tidy! There are shoes and T-shirts lying around everywhere.

"He showed me what he calls his 'shirt collection'—over 400 different T-shirts, stacked away in cupboards in a separate room—and he introduced me to his dogs, Bullseye, an English setter; Sam, who's a hairy mongrel, and his cat, poor little Boots, who was sitting on a cushion with a paw bandaged, looking very sorry for himself.

"David told us he'd wrenched a claw away from his foot while climbing a tree that morning, and that he'd had to take him to the vet to have his foot bandaged.

"Then we sat in the lounge for a while, and he told us about the house he wanted to build in Hawaii. He said he really wanted to live there, because it was the one place where he could get away from everything. He said he liked the people of Hawaii very much, because they always left him alone.

"And when he noticed I had on platform boots, he laughed and said he didn't know how I could wear them, because he always fell over when he wore them!

"That's one of the nicest things about him—he's a natural joker. When I first met him I said, 'How's your dog?' and he put out his hand at about waist height and said, 'About that high!'"

All too soon, it was time for the girls to go—but not before Nicole got David to autograph two LPs she'd been given by his record company.

So, what did she think of him?

"He's lovely," she said. "He was very kind to us. He struck me as a very honest person, and he's very good-looking—but he likes to think of himself as just an ordinary guy.

"In fact, he was just as nice as I'd expected!"

That's me. Can you tell I'm shaking?

146

David

Slade laugh over some incidents which weren't so funny at the time . . .

No, dear, that's NOT part of the act!

WHEN you have a group made up of four crazy lads like Noddy Holder, Dave Hill, Jim Lea and Don Powell, you might expect that anything could happen—and it does!

During the years they've been together, Slade say they've had lots of hair-raising experiences—the sort of thing that is very frightening at the time, but can be quite funny when you look back on it.

"Some of our worst moments, as you might expect, have been on planes," Don told me. "None of us are actually scared of flying itself—but some of the planes we've travelled in would scare anyone!

"I remember once we had a really scary flight during a Scandinavian tour. We were flying from Copenhagen to Aahus, and the flight was delayed by snow.

"Then when it finally arrived we discovered the plane was very old—with an ancient propeller!"

The boys were a bit doubtful about the safety of the plane, but since it was the only transport available, they decided they'd just have to risk it.

"It was all right until it came to taking off," Don said. "Every time it tried to leave the runway, it hit the ground again! It did it four times—and each time there was a terrible bump.

"Eventually it did take off—and somehow, we got safely to our destination."

As far as the individual members of the group are concerned, Noddy says Don is the one who gets into trouble most often.

"I wouldn't say Don's accident-prone," he said, "but whenever he touches something, it breaks!

"For instance, I remember when we were in Holland, Don went round to Dave's room.

"He knocked on the door and Dave shouted 'Wait a minute.' So Don knocked again—and the door fell off its hinges!"

Dave says he's terrified of heights—and this led to one of his most frightening experiences.

"We were making a special film for 'Top Of The Pops' at a power station. I was wearing a silver suit, so they decided to film me walking along an overhead ledge, as though I was a spaceman who'd just landed.

"It was very high up, and I suddenly looked down at the ground. That was a mistake, because I just froze.

"I had this terror of falling and I just froze completely, like a cat does when it gets stuck up a tree.

"You know, you watch that cat and you know it could get down the same way it came up—but the cat's too frightened, and it just sits there till somebody rescues it.

"Well, that was exactly what happened to me. I've never been so scared in all my life!"

Another frightening moment for Dave came when the group were in the Bahamas a few years ago.

"There was a girl I really liked," said Dave. "I'd been trying to make a date with her for ages, and when she finally invited me to go snorkelling with her, I was really pleased.

"I didn't know what snorkelling was, but I was quite pleased to have a go, as long as I was with her. But I got a shock when I met her on the beach and she gave me all the gear she'd borrowed for me. You see, I can't swim!

"But I didn't have the courage to tell her that. I figured I'd be okay if I walked along the sea-bed, pretending to swim—and that did work, for a bit. But unfortunately, the sea-bed suddenly shelved away while I was going along, and I went down with it!

"Luckily the girl noticed I was in trouble and helped rescue me—but that was the end of my attempt at impressing her!"

Although all the boys love seeing their fans reacting enthusiastically at their concerts, they admit it can be frightening if this gets out of hand.

"We're always afraid someone will get hurt in a situation like that," said Jim. "It can be really frightening if you're going through a big crowd in a car, and they're all mobbing around you.

"When we played the Apollo Theatre in Glasgow in the spring, there were so many fans outside, we had to escape in a police Land-rover.

"That was scary enough, but the person who really came off worst was Swinn, our roadie. He had the job of acting as decoy in the Rolls Royce we usually travel about in.

"It took him ages to make his way through the crowd, and he told us afterwards he'd been petrified!"

Slade spent the early part of this summer in America and it was while they were playing in New York that Noddy had a rather nasty experience.

"While we were onstage, someone threw a firework on stage," he told me. "It landed right at my feet, and for a moment I just stood there in horror, wondering what it was going to do!

"It turned out to be a smoke-bomb, which of course brought us to a halt right in mid-act! There we were standing among great clouds of smoke. We couldn't see the audience, and they couldn't see us!

"When the smoke finally cleared, we noticed nobody in the audience seemed to be very upset by what had happened.

"But afterwards we found out why—they thought it was all part of the act!"

ON-THE-SPOT INTERVIEWS
where our roving reporters find out what you think.

Do you remember your first kiss?

Moira Garland, Middleton, Leeds.
My first boyfriend took me to the fair for a special treat one night. We went on the ghost train and suddenly, in the dark, he kissed me — it was the first time he'd dared! I nearly screamed, because I wasn't sure if it was part of the horror show or not!

Marsha Dun, Liverpool.
We were walking hand. in hand along the sandy beach, the water lapping gently over our bare feet, when David turned to me, kissed me passionately, and said, "I'm gonna make you a star!"
Then I woke up!

Tanya Saunders, Brighton, Sussex.
I'm afraid it was a great anti-climax! We were coming home from a lovely party, it was a beautiful starry night, the moon was full — and when he kissed me all I could think was, "Oh, is this what it's all about?" Now I come to think about it, though, everything else was perfect — he obviously wasn't!

Mick Robertson.
It was when I must have been about ten or eleven. I was cycling home from school with my little girlfriend. We stopped and I just kissed her. It was so nice I just kissed her and kissed her.
. Unfortunately, some friends of mine had been standing behind the trees — they told me that they'd counted up to 175!
In those days I believed in quantity. Now I've grown up I appreciate quality . . .

Sandra Pearson, Birmingham.
My first kiss was from a boy called — would you believe — Ivor Fowler! He was tall and skinny and he wore big, thick glasses. I didn't fancy him at all. In fact, I thought he was hideous. The worst thing was, after that first kiss, he followed me around for weeks.

Mary Butler, Stirling.
I think I'd rather forget it. I felt really chuffed when the boy next door kissed me on the way to school, but then my brother told me he'd only done it for a bet!

Geraldine Clarke, Exmouth, Devon.
My first real kiss was just like in the movies. There we were in a grotty old street under an even grottier old lamppost, then suddenly, at that first kiss, I saw stars and went all weak at the knees. That grotty old street suddenly seemed beautiful. It was unforgettable!

Alison Ross, Plymouth.
My first kiss wasn't really very romantic. I was at a party with six boys and only four girls . . . the boys decided we should play postman's knock, but I was terrified as I'd never been kissed before. I soon got the hang of it after the first one though!

Sheila Knox, Glasgow.
Last year, I had an enormous crush on this boy who'd bright red hair, glasses and loads of freckles. All my friends thought he was horrible, but I thought he was wonderful. He took me home from the school dance and kissed me outside my front gate. After that, I went right off him!

Martine Howard (Guys and Dolls). —
I had my first kiss when I was 11 — it was horrible! His name was Dave and I was absolutely petrified. I thought he was going to eat me!

Sarah Roe, Chichester.
I went to this party, and about half way through, all the lights went out, and I got my first kiss. The only thing is, I don't know who gave it to me!

Rob Davis (Mud).
It was when I was 13. I had no idea at all what I was meant to do — so I stood there with my eyes shut and let her do the rest!

Dave Hill (Slade).
It wasn't bad. I was 9 at the time and on holiday in Rhyl in North Wales. I met this girl there who was also on holiday — she had lovely long blonde hair.
It was only a typical kid's kiss, but at the time I thought it was pretty hot stuff!

Moira McGrath, Glasgow.
First kisses are meant to stay with you forever, but I really can't remember mine, or even who it was. It was either the boy who lived near me at home, or the one in my Maths class at school. I went out with them both at once and can't remember which one kissed me first!

Alan Gardner, Grimsby, Lancs.
It was really romantic, actually. I was walking home with this girl, when it began to rain. It was a real downpour — thunder, lightning and everything. She was a bit scared, so I thought I'd be all protective and put my arms round her. She was soaking wet and her hair was all straggly but I thought she looked lovely — so I kissed her!

Andrea Maxwell, Newcastle-upon-Tyne.
My first boyfriend was dead nervous about asking me out, even though it was obvious he wanted to. So, eventually he managed to work up the courage. When I agreed, he yelled, grabbed me and kissed me! Then he went really scarlet, which made me feel even better.

Rosy Hanlin, Stockton-on-Tees, Cleveland.
Oh, yes! I remember it well! My first boyfriend tried to kiss me goodnight romantically at my door. The trouble was, he was about four inches shorter than me, so he couldn't reach! We soon solved that problem though — he stood up on the doorstep!

David Cassidy's idea of Paradise is Hawaii, where he owns a plot of land on which he's building a house.

"I'm building it myself, with the help of two friends who know a bit about building," he said. "I'm really looking forward to getting it finished, so I can spend as much time there as I like.

"I love Hawaii. When I'm there, I feel as though I'm in a world of my own, away from the music business and all that.

"That's why Hawaii's so important to me — when I'm there I can forget everything else."

MICK'S STAR

(Where you might just find your

Mick Robertson, as you know, writes a fortnightly column for 'Jackie' telling us about some of the exciting places he's travelled to during the time he's worked for Thames TV's "MAGPIE".

And his column is so popular we thought it would be nice if he, and some other stars, could tell us which are their favourite places.

Here's Mick to tell you more about it.

1

"In the time I've been with Magpie, I've been lucky enough to travel all over the world and see some places I thought I'd only ever be able to read about.

"Every country has its own special memories for me — but, at the moment anyway, my favourite place of all is New Orleans.

"The atmosphere there is incredible. New Orleans is the home of blues music, and the city is full of it — you can hear it coming from every café and bar you pass.

"The city is also beautiful to look at — the houses are all very ornate, and everywhere you go you find lovely flowers, thriving in the hot, humid climate.

"I think it's a very romantic city.

"Well, that's my choice of favourite place — but everyone has their own ideas on the subject, as you'll find out if you read on!"

4

Bryan Ferry decided to get right away from it all this year — so he flew off for two weeks on the remote West Indian island of Mustique.

Mustique isn't a very big island — in fact, according to Bryan, it consists of one hotel, a few houses and seven sandy beaches!

"As you can imagine, I spent most of my time on one or other of the beaches!" said Bryan. "I also did a lot of swimming, and I played tennis — in fact it was quite an active holiday!

"The only trouble was, I really got used to the lazy pace that everyone lived at out there. I found it difficult to adjust to life in London when I came back again!"

The Bay City Rollers, who usually go on holiday together, spent a few weeks in Tunisia last year — and they loved it!

The highlight of the holiday, according to guitarist Eric Faulkner, came when the boys decided to sample the local night-life.

"We went to a big night club, where the cabaret was a company of belly-dancers," said Eric. "I don't know why they picked on us, but they came down into the audience and dragged us up on stage — and made us join in the belly-dancing!

"We must have looked a real sight, but it was fun, all the same!"

Mott the Hoople spent the early part of this summer doing an extensive American tour. And when they finished it at the beginning of June, lead singer Ian Hunter and guitarist Aerial Bender decided that what they needed after all that work was a holiday in the sunshine.

"We were nice and near the West Indies," said Ian, "so we decided to fly down to Barbados for a few weeks, and have a proper rest.

"We had a super time, lazing about on the beach — it was just what we needed after a strenuous tour."

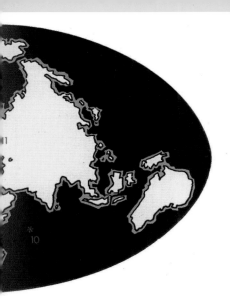

TREK

favourite pop star next summer.)

6

Ron and Russell Mael, that incredible pair who lead Sparks, say their favourite holiday place is Paris.

"We love the whole of France," Russell told me, "but Paris is, of course, the centre of it all.

"Everything about Paris is nice — it's a beautiful city, and the atmosphere is incredible."

Another thing the brothers love about Paris is the fashion scene there. They both love French clothes, and whenever they're in Paris, they like to have a look around the city's boutiques and clothes shops.

And there's one other thing Ron and Russell love about France — the food!

"We're both crazy about French food," explained Russell. "We could live off French bread and the gorgeous cheeses you get over there!"

7

Elton John likes to go to Los Angeles every July for his four weeks' annual holiday.

"I love going down to Malibu Beach," said Elton, "half an hour's drive down the coast from Hollywood. It's really nice there.

"It's very hot though, I'll tell you that! Step on the sand and you've got instant fried feet!

"One year I rented a house there which used to belong to Cole Porter. It was beautiful — you stepped out literally from the kitchen onto the beach and you could watch the sunset and people riding horses along the sands.

"I don't really like swimming in the sea very much, because I'm afraid of getting bitten by things like Piranha fish! But I did a bit of surfing while I was there, and that was nice."

8

During the 1960's, Alvin Stardust "dropped out" and spent a couple of years just wandering around Europe. And out of the whole of the Continent, he says his favourite city was Amsterdam.

"Amsterdam's a great place for young people," said Alvin. "The nicest thing about it is that you have the freedom to live just the way you want.

"If you want to rave it up, you can — but you can live quietly too. I used to love walking along the banks of the canals at night, where it was peaceful and quiet — but there were some great clubs and discos too!"

9

David Essex's favourite holiday area is the South of France.

"Apart from Britain, of course, my favourite place is the area around the Mediterranean," he says. "The South of France is particularly nice, because of the cool breeze called the Mistral which always blows through there.

"That means that, although it's beautifully warm and sunny, it never gets too hot. In fact, it's just right!"

10

Noel Edmonds and his lovely wife Gill spent their summer holidays in the Seychelles this year, and Noel liked it so much he got quite carried away just telling me about it!

"It was a real tropical paradise," he said. "The trouble with most of these places is that they're either very primitive, or, like Jamaica, they're totally commercialised.

"In Jamaica, you can go to a beach and there's likely to be a concrete factory just around the corner — but the Seychelles weren't like that at all.

"They were perfect — we could go and have a whole beach to ourselves during the day, but still come back to an air-conditioned hotel at night, where everyone was very friendly and only too eager to help us.

"The only thing lacking in fact, was any night-life — but we didn't mind that. We get enough of that in London."

11

David Bowie was very impressed with Moscow when he passed through it last year on his way back from Japan on the Trans-Siberian Railway.

"When I was there, the May Day celebrations were going on," he said, "and I was lucky enough to see the big parade, which is the highpoint of the celebrations. It's an incredible sight."

But according to a friend of David's, none of the Russians were watching the May Day Parade on that day — because they were all too busy gazing at David himself!

I can believe that!

David with his wife Angie just before he set off for Moscow.

THERE'S a new theory about choosing your ideal mate which has absolutely nothing to do with computers, signs of the zodiac or Chinese horoscopes. It's based on your age-position in your family.

Recent investigations show that most happy, secure marriages involve couples who are "complementary." The idea is that having older brothers, younger sisters or whatever influences your character, and likewise, your prospective boyfriend is affected by his place in the family.

We've simplified the theory and come up with this analysis.

N.B. We can tell you which category you fit into, give you a character analysis, tell you what your boyfriend should be. Afraid we can't find him for you, though. That's NOT part of the service!

SO—
If you are:
AN ONLY CHILD
Only children have absolutely no-one with whom to compete for their parents' attention. They're more used to adult company and can also be left a lot on their own.

You're likely to be shy and sensitive, yet self-sufficient. Chances are you're extravagant, generous and altruistic. You tend to lack drive, though.

You're constantly seeking attention, and you'll find it in a boy who has a natural inclination to spoil girls and shower them with gifts and affections.

Your worst fault, however, is that when you have a row with your boyfriend (as you're bound to do, occasionally, being rather self-centred) you tend to rush off in tears rather than have a fair quarrel. Most boys will find this infuriating.

So your ideal boyfriend is:

BROTHER WITH YOUNGER SISTERS
He's definitely the one for you. Having younger sisters of his own, he's something of an expert on handling rather spoilt females!

He'll give you the pampering and constant reassurance you need to be happy, whilst still remaining sensible and fair in his judgments.

He's not a loner, and will enjoy company of both sexes, but he's not only "one of the boys" — he'll be just as happy to spend a cosy evening with you, watching TV or having a chat.

His main fault is that he's not very

ambitious, but we'd say he was a reliable, steady, super boyfriend to have!

If you are:
DAUGHTER WITH YOUNGER SIBLINGS (THAT'S BROTHERS OR SISTERS!)
You're a friendly, but very responsible person, with a very practical streak. It seems to be your natural role in life to settle quarrels and calm other people's hot tempers!

You're good at making decisions and don't often change your mind, but this can become an obsession to the extent that you can become unreasonable over trivialities.

If you have more younger brothers than sisters, you'll tend to be calmer than someone with more sisters than brothers. Girls with younger sisters can be a little too dominant, if they don't get their own way, and have a tendency to sulk at the unfairness of life!

You need someone you can boss about a bit! Could be he's a couple of years younger than you, in maturity at any rate, but you'll soon straighten that out! So your ideal boyfriend is:

AN ONLY SON
Although he often demands more attention than is strictly necessary, and can be infuriatingly selfish at times, he's the one for you.

Being used to looking after younger children, you can dominate him when necessary, and soothe him when he's feeling low.

It's essential that he has someone to rely on, someone concerned about him whom he can turn to. You'll have to use all your patience with him occasionally!

On the brighter side, though, he'll bring out your maternal instinct and provide a suitable balance for your temperament.

He has a lot of affection and generosity to spare, and you'll probably find him so lovable you'll forget all about his faults — till the next time!

If you are:
DAUGHTER WITH OLDER BROTHERS
You're definitely a female female! You like to feel protected by a boy, and tend to go along with his opinion, even if you know at heart you disagree. This is probably a throwback from the days when you were teased by your elder brother(s) to the extent that you went along with their opinions rather than risk more teasing.

You're not over-ambitious, and may well decide to give up your career, if you get married, for a state of housewifely bliss.

The only thing you have to watch out for is that you treat your boyfriends like boyfriends, not as substitutes for your big brother.

You could become dominated by your boyfriends, if you let them, but as you don't really mind this, you should get on really well with your ideal boy, who is:

SON WITH OLDER SISTERS
He's your ideal male! He's a perfectionist, and can be a bit domineering at times, but he'll always try to see your point of view in an argument and will stick up for you if he thinks you're right.

As your "opposite number," so to speak, he understands what it's like to have elder siblings of the opposite sex, and has come through many of the same problems as you.

You'll find he's someone it's very easy to fall for — he's such a genuinely nice person. However, he has a tendency to be forgetful and unreliable, so don't expect him to turn up on time for a date!

If you are:
DAUGHTER WITH OLDER SISTERS
You're enthusiastic, adventurous and have a definite character of your own. This means you're very attractive to males and probably have lots of boyfriends but for one reason or another you never manage to keep them.

Either you begin to feel tied down and move on to pastures new, or the boy gets bored with your moodiness and lack of responsibility.

You tend to get wildly enthusiastic about things at first but can never be bothered to finish them — and unfortunately, this applies to boyfriends too! The idea of a new boyfriend appeals to you, but possibly because you're used to all these sisters, you tend to shy away from any deep relationships with the opposite sex.

You need someone with a remarkable degree of understanding to calm you down

fit in?

a bit! That's why the person most suited to you is:

SON WITH OLDER BROTHERS

Again, this is the case of someone with elder siblings of the same sex knowing how you feel.

He's imaginative and thoughtful, with a rare degree of understanding, which is great, as he'll need it all with you!

Having older brothers, it's unavoidable that he'll enjoy the company of male friends, but that only means he's doubly interested in you when it comes to romance — so make sure you always look your beautiful best for him!

If anything, he tends to be a bit over-romantic with his girlfriends, but we don't think that's a reason for complaining!

You'll be able to give vent to all your crazy ideas here without him taking you too seriously — he knows how fickle you are! He, too, likes freedom and independence, so you should make a super couple!

If you are:
DAUGHTER WITH OLDER BROTHER(S) AND SISTER(S)

Phew! What a mouthful! But despite the long-winded title, you have the distinction of being the most settled and happiest person of the whole bunch!

Being brought up with elder siblings of both sexes, you'll have had the advantage

of a well-balanced childhood emotionally.

Although you probably argued with your brothers and sisters as a child, this actually served as a good basis for later life, when you're more interested in boys than toys!

Used to being with people of both sexes, you don't suffer from the inhibitions of shy people, or the selfishness of extroverts.

You tend to be rather middle-of-the-road in your opinions — but don't dare let anyone call you dull, as you're far from being that! You're the sort of girl the rest of us would like to be — happy-go-lucky, yet stable.

Although you would be suited to any of the boys previously mentioned, your ideal boyfriend is probably the one nearest to you in family placing, i.e:

SON WITH OLDER BROTHER(S) AND SISTER(S)

Like you, he has elder siblings of both sexes to contend with, so he is exactly on your wavelength as concerns family relationships.

Much of his character rating, of course, is just the same as yours with the same basic qualities of stability and fairness.

He's come from a well-adjusted family, too, so both of you are really ideally suited (do we hear wedding bells?).

Anyway, with two people as well suited as yourselves, you've no excuse for *not* being the perfect couple!

OUTRODUCTION (as opposed to Intro)

Of course, there are exceptions to every rule and you may find your ideal boy in entirely the wrong age-position. And there's also a four-letter word we haven't mentioned so far, which is rather important — love!

But it's really uncanny how one's character can unfold to fit into the categories once the family gets older and more settled — so bear our twosomes in mind next time you're stuck for something to say to that gorgeous guy sitting next to you on the bus. ''Em, excuse me, I was just wondering — do you happen to be the middle sibling of three brothers?''

It's certainly a startling opening for a fascinating conversation.

Happy hunting!

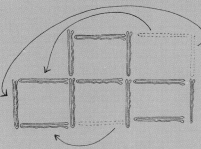

The Most Beautiful Man In The World...

... what would he look like?

That's what we were discussing the other day in the Jackie office. And though we all had our own ideas (!), we finally managed to agree on one man.

First of all, we decided he'd have hair just like RUSSELL MAEL, the lead singer of Sparks —his curly dark hair looks stylish, but still lovely and natural.

When it came to eyes, everybody wanted different people, so we gave the tea lady the casting vote, and she decided on DAVID ESSEX. And we had to agree—David has beautiful clear blue eyes that positively sparkle when he smiles!

Noses were a bit more difficult—I mean, there's not much you can say about noses, is there?! But everyone agreed that DAVID BOWIE'S is a very fine specimen!

The most beautiful man in the world, everyone decided, would have a mouth that was both friendly AND sexy. Like DAVID CASSIDY'S in fact— lovely!

Last, but not least, his chin would have to be just right— and we all agreed that one of the nicest chins around belongs to DONNY OSMOND.

So there's our choice for the most beautiful man in the world —he sounds gorgeous, doesn't he?

Well, with the help of some miracle-workers in our art department, we've made up a photo of him, and if you turn to page 93, you'll see what he looks like!

SECRETS O

ALTHOUGH the Jackie office is a very happy place, we have been known to have little disagreements from time to time! But when it comes to our favourite T V show we are in total harmony. Our vote just has to go to "Top Of The Pops". The Top Thirty rave-up has been happily bouncing along since David Bowie was in short trousers and Gary had never heard of glitter. But the amazing thing is that it's still as fresh as a mountain stream. (This is beginning to sound like a cigarette advert!)

We thought you might like to know what goes on behind the scenes at "Top Of The Pops" so Pete donned his Sherlock Holmes hat and yellow woolly socks and set off to investigate . . .

I ARRIVED at the BBC T V Centre in Wood Lane, London, bright and early one Wednesday morning and soon found myself deep in conversation with Programme Director, Bruce Milliard. He told me the TOTP team had already been working on the show for 24 hours. On Tuesday mornings the new Top 50 chart gets the Hot Line treatment and Bruce knows the week's placings almost before the ink has dried on the new chart.

The next move is to decide who is going to guest on the show and a series of quick phone calls to various corners of the pop world let the lucky stars know they are wanted.

Every pop star wants to be on TOTP. It's the best possible way of getting across to millions of people and just one exciting appearance can make you a chart-topper overnight. Remember what happened with the Rubettes back at the beginning of summer?

Once the final list of names is ready, the backstage team can start to relax. Work starts again around eleven on Wednesday morning, when the stars start to arrive. Each group is given a separate rehearsal and the lighting is organised to make them look their best. As Bruce puts it "If someone has a big nose, we try not to make it too obvious." They're very considerate people down at the T V Centre!

Everything is now ready for the dress rehearsal at five in the evening. The disc jockey is on the scene by this time and he runs through his introductions and now the show is getting very close to what you'll see on your T V screen.

THE TOP POP SHOW

Cameramen and floor managers scurry around and you have to be very careful where you step or you're likely to go flying over one of the curling black tails of cable that run in crazy patterns across the studio floor. The guys behind the cameras look very cool and professional and the only time they get a little hot under the collar is when Pan's People run through their latest sizzling dance routine!

The night I was at the studio, the rehearsal was over by six. Various stars chatted together and the scene was like an autograph hunter's dream! Then they wandered off to their dressing rooms in a long corridor running underneath the TOTP studio.

It's a long day for the stars and they pass the time by joking around in the dressing room, strolling over to the canteen for lunch and coffee (the chips are delicious!) or maybe popping into the BBC Bar for something a little stronger.

Boredom can set in during the eight hours from when they arrive to when the show is actually recorded, but as the big moment approaches a tingle of excitement touches the air and the stars suddenly come to life. Very soon they will be in front of the cameras. Like footballers before a big game, they feel the butterflies whirling and circling in their tummies.

Upstairs in the studio, it's seven o'clock and the audience are swarming through the doors. The first thing that hits them is how small the studio is. Cameras can play funny tricks. When you see the show at home you get the feeling TOTP is held in a huge discotheque but the studio is only about the size of an ordinary school gym.

The disc jockey of the week welcomes them and gives them a few friendly words of advice. The main thing is to watch out for the cameras. They whizz around like angry Daleks and it doesn't pay to get in their way. There are other hints and tips but the most important message is . . . have fun!

For half-an-hour, I joined the lucky 132 fans who had been given tickets for the show and we danced and laughed and almost forgot we were in the TOTP studios. It started to get very warm and

with the lighting dimmed, the atmosphere was great. Then, suddenly, it was seven-thirty and the show was on the road. The lights went up, the cameras started to move and the familiar theme music blared in my ears.

Noel EDMONDS, surrounded by pretty girls and looking full of health and confidence introduced the first group and another successful show was being recorded. The programme seemed to whizz past at an amazing pace. No sooner had one group left one of the small stages spaced around the studio, than another appeared to get ready for their spot. Noel sprung around various cameras making his introductions and the dancers generally had a ball, while keeping a careful eye open for cables and runaway cameras.

The groups seemed interested in what they looked like and kept looking up at the monitor screens above them, while they sang their songs. Next time you

watch the show see if you can spot the stars gazing up at the roof. They're not admiring the ceiling, they're admiring themselves. Conceited lot!

Suddenly, before you knew it, the show was over. It had been a great experience seeing it all from the studio and you certainly get to know a few tricks of the trade when you are behind the cameras. Some of the best scenes never get on the telly.

"Gary Glitter was on the show once and we wanted him to stand on a little platform a couple of feet high," smiled Bruce. "D'you know, we had to have him lifted up there. If he'd climbed up by himself, he would have split his tight trousers!"

It's amazing what goes on . . . behind the scenes at "Top Of The Pops"!

If you want tickets for the show, you must be prepared for a long wait. It could be six months. But if you've got the patience, here's the correct address: "Top Of The Pops," B.B.C. Television Centre, Wood Lane, London W.12. Have fun!

JOIN THE MAGIC CIRCLE

♠ ♥ ♣ ♦

THERE are many methods of fortune-telling, from palmistry to peering into a crystal ball, but the easiest one to learn is by using playing cards.

It's easy — all you need is the basic meaning of each card and a little concentration. We'll give you one if you'll supply the other!

Cards were originally made for telling the future. It was only later they began to be used for playing the card games we know today. There are lots of different ways to read the cards. Our method is simple and needs only a little practice.

HOW TO START

Study the circle drawn here. As you see, it's divided into twelve sections, each section representing an area of your life. The card dealt on this section shows your future in that area.

First, remove the jokers and all cards under seven from the pack. Aces, of course, count high and they stay in Shuffle the remaining 32 cards, cut three times, and dea them face up, clockwise, starting at "one o'clock" an finishing at twelve.

Unless you've a set of miniature playing-cards, it's bette to draw your own magic circle on a really big piece c paper. Then, as you deal the cards, you can place the directly on your chart.

To interpret correctly, you must know the card's meanin and how this applies to the particular segment it lands ir Under "Card Meanings" you will see a list of what eac card means, first in a general way, then its special mean ing should it land on the particular section mentioned.

As an example, take the Jack or Knave of Diamond which means "A stranger in uniform." If this lands o No.3, "Travel," it looks as if you're taking a trip with hin

CARD MEANINGS

Court cards—Ace, King, Queen and Jack—represent PEOPLE in your life. The other cards stand for EVENTS.

General — SPADES — Special

ACE
Someone connected with music you have dreams about.

KING
Your boss or head teacher.

QUEEN
Mother or female relative.

JACK
A surprise compliment sets you thinking.

TEN
Young male acquaintance or relative.

NINE
You'll suspect a boy of deceiving you.

EIGHT
Arrangements you had been looking forward to may be changed.

SEVEN
The luckiest card in the pack!

WISHES
News of forthcoming visit has you in a tizzy.

SCHOOL CAREER
Punishment over a misdeed turns out to be less severe than you feared.

HOME LIFE
Temporary upset means more work for you.

LUCK
Stroke of good fortune for him has lucky repercussions for you.

ENEMIES
Someone you thought of as an enemy makes overtures of friendship.

LOVE
You have some heart-searching before making an important decision.

COMMUNICATIONS
A phone call brings a disappointment and a ray of hope.

***
Wherever this card falls it promises good news to come.

General—HEARTS—Special

ACE
A talented someone you have heard of but never met.

KING
Parent of older relative who has deep concern for your welfare.

QUEEN
Close friend or relative in same age group as yourself.

JACK
An admirer, though by no means a secret one!

TEN
A major change in your way of life.

NINE
Your bad patch will soon pass.

EIGHT
News of an old flame.

SEVEN
Danger from an unexpected source.

WISHES
Unexpected offer could have strong influence on your future plans.

MONEY
The outlook will soon be more hopeful.

FRIENDS
An annual event you are looking forward to could result in a long-lasting foursome.

LOVE
Information from a friend makes you view him in a kindlier light.

TRAVEL
Permanent move to another district possible.

HEALTH
Brief and minor health upset will be over shortly.

COMMUNICATIONS
Letter from a friend has interesting news of boy who may come back into your life.

ENEMIES
Unfounded rumour about you could cause a boy heartache.

General — CLUBS — Special

ACE
Attractive male who is the friend of a friend.

KING
A stranger, soon to come into your life.

QUEEN
Someone you disliked at first now proving to be a true friend.

JACK
An older boy at school or work.

TEN
Your second meeting with a boy takes place in very different circumstances from the first.

NINE
You're the subject of discussion among a group of girls.

EIGHT
You have cause to regret an impulsive action.

SEVEN
Be prepared to sacrifice a little pride to help a new venture.

COMMUNICATIONS
Phone call for you sends your hopes rising.

TRAVEL
A journey over water is indicated.

SOCIAL LIFE
Two late nights in succession for you.

LOVE
You're directly concerned in an exciting piece of gossip.

WISHES
You've longed for a second date with him and chances look bright.

SOCIAL LIFE
You'll be back in circulation and this could have surprising consequences.

LOVE
You would be wise to make the first move in patching up a quarrel.

HOME LIFE
You are given the extra freedom you wanted — and more responsibility too.

General — DIAMONDS — Special

ACE
Someone who attracts you strongly but is unattainable.

KING
Your dentist, doctor or some other person concerned with your physical health.

QUEEN
Girl friend at school or work.

JACK
A stranger in uniform.

TEN
You change your former opinion of a boy.

NINE
You regret an extravagance which proves unnecessary.

EIGHT
A disappointment is indicated.

SEVEN
As one door closes, another opens to you.

SCHOOL/CAREER
New turn of events leaves you with a difficult decision.

HEALTH
A visit to do with medical matters has a happy outcome.

ENEMIES
An unjust accusation angers and upsets you.

SOCIAL LIFE
A flirtatious offer is made to you.

FRIENDS
The group you have gone about with may soon split up.

MONEY
An emergency leaves you practically broke.

HOME LIFE
Some restriction or difficulty you hoped you'd resolved still persists.

SCHOOL/CAREER
You discover hidden talents in yourself.

Perhaps he's the bus conductor! If it lands on "Communications" that could mean a lonely soldier wants you or a penpal. Or it could be that new young postman is thinking about you—the choice of interpretations is up to you.

But if the Jack lands on Section 10 "Social Life" you'll see the special reading "A flirtatious offer is made to you." This is when you can start worrying if you see that the French Navy are to pay your town a visit!

Are you beginning to see how it works? It's your judgment to decide what each combination means in the particular circumstances. If you become good at it, you could find yourself in demand at parties once the other girls find out about your powers!

But practise on your own for a while till you gain fluency. And remember to write down the results in your diary so you can look back a few weeks from now and see how many of your predictions came true!

WHAT DARK SECRETS WILL

YOU'LL need about half an hour to do justice to this Superquiz, so leave it for an evening when there's nothing good on telly and your tranny needs new batteries. It would also be a giggle doing it at an informal hen-party, as long as everyone is able to laugh at themselves! You never know which beastly side of your nature it might reveal to the others!

If you answer honestly, we'll provide a character reading which might surprise you, and add some hints about the career which would suit you best.

What You Have To Do

Just read the questions and jot down your answers on a piece of scrap paper. Don't write on the page — you may want to have another bash later on. We'll tell you what to do when you've finished. Remember, the more truthful you are, the more accurate will be the picture.

1. Imagine you get a book-token on your birthday. Which of these is your most likely choice?
(a) book of poetry?
(b) book on travel or adventure?
(c) book to help with study or hobby?
(d) historical romance or biography?

2. Your boyfriend is late and the rain is lashing down. Do you . . .
(b) listen to his explanation but secretly believe he was chatting up another girl?
(c) tear him off a strip, and hop on a passing bus before he can explain?
(d) forgive him on sight because you really didn't expect him to turn up anyway?
(a) wait for his explanation and if it sounds genuine, believe it?

💙 **3. You're shopping with a girlfriend and** she's set her heart on a dress that doesn't suit her. Would you . . . .
(c) tell her she looks like Dracula's mother?
(d) refuse to offer an opinion?
(a) say you think another dress suits her much better?
(b) tell her you don't care for it, but she knows best what suits her?

4. Which of these would make you cry most?
(a) unkind words from your boy?
(b) peeling onions?
(c) you're given the sack or expelled from school?
(d) your beloved but elderly family pet has died in its sleep?

5. What appeals to you most about going steady?
(a) the romance and love angle?
(b) going out to interesting places?
(c) the envy in the eyes of girls still on the shelf?
(d) the feeling that someone understands you?

6. A boy takes you to a party then disappears for a few minutes. When he comes back, he has lipstick all over his face — the rat. Do you . . .
(a) say nothing but think he has very bad manners?
(b) start thinking how you'll get your own back?
(c) tease him about it?
(d) think he's only asked you for a laugh?

7. When you really dislike someone, do you . . .
(a) remain polite but keep your distance?
(b) find you can't help being rude?
(c) chat to them regardless in a friendly way?
(d) ignore them completely?

8. Friends arrange to meet you at the disco but don't turn up. Would you . . .
(a) feel awkward on your own but wait about twenty minutes?
(c) wait a few minutes then walk out in a temper?
(b) decide to enjoy yourself anyway and catch a nice boy's eye?
(d) feel too embarrassed on your own, so go outside to wait?

9. You're having a colossal row with your parents and have just threatened to leave home. What's the most likely cause?
(b) Their strictness. They won't give you enough freedom.
(c) Money. The pocket money you get, or the board you pay from what you earn.
(a) Boyfriend trouble. They don't like your latest, or think you're too serious.
(d) The state you leave your room in, or not helping enough around the house.

Right, that's all for this section, but you haven't finished yet. Score 1 for every "d" answer, 2 for "a's", 3 for "b"s and 4 for "c"s. OK?
If you're between 9 and 15, go on to section H.
If you're between 16 and 22, go on to section E.
If you're between 23 and 29, go on to section F.
If you're between 30 and 36, go on to section G.

SECTION E.

10. When you play Monopoly, what symbol would you choose?
(x) racing car
(w) top hat
(y) boot
(z) thimble

OUR SUPERQUIZ REVEAL?

11. The smashing new bus conductor has short-changed you by 10p. Would you . . .
(y) ask him in a jokey way if he's saving up for something special?
(x) point out the mistake immediately you notice it — with a smile?
(z) say nothing and hope it was a genuine mistake?
(w) ask in a quiet voice, just before you get off the bus, if he's made a mistake over the change?

12. At a wedding reception, you're dancing in a Paul Jones. After dancing with a big fat man, over twice your age, your next partner is much more your style and you'd like to get to know him. Chatting him up, you remark he's quite a change from the awful elephant who reduced your feet to jelly. He tells you the fat man is his dad. What do you do?
(x) say calmly, "Yes, I see it now — you both have the same marvellous smile!"
(z) pass hurriedly on to your next partner
(y) say "Well, you're lighter on my feet than your dad was!"
(w) say "Well, don't tell him what I said. I'm sure he didn't mean to tread on my toes!"

13. You ring up to answer an ad. for a job you like the sound of. Only when you put down the receiver you realise you've forgotten to ask for the address. Would you . . .
(y) ring up, pretending to be someone else?
(x) ring up and say *they* forgot to give you the address?
(w) ring up and admit you forgot to ask for the address?
(z) forget the whole thing?

14. A friend has a juicy piece of information but before she tells you, she swears you to secrecy. Do you . . .
(x) intend to keep the secret but know

you might blurt it out in a heated moment?
(y) ask her to keep it to herself as you never could keep a secret?
(w) make the promise and keep it?
(z) feel flattered that anyone should want to tell you a secret?

Finished? Right, which letter appears most among your answers? If it's W, your key letter is H; if it's X, your key letter is D; if it's Y, your key letter is K; and if it's Z, your key letter is S. Now turn to page 66 and look up your key letter to see what you can find out about yourself!

SECTION F.
15. There's an unexpected power failure one night when you're alone in the house. Then a knock comes to

the door, though you're not expecting callers. So you . . .
(w) pretend the house is empty.
(y) shout out "Go away or I'll set our vicious guard dog on you!" (you don't even have a pet goldfish.)
(z) rush to the door and hope it's a policeman with a torch.
(x) think it's probably someone collecting for charity, but light a candle and answer the door calmly.

16. Your joker of a boy friend puts his arm round you while wearing one of those hideous, hairy plastic hands with claws. When you've stopped screaming what's your likeliest reaction?
(z) tick him off, angrily.
(w) burst into tears.
(y) borrow it to frighten your mum or kid brother.
(x) laugh and forget it.

17. You've missed the last bus and in order to get home before midnight

and avoid a lot of trouble you must take one of these alternatives:
(x) take a short cut through the old haunted cemetery.
(w) ring for a mini-cab
(z) ask the police to get you home in time.
(y) thumb a lift.

18. When you come back after a week's holiday, your boy friend confesses he's been out with a girl or two. Would you . . .
(y) invent some dishy male conquests to show him you had just as good a time as he did?
(x) tell him you didn't expect him to stay at home with his knitting?
(z) smile sweetly and say you hope he had a good time but secretly hope he was bored stiff?
(w) cross-examine him on who and where and finally dissolve into tears or have a flaming row about it?

19. Money is taken from your pocket while you are having lunch at school or factory canteen. A girl you don't like very much has recently moaned about being hard up. Would you think . . .
(z) she must have taken the money and accuse her outright?
(y) she may have taken the money but you can't prove it?
(x) anyone could have taken the money and it's just as likely to be someone else?
(w) it's unimportant who took the money — it's your fault for leaving it carelessly around?

Jotted down your answers? Which letter have you written most? Ws take O as their key letter; Xs take P; Ys have M; and Zs, your letter is R. See what is said about you on page 26/27/28!

♥

159

SECTION G.

20. You and a girl-friend sneak into an X-certificate film for a giggle but get spotted by a neighbour coming out. Her parents think it's a joke, but yours throw a blue fit and ban you from seeing your friend ever again. It's unfair, but what do you do about it?

(x) sulk and throw tantrums till the ban is lifted.

(w) argue constantly about it, trying to keep your temper and pointing out it was more your idea than hers in the first place.

(y) let the whole thing cool down before raising the subject quietly.

(z) admit you were wrong but say their reaction is stupid and refuse to give up your friend.

21. Your girl friend is crazy about a boy she met at a party in a friend's house. He was only in town on a visit and lives 200 miles away. What do you advise?

(w) keep in touch by letter and phone.

(x) go for a visit next weekend.

(z) forget all about him.

(y) get a job in the town where he lives.

22. Your boy's supposed to be at evening classes and you spot him having a cosy cuppa with a girl who used to be at school with you. Would you . . .

(z) pretend not to notice him till the last moment, then say "Oh, I'm glad I've seen you. I shan't be able to make our date tomorrow"?

(w) go up to the girl and ask what she's been doing with herself since she left school "five years ago, wasn't it" (although you know quite well it was only two)?

(y) wave to him and try not to torture yourself until you've heard his explanation?

(x) march in and "accidentally" knock a cup of coffee over the girl?

23. An argument with your boyfriend develops into a blazing row. But after you cool off, you find out you had your facts all wrong. Later, when he calls round to see you . . .

(w) you yell at him some more to cover your confusion and say he had no business shouting at you in the first place?

(x) you don't want to admit being in the wrong but make up the quarrel without really apologising?

(y) you make up first — admit your mistake later?

(z) you humbly admit your mistake and explain you must have got your facts mixed up?

24. You're going to share a flat with three other girls and you agree to make a few rules everyone must stick to. Which of these rules would you put forward to make it easier for everyone to get along?

(y) share everything, bills and chores.

(x) everyone choose a chore and stick to it.

(w) no borrowing other people's things.

(z) the one who makes the mess cleans it up.

Look over your answers. Which letter appears most? If it's W, your key letter is A; if it's X, your key letter is V; if you've more Ys than anything else, your key letter is E; and if you've two or more Zs, your key letter is T. Now look up your key letter on page 66.

SECTION H.

25. Your boyfriend remarks how pretty a certain girl is. Do you . . .

(x) take it as a challenge and really put yourself out to keep his interest?

(y) agree with him and say she's a bit like his sister (provided he has one)?

(z) admit she's prettier than you are?

(w) let it ruin your evening?

26. On a long train journey, do you . . .

(y) chat to fellow passengers if they talk to you first?

(x) get stuck into a magazine or paperback?

(w) start chatting to the person next to you?

(z) dream out of the window?

27. You know for a fact your bloke dated another girl while you were out of town. So he's for it! How does he get the message?

(w) face to face?

(x) by phone?

(z) via a friend?

(y) a "Dear John" letter?

28. Imagine you have an older sister who is prettier, cleverer and more talented than you, but is nice with it. One day you overheard your mother telling a friend she wished you were more like your sister. Would your reaction be . . .

(y) to go upstairs and tear something of your sister's into tiny shreds in an uncontrollable fit of temper?

(z) to burst into tears and tell Mum you wished you could leave home and never come back?

(x) to burst into tears, but keep it to yourself?

(w) to decide to ask your sister's help in making the best of yourself in future?

29. If your boyfriend rings up to break a date because he has to take his mother to hospital, would you . . .

(w) ask him to meet you when he IS free?

(y) offer to go along too for moral support?

(z) think it's an excuse & he's really meeting another girl?

(x) tell him all about the time YOU had to go to hospital?

Look over your answers for this section and see which letter appears most. W? Then your key letter is L. X? Your key letter is C. Two or more Ys means your key letter is G. If you've put down more Zs your key letter is B. Now turn to pages 26/27 to see a picture of yourself.

Elton talking colourfully.

I looked at the towel and thought "Oh no!"

AS you know, Elton John likes to look spectacular when he's on stage. And unlike a lot of pop stars, that doesn't mean he just wears outrageous clothes—for Elton also creates his own fashion in specs and hairstyles!

"Everybody wears beautiful clothes nowadays," explained Elton. "So I just take it a stage further!"

When I spoke to him, Elton's hair was looking a fairly normal fairish brown colour, except for a small green streak above his ears—but at various times during the last couple of years, he's had it about every colour of the rainbow!

"I think hair's such a boring colour normally," said Elton. "Why shouldn't it be orange or green for a change? I think hair that matches your clothes looks rather good!

"To get it done like that, they bleach it first of all, then they paint it the colour you want—they use Dulux!

"No, seriously, they do it with carpet dye or something like that. It fades out after a few weeks. I remember I once had it done in New York and they really made a mess of it.

"I decided I wanted it green, and they'd never done it before. They thought I was stark raving mad! After they'd done it, they told me not to wash my hair for three days to let all the green settle in.

"So there I was, walking round for three days with filthy hair. On the first hour of the fourth day I leapt in the shower and washed it.

"I came out of the shower and rubbed my hair dry. Then I looked at the towel—green towel—and I looked at my hair—white hair!

"So I took it back!"

Now Elton makes sure his hair is done right by going to the same place every time.

"I always go to Smile in London," he said. "They're very good there—they know exactly what I want."

If you're looking at Elton's hair, you can't help noticing the other things that distinguish him at eye level—his specs!

"I first started wearing them when I was at school," explained Elton. "My hero at that time was Buddy Holly—and so I was thrilled to wear specs just like he did!

"Then I decided that if I was going to have to wear them, they might as well look interesting!

"My glasses are all my own creations. I think up the designs, and I get them made up for me at a place in Los Angeles called the Optic Boutique. I have about thirty pairs in all sorts of different colours, and my current favourites are a steaming hot pair that light up in the dark!".

BUT although his hair and specs are outrageous enough, what Elton really goes to town on is his clothes!

"I'm really into suits just now," he said. "Ties, jackets—the whole bit. In fact I have about six suits that I've just bought in Paris, in a place called the Box Shop.

"The jackets fitted me really well, but the trousers were a bit big, so my mum altered them to fit me.

"As far as my stage stuff goes, I get it all specially made up for me. I have several clothes designers who work for me, but a girl called Anne Meesey makes most of my clothes at the moment. She makes them all out of her own head.

"I'd rather designers did that actually, because I'm not much use. Anyway, they get more fun out of it when they can decide things for themselves!"

Every time we see Elton, he seems to be wearing something different! So, I wondered, did he know exactly how many clothes he had?

"Actually, I've got a very good brain for things like **that**," he said. "I know what I've got.

"For instance, I have 300 shirts—but that's counting tee-shirts! I also have about fifty pairs of shoes.

"The only problem with my clothes is that I have a constant battle for space, so every few months I have a grand clean-out.

"Every time I have a clear-out, all my relatives gather—and then they all go to work wearing Lurex suits and platform shoes!"

Well, I bet it brightens up the commuters' Monday mornings!

A

IS FOR ALLIGATOR. Surprised at the description? Not as much as the people who took you for a harmless piece of floating driftwood and got the shock of their lives when they found out how you can bite. You're tough-skinned and though you don't go looking for a fight, when the occasion demands you're a match for most and don't care too much who you hurt.

Temperamentally, you'd suit a post with responsibility. You could make a capable, boss-shielding personal assistant, hold down a job in Public Relations or do well in the Police or Women's Services.

B

IS FOR BEAR. The Teddy type, rather than a fierce, snarling Grizzly. Maybe a little of Goldilocks' charm rubbed off, because boys find you attractive. You've strength in the things that matter most, without making a big thing about it, and you have a relaxed, cool, almost playful attitude which inspires confidence.

Jobs? You can adapt to many careers, but might be happiest in some branch of nursing. Other recommended jobs are in the domestic field — cook, waitress, nursery assistant.

C

IS FOR CHAMELEON. Do you sometimes feel invisible when trying to attract someone's attention? You're so good-mannered and good-natured you've got into the habit of merging into the background. But you have a brighter side under the surface and you're young enough to develop it. For starters now and then try unleashing that temper you keep under such strict control.

Career? If you're good with your hands, you'll find hairdressing or window display rewarding.

D

IS FOR DOLPHIN. You're sympathetic, intelligent and popular, although people don't always understand you. At the same time, you're a bit dreamy and idealistic, assuming people have purer motives than they actually do.

If you're keen on books, you could be an excellent librarian. You like meeting people and you'd also find job satisfaction in a bank or as a sales assistant.

E

IS FOR EAGLE. You're an unusual combination, someone with lofty principles who's a highflier in the career sense. Your main fault is being a perfectionist and trying to handle too much on your own. Popularity doesn't bother you, which is just as well. Ambition, capacity for hard work and desire for success could push you well up the Civil Service ladder, say. You'd make a respected, though, bossy, school-teacher, but your real niche could be in an unusual job connected with long-distance travel. Air Stewardess, travel courier, Air traffic controller, perhaps?

G

IS FOR GOOSE. A highly-strung, excitable aggressive bird, according to those who know, often found wild or flapping about in rage or panic. Sometimes blessed with artistic talent, they are happy in the Art and Design field. They usually prefer a job without too much responsibility as they have a periodic urge to see what's over the next hill. But once the wanderlust is over they settle down contentedly. Well, you've heard of Mother Goose, haven't you?

ANIMAL ARE YOU?

— But you can only find out once you complete our Superquiz on page 38. Otherwise, shield your eyes, dear reader, and pass on.

IS FOR LAMB. You belie your fluffy appearance and people who try to mother or protect you can be taken aback when they find out you're tougher than you look. Over-conscientious in some matters, you tend to follow the flock and you wouldn't be fleeced so easily if there was more of the black sheep about you.

You'd be happiest working at an open-air job. If you have an affinity with animals, a vet's assistant or animal nursing auxiliary job would be right up your country lane.

IS FOR OCTOPUS. Not by any means the sea monster from 100 fathoms with cruel beak and plastic suckers. Generally neighbourly and harmless, more scared than scary. But when she senses competition her instinct tells her to hang on for dear life. In the last resort a diversion of tears can be turned on at will. And when she gets a crush on someone, it can be fatal — for him!

A backroom job would keep her happy — scientific assistant or technician. She often has a knack with machinery and would make a good assembly worker or comptometer operator.

IS FOR HORSE. A stable personality and often a thoroughbred, it's no wonder you're popular. If you bite or kick, it's usually with good reason. You take hurdles in your stride and come equipped with a fair helping of horse sense. You don't mind being saddled with responsibility, have the patience to be a good teacher and would suit most jobs where integrity and getting on well with people counts.

IS FOR MONKEY. A real swinger, aren't you! Playful, confident and a bit of a rebel, you're a terror to timid teachers. You have a following of what you take to be admirers but really they're only hanging around to see what new chaos will result.

If you've the talent, you'd perform well on some branch of showbiz. Jobs involving demonstration or interviewing the public would appeal to the exhibitionist in you.

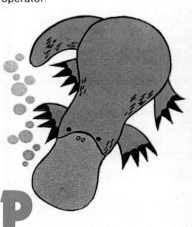

IS FOR PLATYPUS. Look it up, then, and you'll find it's an incredible freak of nature which has a bill like a duck, burrows, lays eggs, yet suckles its young. The original mixed-up kid, in fact. But don't feel so sorry for yourself. All it means is that you haven't developed your adult personality yet. We can't advise on a possible career, either, so wait a few months before you tackle the quiz again.

IS FOR KINGFISHER. You're quick-witted, colourful, like to make a splash and there's an engaging cheekiness about you. Yet there's another romantic, dreamy side which only close friends get to know.

Work in a travel agency, busy hotel, newspaper office or any place which has an atmosphere of excitement would suit you.

HAVE YOU EVER MADE A MISTAKE YOU'D GIVE A YEAR OF YOUR LIFE TO UNDO?

On-The-Spot Interviews

My biggest mistake was having a row with my boy friend Larry. I thought we'd make it up next time we met but he'd already found someone else. Yes, I'd give more than a year of my life to get him back.
Christine Sanderson, Vine Ave., Sevenoaks, Kent.

I was going to this super party and knew the boy I fancied would be there. When I woke up that morning I had a little pimple coming on the side of my mouth. I made the mistake of squeezing it and by evening it was huge and my cheek was all red. I just couldn't go to the party, which I've always regretted.
Cindy Boycott, Vicarage Road, Croydon.

I had the chance to go to France for a year in exchange for a French girl coming to stay with my folk. I refused just because I couldn't bear the thought of some strange girl sleeping in my bed, reading my books, playing my records. That was two years ago and now I realise that an idiot I was and what a chance I missed. I'd give a year of my life, I think, to have the opportunity again.
Diane Crimp, Shelvers Gardens, Tadworth, Surrey.

I was helping Mum with my little brother's party. When the mothers came to collect their kids, one asked how they'd behaved. "Oh, they've all been good," I said breezily, "except for that little horror there." To my horror, it was her son!
Celia Cross, Addison Road, Kensington.

My big mistake was refusing to go out with Martin because he had spots. That was two years ago and now I do go out with him and he's great fun. I missed two years of fun and happiness, so I'd give one for my mistake.
Kay Millard, 12 Axes Lane, Salford.

After a big bust-up at home, I ran away to London and got fixed up with a shared flat and a job in a greengrocer's. Within a week I knew I'd made a mistake but I had too much pride to write home until six months later. I'd give much more than a year to turn back the clock. When I finally plucked up courage to go home I found my mother had died two weeks before.
Liz M., Whifflet, Coatbridge, Lanarkshire.

I went steady with Pete for three years and we planned to get engaged. Then I realised it was all a mistake, I didn't love him enough. I knew he was awfully hurt and that's why I' give a year of my life to undo the mistake of going steady at 14.
Sue Palmer, Cecil Road, Birmingham.

WELL, WHAT KIND OF ANIMAL ARE YOU?

T IS FOR TIGER. A strong, smooth relaxed man-eater, you know what you want and intend to get it. You're not immune from Cupid's darts, however, and if one gets under your skin causing you to lose your self-control, you could be your own worst enemy.

You're efficient and conscientious enough to make a go of most jobs but you're likely to end up in something out of the ordinary. Three suggestions in varying fields are physiotherapist, beauty consultant, receptionist/telephonist.

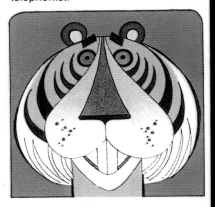

R IS FOR RHINO. Do you find life a series of angry confrontations? Do you tread on toes as you blunder along and cause upsets as you try to explain? Then welcome to the club. Your excellent intentions have a habit of not turning out as planned.

You do have a knack of getting things done, however, which is a consolation when thinking about a job. With your tough hide and boundless energy you could quickly make a supervisory grade. Remember, counting to ten is important in more jobs than a boxing referee!

S IS FOR SQUIRREL. Happiest amongst your own family tree or with a small circle of trusted friends. Apart from a hoarding instinct, you have a great sense of balance which will take you out of many a tight spot.

Jobs? You're neat and a hard worker so bank teller, office cashier and hospital technician are three jobs which suggest themselves. That's it in a nutshell.

V IS FOR VIXEN. Peope who think of you as cunning have the wrong idea. You're just impulsive with a fierce desire to protect those you love. To that end you'd tackle anyone or anything and your friends know better than to take liberties if you're in a fighting mood.

You're quick-witted and occasionally have ingenious ideas or flashes of insight. A normal nine-to-five job doesn't seem right for you. How does being a girl reporter, dress designer, circus acrobat, skating instructor or store security detective grab you?

WOOL DONE!

JACKIE FASHION

EVER thought of all the things you could do with those odd bits of wool? We got to thinking . . . and came up with loads of great ideas like fringing your woollies and scarves and making woolly belts and things.

All you'll need is some wool and a crochet hook . . . have fun.

Put it around the V-neck of your cardigan to make a super furry collar.

Buy 4 or 5 balls of double knitting wool and a crochet hook and put this furry fringing on your woollies. Choose bright colours!

Cut the wool into 12cm lengths. Pick up 4 strands and fold them in half. (1) Push your crochet hook into the garment you're adding the fringing to and underneath one strand of wool (2) Catch the folded strands with your hook and pull them through (3) Repeat this with the rest of the cut wool, fastening each one by looping the loose ends under the folded ends and pulling tight (4) Make each tuft about 1cm apart.

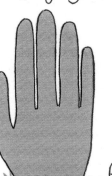

Put it around the wrists of your gloves

or around the cuffs of your jumper.

Put a big cluster on top of your hat, or around the edge.

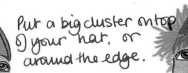

Plait a belt, using double strands of wool, each 2m. long, and sew fringing onto the last 5 cm.

or plait 3 strands of wool, each 1m. long and thread the plait with a darning needle thro' the wrist of a glove - fringe the ends and tie it in a bow.

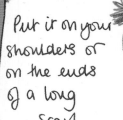

Put it on your shoulders or on the ends of a long scarf.

AN OSMOND A DAY

Monday's child is fair of face,
Tuesday's child is full of grace,
Wednesday's child is full of woe,
Thursday's child has far to go,
Friday's child is loving and giving,
Saturday's child works hard for its living,
And a child that is born on the Sabbath day,
Is fair and wise and good and gay.

You're probably already familiar with this old rhyme — most of us in the Jackie office can remember learning it when we were little.

Of course, we've never taken it too seriously — it's really just for fun. But it occurred to us recently that there are seven singing Osmonds — one for every day of the week. So, just for fun, we decided to see if the family fitted the rhyme. And, to our surprise, they seemed to fit remarkably well — see if you agree!

MONDAY

The rest of the family may be handsome, but there's really only one Osmond who fits the description "fair of face"! Yes, of course, Marie, the only Osmond sister.

Marie certainly does fit the rhyme! It's a safe bet that lots of girls would give anything to have her clear complexion, lovely brown eyes and long shining dark hair.

And not only is she blessed with those natural good looks that all the Osmonds have — she also knows how to make the best of herself. She has her own range of cosmetics specially designed for young teenage girls. They're produced organically, which means they don't contain any animal fats.

Marie says she likes to look casual when she's at home, but she still loves to dress up for special occasions.

One thing's certain though — whatever she's wearing, she always looks just right!

THURSDAY

"Thursday's child has far to go" — this just has to be Wayne!

All the Osmonds enjoy travelling and meeting new people, but Wayne is undoubtedly the most adventurous. He loves exploring — both new places and new ideas. And he has a wide range of interests outside music.

Recently, he became interested in ancient Egyptian history, and when we last met up with him, he explained he had been reading all he could on the subject. Another of his interests is the geography of Europe — and he loves coming over to see for himself all the places he can otherwise only see in photographs.

Unlike his brothers, Wayne isn't content to settle down at home when he and his brothers have some time to spend on their ranch in Utah. He likes to get away — to explore the countryside surrounding the family home. And, to do this, he has his very own plane to fly around in — a Cessna 150. He's a fully qualified pilot, and says he likes nothing better than to take off for a few hours at a time.

So you see, Wayne has far to go — in more ways than one!

FRIDAY

"Loving and giving" — we think the Osmond who fits this description best is Jay.

When you first meet him, Jay seems to be rather quiet. As the drummer, he tends to be the man at the back, perhaps not noticed as much as the 'front-line' of the group.

But once you get to know him, you realise there are hidden depths to Jay's character. For instance, he's very affectionate — it's Jay who looks after the family pets, and he's always the one who's the most upset if a beloved dog or cat becomes ill.

In complete contrast, Jay is also the joker of the group. The others may groan and tell how awful his jokes are — but they know when they're feeling depressed, Jay will be there, cheering them again by making them laugh.

And we can't think of anything better to give than that — a little happiness.

TUESDAY

"Full of grace" — in the rhyme, grace is used in the old-fashioned sense, meaning good manners and politeness.

Of course, the Osmonds are all very polite, but since we've to pick out one person, we'd choose Merrill as Tuesday's child.

Merrill is the diplomat of the group — when you first meet the Osmonds, it's Merrill who's usually first to say hello and introduce himself. He's always pleased to tell you all about what he and his brothers have been doing — and if you're lucky enough to meet them again, Merrill's sure to remember having spoken to you before.

He's one of the quieter members of the family, with a soft, gentle voice. His manner suggests he can sometimes be a bit shy — and that's why we were all especially pleased when, in the autumn of 1973, we heard that Merrill had fallen in love with a lovely girl called Mary, and that they were getting married.

Don't you feel pleased that such a nice guy has the happiness he deserves?

WEDNESDAY

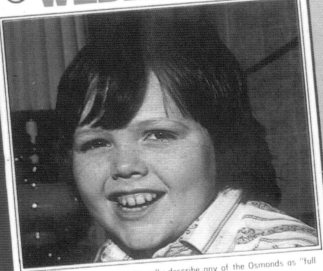

To be honest, we couldn't really describe any of the Osmonds as "full of woe" — because they are a happy family.

But if anybody fits the description, we'd say Jimmy does, simply because, up till now, he's sometimes had to be left out of things. He was just too young to join in everything his elder brothers and sister were doing.

And in a way that was good — because it made sure that Jimmy could be like any other little boy, with the normal boyish interests — football, toy cars and comics.

But now Jimmy is growing up and joining more and more in the group activities. As well as making his own solo records, he now tours with the group and appears on stage with the rest of the family.

So it looks as though he doesn't have much reason to be "full of woe" any longer!

SATURDAY

"Saturday's child works hard for his living" — although it's true that all the Osmonds work very hard, we reckon the hardest worker of all must be Alan.

He's the oldest of the group, so he tends to be the most responsible. He keeps an eye on his younger brothers, giving them advice when they need it, and making sure they keep out of mischief!

He's also the most dedicated musician in the family, and as well as lead guitar, he can also play the piano, saxophone, banjo and bass guitar.

Alan too is the main writer of the group, and he takes the tape to Los Angeles, and works on it until he's satisfied it sounds just right. The finished product is then put on record — and that's when we get to hear it!

On top of this, Alan now wants to involve himself more in filming. His big ambition is to direct an Osmond film.

We just don't know where he'll find the time!

SUNDAY

"And the child that is born on the Sabbath Day Is fair and wise and good and gay" — well we're sure there are plenty of readers who'd agree that Donny is all of those things!

When you meet Donny, it's easy to see why he's so popular. Since he first began to capture girls' hearts four years ago, he's changed tremendously. He's grown from a rather shy boy to a self-confident young man — and he's grown physically too. He's now tall and handsome and, we're sure you'll agree, even more beautiful than in the days of "Puppy Love" and "Too Young".

But Donny himself is basically still as charming and friendly as ever, with the same politeness that makes him so likeable. He always has a smile for everyone he meets, and if he gets fed up being asked the same questions over and over again, he never shows it.

Like the rest of his family, he really is a genuinely nice person — and that's why we love him!

How can you tell the difference?

As most girls probably know, you can love a guy without being 'In Love' with him. But what's the subtle difference that's really the great divide? Are you just a loving friend or are you fooling yourself and secretly in love with the guy? Answer these simple questions and find out.

When he walks into the room, do you
(a) Have to make a superhuman effort to appear normal, as your legs have gone weak and your head's so light you think you've just been deprived of your oxygen supply?
(b) Feel a pleasant sense of security and think it's nice to see him again?

When he makes a joke or a funny remark, do you
(a) Always laugh like a drain, just because he makes you feel so happy and bubbly you've got to let it out somehow?
(b) Laugh easily if the joke happens to be funny, but make a sarky comment if it isn't?

If your knees or hands accidentally brush, do you
(a) Leap away from the contact, as an electric shock has just zoomed through your senses?
(b) Feel warm and comfortable?

When somebody mentions his name in conversation, do you
(a) Immediately leap out of the deepest somnambulant trance and take a sudden enthusiastic interest in the conversation?
(b) Wonder what they're saying about him, and make it your business to find out?

When you're out with your friends, do you
(a) Proudly tell them his opinions, as if they've just been handed down from the Holy Grail?
(b) Tell your friends what he thinks, but make it clear that you don't always go along with his views?

If you see him dancing with another girl at the disco, do you
(a) Think it would be worth twelve years' solitary in Holloway for the pleasure of wringing her neck? Tell the bouncers to tear them bodily apart?
(b) Feel sure he'll come over to you when he's finished, and go off and dance with someone else yourself?

When he comes round to your house for tea, do you
(a) Leap about, running after him, until your mother's worried that you've undergone a serious personality change?
(b) Make him feel very welcome and expect him to help with the washing up?

When you're chatting with your friends, do you
(a) Subtly keep dropping his name into the conversation at every opportunity, until they get up a petition to Somerset House asking for his name to be struck off the records and made illegal?
(b) Or do some of them have to ask what he's called because they're not sure who you're going out with?

If you walk down the street and happen to bump into him
(a) Does the whole day suddenly become glittery and sparkling and do you feel tongue tied and very shy?
(b) Do you immediately feel more cheerful and ask him to have a cup of coffee with you?

If he mentions that he doesn't like skinny girls, do you
(a) Drink a bottle of Guinness a day, pinch other peoples' rolls in cafes, insist on chips with everything?
(b) Wear more clothes so he can't see what shape you are, buy a padded bra?

If he takes another girl home from the disco, do you
(a) Rush home and cry solidly for hours so that no-one's able to console you?
(b) Think you'll give him a row he'll never forget next time you see him. And gladly accept a lift from his friend?

If he says he hates fat girls, do you
(a) Go on a fast that Gandhi would admire?
(b) Promise yourself to diet next month and throw away your padded bra?

When you're out with him, do you
(a) Feel a tremendous exhilaration and excitement as if all life apart from him is just meaningless, drab, existence?
(b) Feel contented and happy, but sometimes wonder what other people are doing?

If you're going to a party together where your friends are going to be, do you
(a) Feel really proud and elated that they're going to see you together?
(b) Worry slightly about what their reaction to him will be, but tell yourself that you love him, so what does it matter what they think about him?

When he kisses you, do you feel
(a) As if the whole world is just made up of the two of you, and that nothing else exists except his kiss?
(b) Warm and cosy and romantic and loving?

CONCLUSIONS

If you've answered all A's, then yes, you're in love. You can tell the difference because all your senses are incredibly heightened. You're deeply aware of his every movement and feeling. Every moment that you're with him you feel on top of the world. You're a very lucky girl, because although your elation is often followed by deep depression, when things aren't working out, you're experiencing the most exciting emotion any human being can achieve.

All B's — You love your boy, but as you realise only too well, you're not in love. You need that extra excitement, that breathtaking tension that makes being in love so much less cosy and safe, but so much more rewarding!

A mixture of A's and B's — You're still not sure of your feelings. Although you love your boy you still don't feel ready to commit yourself totally and proclaim to the world that you're in love. At the moment you're playing it safe, but as time goes on you'll find your emotions taking over from your reason and your B responses turning into A's.

DO BOYS HAVE MORE FUN THAN GIRLS?
A JACKIE ON-THE-SPOT INTERVIEW.

Joan Curry, Hayes Drive, Barnton, Northwich, Cheshire.
Everything seems to be geared to boys having fun. Even at youth clubs there are lots of boys' games, like darts, and very little for the girls. There's not much to look forward to either. Marriage is the same idea, with the men going out to enjoy themselves, while women are tied at home with children.

John Lawless, Glebe House, Great Smeaton, Yorkshire.
I think it's about equal. Girls have a different idea of fun, that's all. Fellows like spending Saturday at a football match and sensible things like that — girls like to sit outside hotels all night hoping for a glimpse of the Osmonds. I think girls who complain about there not being equality are stupid — it's there if they want it.

Raymond, Penn Road, Wolverhampton.
Hard to say for sure, having never been a girl to test it out, but I reckon they have a far better time than us. They get taken out and paid for and bought presents. Then they can retire when they get someone to marry them, and spend their lives having fun, while the poor bloke has to slave away to support them!

Dianne Flynn, Purcell Road, Bell Green, Coventry.
You can't generalise. Life is what you make it, whatever your sex. I don't have any brothers, but my boy cousins don't get any more freedom than me and my sisters. I think you have to be sensible and come to an arrangement with your parents about where you can go and how late you can stay out.

Cathy McDonald, Mains East, East Kilbride, Glasgow.
Boys have it made before marriage, and after. They can ask up any girl at a dance or disco. All we can do is dance with friends or be wallflowers. And until kids come along, most girls have to keep on their jobs when they marry, as well as look after a house. If husbands are asked to dry dishes they think they're being hard done by.

Sue Brown, Lansdown Road, Bath, Somerset.
People are all different. I've known some girls who give you the impression of being very dull and stuffy but are great fun once the barriers are down. It's just that they get their enjoyment in more serious, introspective things. Certainly it's easier for a boy to have fun in a rowdy way than a girl — at least in this area!

Fiona Lawson, Easson's Angle, Dundee.
They certainly ought to — they don't have to sit around hoping someone will ask them out. That's one thing I'd really enjoy, being able to ask a boy I fancied for a date. All a girl can do is try to be noticed. The other week I was trying to catch the eye of a boy who worked in a newsagents. It cost me a fortune in magazines, with nothing to show for it.

Frances Connolly, Queens Drive, Liverpool.
No, I think girls have more fun. We're more light-hearted. I work with a crowd of girls and we never stop laughing, mostly about boys and their funny little ways. Boys are too intense. They turn any casual discussion into a heated argument, particularly if it's about sport.

Cathy Cleer, Parade Street, Passage East, County Waterford, Ireland.
Yes, boys get away with murder. If a boy has a dozen girls on a string everyone thinks he's great. If a girl acts like that, she is something unmentionable. I think things are getting better, though. Girls are getting not to feel so downtrodden.

Pauline, Greenbank Road, Darlington.
I enjoy being a girl, as the song says, and I don't think I've missed out on much fun. I think, though, some girls envy boys their freedom. A boy can walk into a pub or a club on his own and have a good time, but it takes much more nerve for a girl to do it. So girls tend to stay home if they haven't a boy to take them out.

A CATHY AND CLAIRE SPECIAL
CONFIDENCE
AND HOW TO GET IT!

PHOTO BY JEANY

IT makes all the difference between success . . . and failure, happiness . . . and despair, a full social life . . . and a diary of blank pages! It's CONFIDENCE. But never give up — even if you feel you haven't as much as a shred of the stuff to your name. Although some lucky people do seem to be born with it, ANYONE can acquire it!

Here's another good thing to bear in mind. A girl can't successfully PRETEND she's slim — when her hips are a robust 40 inches, plain for all to see! But *confidence* — or lack of it — is a personal, not a physical quality. You can PRETEND to a lot more confidence than you've actually got. In fact, if you keep on pretending long enough, you'll get so good at it, you will actually BE more confident.

So the first rule is — NEVER ADMIT HOW NERVOUS YOU FEEL. Not even to a best friend! It undermines what confidence you do have, and even best friends have been known to let you down. They'll maybe let slip, right in front of the gang, how you nearly didn't come to the party because you felt your knees knocking so much — and you'll feel so stupid, it will take a lot more courage to drag you out of your shell next time a party's in the offing!

For the same reason, NEVER UNDER-SELL YOUSELF. You know — none better — if your hair is like a hay-rick, face more spotty than a currant cake, etc.,etc. But most people will be far too busy worrying about their own looks to make a very close study of yours! So if you don't moan in public about the way your hair looks, and providing it's not actually three inches deep in grease, you'll get by!

DO THE BEST YOU CAN . . . AND THEN FORGET IT

OF course, some things are bound to nibble away at a girl's self-confidence. If you're worried that your breath may be a wee bit stale, or feel a wave of perspiration come on and wonder nervously if there'll be a wet patch under your arm . . . you can't look poised and calm!

So, when you're out to develop confidence, the very first things to tackle are the basic, simple things that affect you physically. People who are lacking in confidence and easily upset do tend to suffer more with bad breath and body odour problems than anybody else. It's no good leaving it and hoping things will be all right. Take precautions, first!

There are lots of products which deal efficiently with bad breath when nerves are the cause. You can get breath-freshening tablets (Amplex), capsules, sprays (Gold Spot), liquids and mouthwashes (Vademecum). Just try one or two, find which you like best for taste and performance, and use them regularly before nerve-racking personal appearances!

Of course, you must be CERTAIN that another cause of your bad breath isn't a tummy upset or dental decay, but the signs of either of those are pretty obvious, and in that case a fast visit to the doc. or dentist are called for!

Perspiration and body odour is easier to solve than suffer with. A daily all-over wash with a reliable brand of soap, either deodorant or a general family soap bar, is a must, plus a reliable anti-perspirant for under-arms, a spray for feet, and a third one for body use.

There are lots of brands available, and some work better for different people, depending on your body chemistry. We're sure you'll be kept cool and dry if you pick from Cool, Mum, Femfresh or Sure. Just remember that if the product is to work, it must be applied to clean, dry skin, and sprayed from a distance of eight to twelve inches, in a short, quick burst! Underarm hair should be removed 12-24 hours beforehand, too.

Spots can make you shy of taking your face out of doors — so do something about them, too. If you can't put a finger between them, you'd best see your doctor because there are now medically-prescribed treatments which might work wonders — he'll know what's best.

If there aren't THAT many, but still enough to make you wish masks were in fashion, follow a strict rule of spot treatment, being careful not to eat too many greasy foods, using a good spot-healing cream on your skin, and deal with a greasy complexion with an astringent solution such as in the Innoxa 41 range.

Practise, in spare time, until you can do a really good camouflage job on the nastier spots. Here's how! First dry out the surface by patting it with Innoxa 41 lotion, or TCP or even a dab of cologne (provided the spot isn't open or bleeding). Then put a tiny dab of spot cream in the centre, choosing a cream that matches your skin tone, of course.

Gently pat it outwards until it blends with your skin at the edges, but remains sufficiently thick in the middle to hide the spot. Let it dry for at least two minutes. Film on your usual light skin make-up, all over your face, spot and all. When THAT is set, dab a LITTLE transparent powder over the spot — it'll prevent any grease seeping through. But only apply this rather heavy make-up treatment to bad spots, and never leave it on for more than a few hours without thorough cleansing and a fresh make-up.

"Thank goodness — it's only measles!"

Hair a worry? If it's constantly a headache, get some advice from a sympathetic hair-stylist. If it is totally unmanageable, it means you are either using completely wrong products for the degree of dryness or greasiness your hair displays, or you have chosen a hairstyle which is unsuitable for the texture of your particular hair. A change — or changes — are called for!

Having sorted out the Big Four, and done the best you can for face and hair, don't give yourself a second thought. Force yourself to stop carrying a small portmanteau with your make-up needs in

it! Break the habit of looking in every mirror you pass, staring in shop windows for a glimpse of your reflection, dashing for the loo at every chance, and fiddling with your hair in between times.

If you've done the best you can, you won't improve things with odd dabs and touches while you are out, and you simply make yourself look more nervous and self-conscious, and draw attention to any teeny little faults! So . . . FORGET YOURSELF.

BOYS ARE HUMAN TOO!

THE main idea in developing confidence, of course, is to help you get and keep a boyfriend! If you're very shy, the very idea of being left alone with a BOY is enough to frighten you into fits, and you feel certain you'd never manage to say anything to keep him interested for five minutes, let alone a whole evening!

But there is truly nothing to be scared about. In fact, boys are usually much less self-confident than girls, only they hide it better! All you really have to remember is that most boys dislike extremes — the girl who never says a word, and also the one who never leaves off! And they don't like a false, insincere approach, either.

Also, they're totally against being made to look stupid, so you don't have to bash your brain to a jelly thinking of smart things to say, because the average chap would rather HE made the funnies!

In other words, all a boy wants is someone to boost HIS self-confidence — and that's very easy. Give him a nice, friendly smile, show interest in the things he wants to talk about, and you'll hardly need to open your mouth to keep the evening going nicely. If he's a boy who finds talking difficult, you may need to give him a starter, but again, you don't have to think of anything terribly clever.

Ask him how his football team is doing, or if his car is running well, or if he liked the telly programme last night, something like that. It's best to keep off anything which might be embarrassingly personal till you get to know him.

The problem may be that you don't seem to have much chance of talking to a boy . . . because you never get one to yourself. The difficulty here is working up enough confidence to make contact — but it can be done. Don't aim too high — try to get on friendly terms with any boys there may be, even if they aren't the sort you particularly want to date!

Smile at the paper-boy — exchange a few words with the milkman — have a greeting ready for the fellas who live or work nearby. Eventually, it comes naturally, and you'll find that when someone you WOULD like to date makes an approach, you have the confidence to answer back!

YOUR DAILY CHALLENGE

The important thing about confidence is that, like a precious plant, it must be tended every day! Then, showing a poised and confident face to the world becomes second nature. Make a list of all the things you would seriously like to be able to do, but feel you are much too shy to tackle. It might go something like this — put the list in order of difficulty, by the way, as it applies to *you*.

1. Speak up for yourself when ticked off in class
2. Go up to a girl you know by sight and make friends with her
3. Join a club or social group

4. Go to dances
5. Be more friendly with the boys in your group
6. Be able to talk to a boy in a natural way

Start with the easiest item on the list, and work at it. You don't have to plunge in and do the whole thing in one go! But each time a situation comes up when shyness in that department causes a problem, try to take one more step forward in overcoming it.

When you really feel you are able to deal with it without too much embarrassment, tick that item off and start working on the next one. The first two or three stages may seem to go awfully slowly, and it may seem impossible that you'll ever be able to tackle the more difficult things, but it really does get easier all the time, and suddenly you'll get the hang of the game, and swoop through the last ones quite quickly!

As well as this, make it a game to do SOMETHING to beat that nervousness, every day. There are perfectly ordinary things you can quite easily do which help to get you used to talking to people and standing up for yourself.

Go out on your own more, to shops, libraries and launderettes. When you have a job to do, you don't worry so much about confidence — it's not like going to a dance on your own, with nothing to do but prop up the wall! And the more you talk to people, the easier it will be, later on, to talk to BOYS.

Join in with school clubs as much as possible. Yes, even if the subject doesn't specially interest you! It's good to have a wide circle of acquaintances — lots of the girls will have brothers — and having more interests makes you a more interesting person. You may be glad you have a sketchy idea about stamp collecting some day, when you are on a date with a boy whose hobby this is, and there is a gap in the conversation!

Finally — BELIEVE IN YOURSELF. When you think seriously about the things that handicapped people can manage to do, you will realise that it doesn't take THAT much effort for you, with good health, a normal brain and the right number of arms and legs to do ordinary things like making friends, talking to people and going out to enjoy yourself.

You can do it . . . so why not start today? You can develop confidence more quickly than you can develop a perfect figure, and once you've got confidence, unlike people with figure problems, you never lose it! ●

I LET MY PARENTS RUIN EVERYTHING!

I WAS never one for saying goodbye, Pete, and I'm not proud of the way I said it to you. I mean, in the middle of the High Street, on a busy Saturday morning: it was a bit much really. I didn't offer any explanation, didn't give you a chance to talk about your side of things. I just dropped my bombshell and walked away from you.

By now you'll have guessed that my parents were to blame. You know they were never keen to meet you. I told you that, as I told you everything.

"Dashwood Road he comes from, you say? That's not a nice end of town, Margaret." I can hear my dad saying it now.

"Oh Dad, don't be ridiculous," I said. "I'm not going out with a road, I'm going out with a boy. And he's nice, you'll see."

Then he'd replied: "I can't pretend I'm happy about it, Margaret."

Mum was no better, although I'd expected a bit of support from her. "I know these Dashwood Boys have an exciting air about them, Margaret, and no doubt your friends think it's very daring of you. A sort of challenge to be dating one of them. But mark my words, these roughnecks just don't mix with our sort of people."

"Will you please stop judging Pete before you've even met him?" I demanded. "He's not a roughneck — he's a quiet, decent boy and he means a lot to me. You'll like him too if you'll just let yourselves forget that he lives in a council house!"

That was a bit underhand of me, because Mum and Dad used to live in a council house until, in Mum's words, they "bettered themselves" and bought the pokey little semi-detached we live in now. I knew what Mum meant by "our sort of people" — small-minded snobs who were always trying to "keep up with the Joneses" and thought they were better than everyone else. Well, I didn't want to be one of them.

And it wasn't as if I'd suddenly sprung the news of you on to them, Pete. I led up to it for ages. They knew we were in the same tutorial group at school; they knew we were both involved in forming the fifth-year Drama Society; they knew our friendship had gradually deepened into something more. But they wouldn't accept it.

I guess that, as long as they never actually met you, they could put you out of their minds. After all, it must be quite a wrench for devoted parents when their only child gets her first serious boyfriend. They probably torture themselves thinking that she's going to up and leave them all alone in their old age.

It's all so silly. I kept telling them that marriage just wasn't in our minds. Certainly not for years yet. We both want to go on to college, which means that we'd have to rely on parental support for quite a while yet! But right now we're in love, we need each other. Surely a mother would understand that?

I even tried talking to Mum about her own first love, trying to get things across to her. I told her that I realised our love might not last forever. I mean, it's real and serious while it's happening, like with you and me just now, Pete; but let's face it, most people go through the same sort of thing — at least a few times, before they finally settle down for life.

Not Mum, though. She swore that she'd only ever loved Dad — and that was since she was thirteen years old!

So I tried to explain instead about how good you and I were for each other, Pete. How you made me happy, helped my shyness disappear, kept me in fits of laughter with your crazy, happy nature! How they'd love your sense of humour.

But after a while I felt I'd tackled all the possible approaches. They listened, but they didn't understand. I really felt it was time they came to meet me halfway. So I invited you to Sunday tea. And then I told them what I'd done.

You'd have thought I'd stolen the crown jewels from the scene that resulted.

There were tears from Mum and a lot of, "Look here, young woman" stuff from Dad. In the end they had me crying, too.

"Look, I'm not asking your permission to marry him! I'm just asking you to have him to tea, to meet him, to get to know him. He's the person I love best in the world next to you two. You've brought me up — you've made me what I am — surely you can trust my judgement? Pete is a warm and good person."

"But think of your mother's feelings," Dad had replied. "The neighbours are sure to start talking. They'll say things to upset her."

"They'll probably say how pleased they are that your plain little daughter has got herself such a lovely boyfriend!" I retorted recklessly.

"But Margaret," Mum whispered tearfully, "a black boyfriend!"

THEY'RE so stupid, the labels we use to tag on people. Black is what coal is, Pete, it's not the lovely sunny colour of your skin. And is white any better a description of my wind-burned face?

But they just wouldn't understand the way I felt. They tore holes in all my arguments and talked me into the ground — cruelly, relentlessly, hour after hour.

Oh yes, they were cruel. They said some wicked, untrue things, and I knew I couldn't bring you here to have them verbally attack you the way they'd done me.

That's why I came to see you at your Saturday job and told you not to come to tea after all. And not to try to see me again either. Ever. Because when it came to a fight, I wasn't

strong enough to defend you against my parents.

It wasn't their fault that we parted, Pete. It was mine. I should have been stronger — you deserved that loyalty from me.

They've got their opinions — wrong ones, I happen to feel — but none the less, they were true to their principles.

I didn't stick to mine. I let you down because I was too weak to stand against my parents. I just couldn't speak up and say that your colour didn't matter to me; that none of our differences mattered because we had so many much more wonderful things in common. I just sat there silent while they threw all their arguments at me.

And when I didn't fight for you, it convinced Mum and Dad that they'd been right all along. That you were a roughneck and I'd only gone out with you as a gesture of rebellion against them. They thought I wasn't arguing back because I'd realised that what they were saying about you was the truth . . .

Well, it's been two weeks now. It's the school holidays, so we haven't met, and although it's been painful, missing you, I've been able to get by, even think about day-to-day things.

I'm not angry with my parents any more — after all, they only wanted what they thought was best for me. And for their kind of person, mixing colours is an idea that takes a bit of getting used to.

But I'm not that sort, Pete. I want you to understand that. I was weak, I admit it; but having found out the truth about myself in time, I believe I can be strong in future when it truly counts. For many people, black and white don't mix — but for many others, they do, and I believe they could for us.

I'm asking you to forgive me, Pete, because I believe we had — and still could have — something special. I love you, and if I haven't hurt you too much, I'd like to try again at being the girl you love. I can only hope you'll let me, Pete . . .

SO FAR SEW GOOD — CHEAP & CHEERFUL FASHION IDEAS

Here's how to make this super tiered skirt. Buy 2 metres of one fabric, 1½ metres of another, and 60 cm. of a third. Trim the 1½ metre length from 100 cm. to 70 cm. wide (use the left over strip to make the waistband) and trim the 60 cm. length from 100 cm. wide to 60 cm. Cut each length of fabric in half and sew up the side seams to make 3 skirts, leaving 20 cm. at one side for the zip. Now place the middle sized skirt outside the longest one and the shortest one outside that, zip openings all together, and run a gathering thread round through all 3 layers, to the size of your waist. Put on the waistband, put in the zip, check that the tiers are the length you like (if not, shorten one or more) and sew the hems.

Choose 3 really nice fabrics — 3 different flowery prints or silky rayon, or 3 different coloured satins or cotton voile.

three tiers!

APART from Christmas, birthdays are our favourite days. Your birthday is the one day of the year when everyone's nice to you, and you get all the attention- not to mention all those lovely cards and presents!

Every birthday's a nice occasion, but most people have memories of one special birthday that stands out as their best ever. Even pop stars like looking back on their happiest birthdays — and the presents they got . . .

Rick Driscoll of Kenny, for instance, says that his nicest birthday was when he was only six years old!

"I'd always wanted a bike," Rick said, "and I really envied all my school pals who had ones of their own.

"So for my sixth birthday, my parents bought me my first ever two-wheeler push bike. I was really proud of it, because it was newer and much more flash than all my friends' bikes!"

Dave Paton of Pilot is another person who remembers getting a very special present.

"It was my ninth birthday," he said, "and it was very special because I got a Robin Hood set. I'd been a bow and arrow fanatic for ages, and this set had a big bow and three arrows with rubber suckers on the end. It was great!"

HAPPY

Alan Merrill, the singer with **Arrows,** also has special memories of his ninth birthday.

"I remember I had a big party with 25 of my friends, lots of food and a big cake in the middle," he said. "In the other room, there was a huge object, all covered with brown paper, which I had strict instructions not to open until after tea.

"So when we'd finished eating, we all piled into the other room for the grand unveiling, and inside was an eight foot long spaceship.

"A commercial artist who lived downstairs had made it for me out of boxes, luminous paper, silver foil — everything. It was really impressive!"

Eric Faulkner of the Bay City Rollers (of course!) says his most memorable birthday was his 10th.

"That was the best," he said, "because that year, my mum bought me my first ever junior guitar!

"I learnt to play a few chords, and how to tune it, and I used to spend hours playing along with my favourite records."

Pete Phipps of the Glitter Band also remembers getting his first musical instrument — in his case a drum kit.

"When I was little I had piano lessons," he said, "but really I wasn't over keen, because I was always determined to learn to play the drums.

"I made my own kit from biscuit tins, boxes, lids, knitting needles and the like, and I used to practise on them.

"I think my parents must have taken the hint, because for my 14th birthday I received my first proper drum kit. I was thrilled with it!

"So that's a birthday I'll never forget!"

Andy Walton of Kenny says his happiest birthday was just two years ago, when he was 17.

"I've always wanted to drive," he explained, "and so my 17th birthday meant an awful lot to me, because my parents bought me a car of my own, and my dad took me out in it to teach me to drive.

"Within a few weeks, I passed my test. That was some present!"

All these people's memories were of birthdays which happened years ago, when they were still ordinary schoolboys, and no one imagined that they'd be stars some day.

BIRTHDAY ♫

But there were a lot of other stars whose happiest birthdays have been more recent ones. Of course, when you're a pop star, you can expect to get lots of lovely presents, and you can throw fantastic lavish parties — all of which goes to make a pretty exciting birthday!

Elton John, as you know, believes in doing things on a grand scale — and his birthday party of two years ago was no exception!

"We had a party on the 'Sloop John B', which was a boat on the Thames," said Elton. "It was a colossal event, with dozens of celebrities, including Rod Stewart and the Faces, The Who, Paul Simon and my mum and dad! (And the Ed was there too, folks!)

"It was a great evening, and a birthday I'll never forget."

Roy Wood was another star who had a party on the Sloop John B — but this time, he didn't organise it himself!

"A couple of years ago, my manager invited me out to dinner to celebrate my birthday," he said. "People tend to think

I'm a bit vague, and I suppose I am most of the time. As I was sitting there, I thought, 'Oh, there's thingy', and, 'That's so and so', because I'm hopeless at names.

"Everywhere I looked there were mates of mine, and I thought that it was such a coincidence that they should all be there too. It never occurred to me that they'd organised it!

"But it turned out to be a fantastic party. Surprise parties are the nicest kind!"

Gary Glitter also had a surprise party last year, on his 30th birthday.

"I was in New York, feeling very depressed because I didn't know anyone,"

he said. "But when I went back to my hotel in the evening, my suite was absolutely full of people, a lot of whom were English.

"Without me knowing, they'd arranged a party for me with a huge cake, champagne, the lot. I had the time of my life!"

Brian Connolly of the Sweet is another person whose happiest birthday was spent abroad.

"It was three years ago," he said. "We left England on Wednesday, after doing 'Top Of The Pops', and arrived on the following day, my birthday, in the Seychelle Islands for the start of a tour.

"I can remember sitting drinking champagne in the blazing sunshine, and saying to the other lads, 'You know, this isn't bad for October 5th .'"

Another pop star whose birthday falls on the same day as Brian's is **Russell Mael of Sparks.** And October 5th, last year, was a very special birthday for Russell — his 21st.

"That was a good birthday, because I celebrated it on two TV shows!" he told me. "Firstly in the morning on 'Saturday Scene' in London, and then in the evening, on the Nana Mouskouri show in Paris. It was a bit strange, but it was good fun, all the same!

"The other nice thing about it was all the presents I got. I got lots of scarves with my name sewn on them, and lots and lots of homemade cards and drawings.

"Those are usually the best gifts — the ones that are hand-made. Even if it doesn't look all that good, it's nice to know that someone's actually worked on it. It seems to mean a lot more somehow."

Your 21st is traditionally a very important birthday. But for **Donny Osmond,** like all other Mormon boys, another birthday was even more important.

Yes, of course, it was his 16th — because that was when he was allowed to start dating girls!

"It was a big occasion for me," said Donny. "I'd been looking forward to it all year! So when the big day came, I made sure nothing went wrong.

"I was a bit nervous about going on my own, so I took along Alan and Jay and their girlfriends for moral support. We all went out for dinner together, and we had a great time.

"Of course, I've been out with lots of girls since then, but that first date is still a special memory. It was one of the best birthday presents I ever had!"

So you see, whether you're a famous pop star or an ordinary person like us, birthdays are just as much fun!

DO YOU BELIEVE IN GHOSTS?

Before you shake your head and say, "Of course not," wait a moment! Have you ever considered that there might just be something in it?

We asked some of your favourite pop people if they believed in the supernatural and a surprising number of them claimed to have come face to face with a ghost at one time or another!

And here on this page are their answers — Tales guaranteed to send a shiver up your spine! So, to find out what they said, read on — if you're brave enough . . .!

Alvin Stardust

"One ghostly experience I had was the night some friends gathered at my house and decided, quite late at night, to have a seance.

"During the seance, we all heard footsteps coming down the stairs and towards the door — and then there was a knock at the door. But when we answered it, there was no-one there.

"There was one person there who'd been a total disbeliever before the seance and he told me that he'd completely changed his opinion. As for me, I've still got an open mind on the subject — but I'm sure something did happen that night!"

David Essex

"I didn't believe in ghosts until I moved into my last home, which was an old Victorian house in Essex.

"Often, when I was going upstairs in that house, I'd get the feeling that there was a little old lady beside me. She was a very nice, friendly old lady though — not at all frightening.

"I never saw anything, but I had a definite feeling there was something there!"

Bill Lyall—Pilot

"Before we formed Pilot I worked in Craighall Recording Studios in Edinburgh. My boss lived in a big house above the studios and once when I had to get up very early the next day, he invited me to spend the night there.

"Everything went okay until about midnight, when I was woken up by the sound of a chair in the corner creaking, as though someone was sitting in it. Then I suddenly felt my bedclothes being pulled off the bed — though, of course, there was no-one there to pull them!

"I later found out that this was caused by the ghost of a servant in the house who'd committed suicide."

Woody—Rollers

"All the others in the group laugh at me, but I really do believe in ghosts!

"When I was younger, I went on holiday to Inverness with some friends, and we stayed in a youth hostel which had been converted from an old castle. It was really creepy.

"One night I was walking along a corridor when I heard footsteps behind me. I thought it was my friends, but when I turned round to speak to them, there was no-one there!"

Noel Edmonds

"After doing a gig in a discotheque in Leicester, I had a minor dispute with the manager about my fee. I suggested that, to sort things out, we went upstairs to his office to look at my contract.

"To my surprise, he refused, then he agreed to go into the office only if I went too! I thought this was a bit odd, but I went in anyway.

"Once we were inside, he told me that he never went into the office alone because it was haunted. Of course, I laughed at this, but he said he'd prove it to me. He told me to let my mind go blank. I did and I got a real shock.

"Although it was a warm summer evening, and the sun was streaming in through the windows, I suddenly felt the room become icy cold, and I could see my breath condensing in front of me. I was absolutely terrified, I just couldn't get out of there quickly enough!

"Afterwards the manager told me that the building had previously been a funeral parlour, and his office had been the chapel of rest. All the staff of the disco had seen a ghost at least once, and a medium who'd been there had seen no less than six ghosts in the room!"

Roger Taylor of Queen

"I once lived in Cornwall, in a 15th century house which was haunted by a poltergeist — an invisible spirit which throws things about.

"One night I was lying in bed when my bedroom door was flung open and all the hangers were jangling about. And another time, the entire contents of the attic were moved around and turned upside down!

"Someone told me that it was caused by the ghost of a person who'd died in the house in mysterious circumstances."

176

COVER-GIRL LOOKS FOR YOU

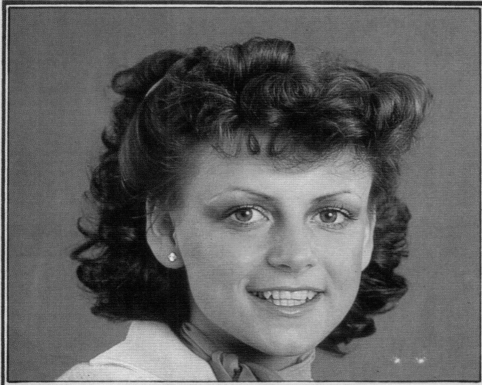

TWO fabulous model-girl looks for you to copy at home . . . we show you two completely different make-ups and tell you how to do them yourself.

DAY-TIME

THE perfect day-time look is a healthy, glowing one . . . skin should
be really clear and eyes should sparkle. Make-up should be
subtle but very flattering, natural but very attractive.

Think of summertime when everyone looks so tanned and
healthy . . . then think of winter when everyone looks pale and
wan. We know which look we prefer and we're sure you agree,
so here's how to look happy and healthy all year round.

STEP 1

Skin care is the first step to natural beauty, of course, so let's
start from there. The latest cleansing theory is that regular cleansing
with creams and lotions isn't enough because they don't remove
the dead cells from the surface. So, even if you do cleanse, tone
and moisturise religiously twice a day, there's still a good chance
that your skin might be looking a bit dingy.

That's not the cue to go back to soap and water, though, try
using cleansing grains and face packs more often to take away those
top layers. Stick to your cleanse, tone and moisture routine as well
and your skin should always look healthy.

Choose skin-care products according to your skin type . . .
normal, greasy, dry or spotty. All the products are marked, so you
shouldn't go wrong and there are always salesgirls to help you if
you're stuck. Follow the directions on the pack and you're well
away . . . if the product doesn't seem to agree with you try something else until you get it right.

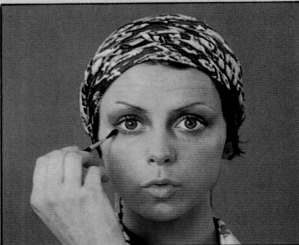

STEP 3

Eyes come next and here's your chance to really make the most
of yourself! Choosing the colour is always a problem, though, and
where do you put it in the day-time so that you look nice without
looking tarty?

The secret of clever day-time eye make-up is choosing colours that
go with the clothes you're wearing . . . not necessarily colours that
match your eyes. Pearly highlights are out during the day, save
those for evenings when lights are low and you want to look
romantic. Stick to fairly basic colours on lids with a darker colour to
outline sockets and a very neutral colour on brow-bones, such as
shell pink or creamy beige.

Use a crayon to outline sockets (brown is good), then the colour
of your choice on lids. Remember that cream shadows are best for
brow-bones, powder shadows for lids and the paint-on powder
shadows last for ages and ages!

STEP 2

After a thorough cleanse, tone and moisturise, the next step is
choosing your foundation. For day-time you'll need one that gives
good coverage without being too heavy or too dark.

There are different types on the market, liquids, creams, sticks and
even aerosol foundations, so choosing the right one can be
difficult. Creams seem to be the most popular as they seem to be
the easiest to apply and give good coverage at the same time.

For those people with skins that tend to look shiny after a while,
there are the matte foundations which combine foundation and
powder such as Max Factor's Sheer Genius, but these will be too
heavy for girls with normal to dry skins.

Applying the foundation is quite simple, as long as you remember
a few basic facts, like blending in under chin and around hair-line.
The secret is to apply dots of foundation all over your face and
then blend in with fingers for the best results. Foundation always
goes on much better if your skin is soft and smooth, so moisturise
well before applying.

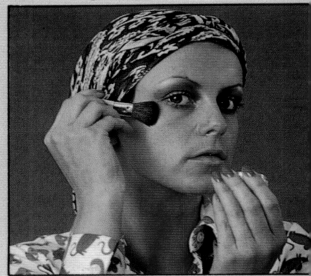

STEP 4

Blusher comes in all sorts of shapes and sizes, sticks, powders
. . . even a roll-on kind from Rimmel, now, so choosing can present
problems. Day-time doesn't really call for too much blusher, though,
so choose your colour very carefully! Experiment with different areas
of your face, always keeping blusher well away from your nose.
Model-girls have a knack of applying it from ear-lobe level along the
bottom of the cheek-bones and up towards temples.

Try all sorts of different ways until you find the one that suits
you best and really makes the most of your face . . . blusher can
make that vital difference that changes you from plain into really
fantastic! Remember to blend in at the edges so that you don't have
huge great circles on your face which can look really ugly.

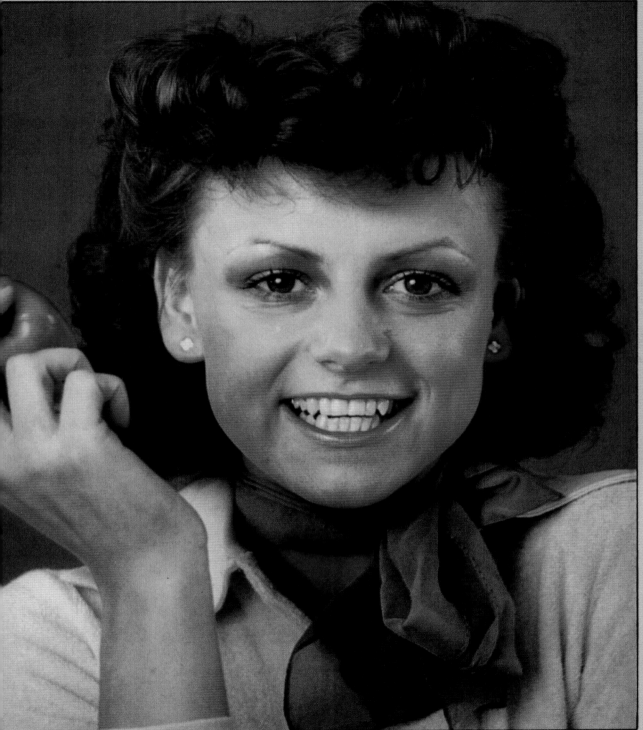

EP 5

e finished look, complete with lipstick and powder. We find that
slucent powder goes over everything and doesn't look caked
tty in any way. Buy it in a compact with its own puff. Lipstick
day-time should be light and bright, and sometimes even just a
of lip-gloss looks great on its own!

ge, scarlet lips don't look nice during the day at any time, so
r clear! Stick to light, shiny colours, perhaps with a lip-gloss
the top!

EP-BY-STEP

e used Boots 17 foundation, cleverly applied with fingertips all
face and neck.

2. Socket lines are outlined with brown crayons, also under lower
lashes. Ginger brown cream shadow over brow-lines, out to the edges.

3. Green crayon all over lids and well into the outer corners of the
eye to meet socket-line. One coat of browny/black mascara.

4. Pale pink blusher applied with a fat brush using
sideways strokes from ear to cheek-bones.

5. Shiny pink lipstick from the Boots 17 range applied
with a lip brush . . . lips are outlined first, then
filled in with colour.

NIGHT-TIME

SOFT and romantic, that's the special night-time look w chosen. Soft colours don't have to look weedy . . . should be pearly so they'll shine in the candlelight (sigh!) and really romantic.

Night-time make-up can be heavier than for day-time, but doesn't mean just heaping on more of the same colours! Go lasting looks so you won't go all streaky halfway through the ever and you shouldn't have to keep disappearing to powder your no

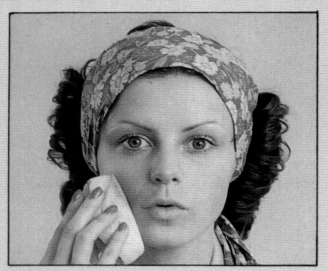

STEP 1

Evening foundation can be tricky. You want that flawless, soft glowing look without looking too heavily made up. Unlike day-time looks, night-time looks call for a pale, less healthy look . . . bright red cheeks don't look nice at all when you're trying to look elegant!

Stick foundations stay on for absolutely ages, especially if you use a moistened sponge to apply the colour. Surprisingly, you can choose a fairly dark shade if you're using a sponge, as the colour seems to be absorbed by your skin and looks several shades lighter.

You must cleanse, tone and moisturise thoroughly before you begin applying your foundation as it will go on much more easily if skin is soft and smooth to start with.

If you're prone to red marks and blushing, try using Boots No 7 Colour-Corrective Moisturiser underneath your foundation . . . It's a green cream which helps to counteract redness.

Sensitive skins need special attention, of course, so you'll need to choose a foundation from one of the ranges specially made for sensitive skins, such as Almay or Max Factor's Swedish Formula range.

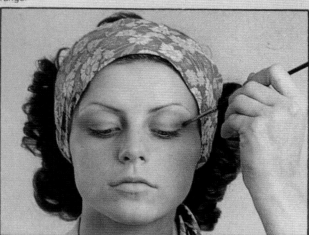

STEP 2

Romantic eyes take time to perfect, so make sure you don't have to rush them. Pearly colours are best, of course, with fairly strong colours for lids, lighter ones for brow-bones.

Decide what you're going to wear first, then choose your eye colours to match or tone. Pinky lilac colours are great for night-time, along with silvery grey and light, shiny blues. Powder colours are easy to apply with a brush and last longest, especially if you use a fairly neutral cream shadow as a base.

Make sure eyebrows are nice, too. Not too thin and finely arched . . . that's out now, but shaped nicely without any stragglers showing!

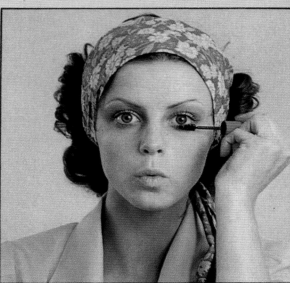

STEP 3

Mascara is very important at night, 'cos you'll want those las to be extra long and fluttery! Try a mascara with built-in l lengthener, in a colour to tone with the eye colour you've chos You can buy all sorts of colours now, such as blue, plum, green a grey as well as black and brown.

Mascara's the last thing you do to your eyes, applying one c very carefully and allowing it to dry before applying the next. Wa out for bits that may get left behind on your cheeks . . . put a tiss underneath your eye as you put on the mascara if you think you likely to make a mess.

STEP 4

Night-time blusher should be light and pearly, applied high cheek-bones to make you look extra soft and romantic. Bright re won't do at all!

Powder blusher will be best for evenings, applied with a nice brush or a little puff. Stroke in from ear-lobe and over cheek-bon but not too near your nose as this will make your face lo unbalanced.

Powder is important at night, too, and this is when you can spla out on some loose powder and one of those lovely, feathery pu Max Factor make a splendid loose powder in their Swedish Form range, it's translucent and has tiny sparkly bits in it . . . looks sup in candlelight! Always remember to dust off excess powder, though

STEP 5

Lips should be soft and shiny and oh-so-kissable, so choose a [li]pstick that's right for the occasion! Outline lips first with a lip-brush [tip]ped in a deep colour . . . mulberry for instance . . . to give [yo]ur lips shape. Then fill in with a lighter, toning colour that's [re]ally shiny.

[F]inish off with a slick of lip gloss if you like, but don't load up your [lip]s with too much stuff . . . you don't want to leave it all on your [gl]ass or his face, do you!!

STEP-BY-STEP

We used Rimmel's stick make-up applied evenly and lightly with a [mo]istened sponge, all over face and neck.

2. Pinky lilac shadow is applied with a brush all over lids and brow-bones, followed by a band of lilac painted straight across, just below the socket line. A pinky beige shiny highlighter at the outer edge of the brow-bone adds the finishing touch.

3. Two coats of navy mascara next, allowing the first coat to dry before applying the second. Wipe excess mascara off the brush to avoid bits.

4. Pearly pink blusher is applied high on cheek-bones and up temples to look extra stunning for evening.

5. Pale pink lipstick applied with a lip-brush adds the final touch, with a slick of lip-gloss (Max Factor's) over the top.

Both looks were created especially for Jackie by Claire of Boots 17, using the make-up that suited Belinda best. You'll find similar colours and products in various ranges such as the Outdoor Girl, Miners, Yardley, Boots No 7, Max Factor, Rimmel and Love make-up collections. Have fun shopping around!

Do you
long to
w clubs?

6. Are you very
healthy, on
the whole?

5. Are you
curious about
new people?

4. Does your
mum rely
on you?

3. Do you think you are a
capable person?

2. Do you enjoy
a good laugh?

Mostly (yes) —
read the
conclusion for
HIGHWAY FOUR

Mostly (no) —
go to the
beginning of
HIGHWAY
THREE

4

1. Do people often
come to you for
advice?

Do you
yourself
eresting
person?

9. Do you often
question the truth of
what people say?

5. Are you
sometimes
stubborn?

4. Can you
switch on the
charm whenever
you want?

3. Have you a
lot of enemies?

2. Do you take
instant dislikes
to people?

1. Do you think you'd
be good at public speaking?

Mostly (yes) —
turn on to
HIGHWAY ONE
Mostly (no) —
turn on to
HIGHWAY TWO

Do you
feel you
missing
n things?

8. Does hope
play a big part in
your life?

9. Do you ever
daydream?

Mostly (yes) — read
the conclusions for
HIGHWAY THREE

Mostly (no) — go to
the beginning of
HIGHWAY FOUR

3

9. Do you think
indifference is
worse than
hatred?

5. Do you sometimes
feel your friends are
making rude comments
behind your back?

4. Do you think
about your own
faults
quite a lot?

8. Do you have
to fight
for what you
want in life?

3. Would
you give
a poor tramp
your last
penny?

6. Are you secretly
jealous when
your friend buys
a super new dress?

7. Do you feel hurt when you're not
the centre of attention?

2. Do you
sometimes
think you
live in
cloud-
cuckoo-
land?

ncy a quick zoom along the motorway? You'll
nd out some surprising things about yourself en route!
arting here in the garage, answer the following
uestions, then choose your route accordingly
nd when you've completed the game, turn to page 79
r the conclusions.

Do you often feel madly happy for no reason?
Do you sometimes fly into fits of temper?
Can you imagine being a television announcer?
Do you find spending an evening at home a bore?
Are you fascinated by murder stories in the newspapers?
Have you more friends than you can count off-hand?
Do you sometimes wear your poor mum out?
Have you more than one boyfriend at the moment?
Do you pride yourself on not being shy?

Mostly (yes), set off along ROUTE A
Mostly (no), set off along ROUTE B

B

1. Does your mum
often complain you
never listen to a word
she says?

*Conclusions
on page 48*

183

QUIZ
CONCLUSIONS
FROM
PAGE 46

HIGHWAY ONE

You whizz fast and furious along the motorway without any regard for your fellow travellers. You're a bit of a road-hog, and can be very selfish at times, but you'll get where you want to go, all right! You are very ambitious, self-confident and determined. Many people envy your vitality and your powers of persuasion, and you have a way of getting people to do what you want, because you have a very strong personality. People can only take so much of you, but with your bull-in-the-china-shop approach to life, it's likely you don't care all that much what people think, anyway! You might be heading for a crash, though, so watch out. Try to consider other people a bit more, and your journey along the road to success will be enjoyable as well as rewarding.

HIGHWAY TWO

You speed along the motorway, enjoying the ride, and managing to consider others along the route, too. You are friendly, easy-going, and you enjoy the good things of life. You should be popular, because you are lively and fun, and get on naturally well with people. You are rather practical, and your sense of humour plus your intelligence will see you very nicely through life. You are a good mixer, you are good at solving problems, and you will be an asset to others wherever you go. You have the ability to spread happiness around you. Sailing through life is fine, but it would be worth your while to look beneath the surface a bit more. Do you really think you are making the best of your abilities and your talents?

HIGHWAY THREE

You are a danger on the roads — you wouldn't see a bright red lorry in front of your nose, because you'd be too busy dreamily admiring the pretty flowers along the hedgerows! You are a romantic, a dreamer and sometimes too emotional for your own good. Of course it's good to be sensitive and to feel things deeply, but you often tend to be *too* affected by events in your life, and too easily led by people around you. Try to get things into perspective a bit more — listen to your head as well as your heart. On the bonus side, though, you are sympathetic to others, you are loving and gentle, and although you are often depressed, you also have the capacity to be very happy. So go on living in your beautiful dream-world, but try to temper it with reality. Concentrate on the road-signs and get going — along the ground, not up in the clouds!

HIGHWAY FOUR

You drive cautiously and with great concentration. You're not in a hurry to arrive at your destination, but when you get there you'll enjoy it all the more. You are a complicated, thoughtful person, and, as a rule, things don't come easily to you. This is partly because you make mountains out of molehills, and partly because you tend to overlook the obvious in your quest to find great meaning and significance in everything around you. You are an individual, a bit of an intellectual really, and you tend to be intolerant of thickies; but perhaps they could teach you to relax a bit more. You'll wear yourself out with tension if you go on questioning everything and accepting nothing. You are very aware as a person, and your soul is always searching for something. Your journey through life will always be interesting because you will never allow yourself to park your car and doze off — your mind is always alert.

FIVE OF THE BEST!

If you could put together your ideal group, who would be in it?

We all have our own special favourites when it comes to pop stars. In every group there's one guy who stands out. No matter how much you like the others, he's the one you love — because there's something about him that makes him extra special!

And we thought it would be fun if we took some of our favourites out of their own groups, and put them all together in one big supergroup!

All you have to do is work out, from the clues listed below, who the members are — so get your thinking caps on!

And if you turn to page 71, all will be revealed in our magic photo of the boys all together!

THE LEAD SINGER

His birth sign is Leo.
He went to the Shipman County Secondary School.
He once worked for a scrap dealer.
One of his first groups was called The China Plate Blues Band!
His favourite food is Indian curry.
He has blue eyes.
He once had a horse called Zelda.
There are two women in his life!
His middle name's Victorian!
He once worked as Tommy Steele's understudy.

THE DRUMMER

He has blue eyes.
His birthday's on the same day as Mick Jagger's.
He was born in King's Lynn.
His family live in Cornwall.
He has blond hair.
He once went to dental college.
His group is very popular in Japan.
He can play guitar as well as drums.
He also writes and sings!
Cats are his favourite animals.
He once worked in Kensington Market.
He's 5 ft. 10 ins. tall.
He has a degree in biology.
His first group was called Smile.
He loves old clothes.

His first record was called "And The Tears Came Tumbling Down."
Football is his favourite sport.
December 18, 1971 was a very special day for him.
His grandfather was an Irish gipsy.
He loves dogs, and has two of his own.

THE LEAD GUITARIST

He has blue eyes.
He plays several musical instruments — including the violin!
He was born in the Elsie

THE BASS GUITARIST

He went to Liberton Secondary School.
He has blue eyes.
He's also a singer.
His dad's a singer too!
He once played with another well-known group.
He's very patriotic!
He has dark brown hair.
He wrote his first hit while he was working as a milkman!
He's also worked as a mechanic and an electrician.
His star sign is Scorpio.
His group went to America for the first time earlier this year.
He has a cat called Pussy.
He's 5 ft. 8 ins. tall.
He enjoys studying classical music.

Inglis Hospital.
He once played in his local schools' orchestra.
He's 5 ft. 7 ins. tall.
He has one brother, Alan.
He went to Morden Primary School.
His very first group was called Witness.
He worked for six weeks as a roof surveyor.
His birth sign is Libra.
He loves horse-riding.
His father's name is George.
When he was eleven, he met the Queen Mother.
He's the smallest member of his group.
He takes size 7 shoes.

THE KEYBOARD PLAYER

He can sing as well!
He has one sister.
He has brown eyes.
His birth sign is Sagittarius.
His middle name is Clark.
Red is his second favourite colour.
His favourite drink is orange juice.
He has a very useful hobby!
He was born in Ogden.
He has lots of nephews and nieces.
He's been going out with girls for two years now.
He's the third youngest child in his family.
He made his first TV appearance at the age of 5.
His brothers call him by his nickname, Corky.

Got A Minute?

Got a minute? Then here's a quick selection of fun games and puzzles to help you fill in some spare moments!

Just Picture It...

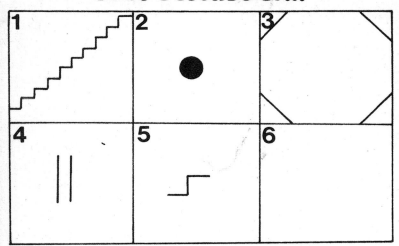

Here's a very simple picture quiz — but one which can tell a lot about you!

All you do is describe what you see in the diagrams.

Answers:

1. If you treated the diagram as a flight of stairs, this shows you're conventional. As anything else this means you have a lot of character and will go far in life.

2. If you saw the dot as the centre of something, this means you're self-centred. As anything else, means you're open and generous.

3. If you saw the lines as a box, this means you're needing to widen your horizons a bit. Anything else, you're fine as you are!

4. If you saw them as matches, this means you're lonely and in need of company. If you see them as anything else, this generally means you're just doodling!

5. If you saw this diagram as part of an object, this means you have a practical, hard-working streak, and like to get problems sorted out quickly. If you see it as part of a design, you're moody and temperamental.

6. The answer to this is simple – the more complicated your answer, the more complex a character you are. If, however, you just answered "a blank space," you're a pretty boring person, I'm afraid!

Penny For Them!

Play the penny game and astound your friends! Have someone blindfold you, and collect a dish full of one pence pieces. Ask them to pass round one penny — any one — and get them all to examine it so that they all know its date, etc. Then tell them to place it amongst the other pennies in the dish and hand the dish to you, lo and behold — you'll be able to pick out the "special" penny, every time! The secret is very simple — the "special" penny will be hot after everyone has handled it, and all the rest of the coins will be cold! Easy!

We've Got Your Number!

To find out someone's personality secrets, just add up his birthdate as follows. Take the month number (i.e. July is the 7th month, therefore its number is 7), then add on his day number (the 8th =8) + add the year number (1960=1+9+6+0) Thus=7+8+1+9+6+0=31.

Now reduce this to one number by adding 3+1=4. Therefore 4 is the birth number. Now look it up on the column below!

1. Confidence, strength, reliability.
2. Sympathy, tact, artistic nature.
3. Always on the go, full of ideas.
4. Steady and unchangeable.
5. Impulsive, unrealistic, lives in the clouds.
6. Home-loving and generous.
7. Very talented, often musical or poetic.
8. Usually ambitious — and usually successful!
9. Has an unusual degree of understanding and intelligence.

Draw Your Own Conclusions

Here's a very simple way to tell the secrets of someone's personality — ask them to draw a flower! The type of flower they draw can tell a great deal about them — see below: —

Artistic and gentle, dreamy and inclined to be forgetful. A true romantic.
The details on the leaves and the difference of petals show a love of detail and an open mind to other people.

Secretive and withdrawn, can be reliable and moody. Doesn't fall in love easily.
The uneven lines represent someone whose life is unsteady and often worrying. The decreasing lines towards the centre mean someone withdrawn and secretive.

Acts on impulse — changeable, moody, restless by nature.
The spiky petals show a certain sharpness of nature and reluctance to give away any secrets. The fact that the flower is drawn from the centre shows selfishness.

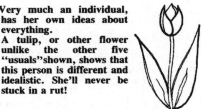

Very much an individual, has her own ideas about everything.
A tulip, or other flower unlike the other five "usuals" shown, shows that this person is different and idealistic. She'll never be stuck in a rut!

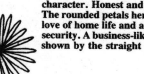

Very basic, down-to-earth character. Honest and reliable. The rounded petals here show a love of home life and a need for security. A business-like mind is shown by the straight stalk.

The five points show a sense of fun, an open mind with lots of interests. The simplicity of the drawing shows an unstable mind.
A bit childish, but full of fun, and makes the best of life.

PATCHWORK

Here's a very special selection of ideas to brighten up your life!

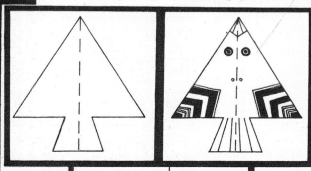

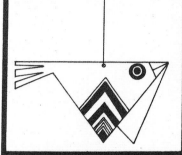

JUST PICTURE IT!

Ask all your friends for a photograph of themselves and stick them onto a sheet of coloured card, to make a friendly poster for your room. Screw the card to the wall with mirror screws.

HAVE A HANG UP!

Cut a heart shape out of thick card – cover it with red satin and stick suction hooks onto it to hang your beads from. Hang it from the wall, or put hooks on both sides and hang it with a pretty ribbon from the ceiling.

WATCH THE BIRDIE!

Make a hanging paper bird — cut the shape out of thin card (use a postcard if you want a little bird). Cut the tail to look like feathers and paint on a pattern (the same on both sides) Fold down the centre and suspend from the edges of your lampshade on a bit of thread. Make lots!

A FISHY STORY . . .

Make a gloomy corner of your room cheery and bright. Buy a goldfish and bowl and some tiny tins of enamel paint. Paint trees and flowers round the outside of the bowl. Put a table lamp beside it to illuminate it prettily.

STICK TO IT!

Stick rubber suction towel holders on the back of your door and hang your scarves in them.

GETTING ROUND IT . . .

Buy some shiny windmills from a market stall or toyshop and put them in a jamjar covered in silver foil for a nice permanent flower display. Put them in a draught and they'll whirl, too!

ON THE SHELF

Ask a shoeshop for some empty shoeboxes and glue them together to make shelves. Paint them or stick coloured paper over them or cover with cooking foil.

CHICKEN AND ALMOND SALAD

Chicken and Almond Salad.

You need some leftover chicken, a small green or red pepper, some toasted almonds, lettuce and mayonnaise. Cut the pepper into strips, lay it, with the chicken, onto the lettuce leaves, put some mayonnaise onto it and sprinkle with toasted almonds.

WHAT'S YOUR REMEDY FOR A BROKEN HEART?

Julie Thornton, Dewsbury, Yorkshire.

If ever I feel heartbroken over anything, I find the best thing to do is to shut myself away in my bedroom and have a really good cry, then go to sleep for a while, and when I wake up, things don't seem half as bad!

Pat Stewart, Hillhead, Glasgow.

Reading poetry. It convinces me there's nothing like being crossed in love to inspire the imagination, and also that however heart-breaking a situation may be, it's happened before, and the people involved managed to use it to develop a better understanding of themselves and others.

Clare Thornton, Portsmouth.

Read a very long, soppy novel, like "Gone With The Wind" or "Penmarric" — you'll get so involved, you'll almost forget your troubles — or at least you'll realise that you aren't the only one!

Steve Yates, Blackheath, London SE3.

Pick yourself up; dust yourself down — and start all over again! As the song goes! Pretty good advice, I'd say!

Julie Cave, Corby, Northants.

Fortunately this is something I've never experienced, but I think that if I ever did I'd try to make every effort to forget him and concentrate on finding happiness with somebody else. But if you've been really serious about somebody, everything you possess, records, presents, photos, anything at all is bound to remind you of him for a long while, so you have to be very strong willed and make up your mind that you're going to mend it again. But as I've got such a fabulous boyfriend I hope I'll never be in this position.

Crazy Mary, New Addington, Surrey.

Stick it up with sellotape — then no-one will know it's broken and you can recuperate in peace!

Jackie Nicholas, Bemerton Heath, Wilts.

Oh, if it was me I'd get a new boyfriend as quickly as possible. One that's much better-looking than the last. It's a good way to restore your confidence! And of course I'd get out and about as much as I possibly could.

Sharon Gillingham, Harlow, Essex.

I don't take boys as seriously as most girls do, so I don't ever suffer from having a broken heart. So having never been in this position I find it difficult to answer. But if I ever did have a steady relationship with a boy and suddenly it ended I'm sure it would be a very long time before I'd want to go out with anybody else. I think it's just true to say that 'time heals' and you just can't rush it.

John Lumley, Bury, Lancs.

Work. I have a market stall, and work is not only hard graft to me, but also my hobby and way of life. It may not mend a broken heart — I wouldn't know about that — but it can be guaranteed to ensure you don't go broke financially as well. And that must be some comfort.

Suzie Lofthouse, Swindon, Wilts.

Fall in love again as soon as possible — it may be superficial, but it works.

Lindsay Fraser, Northampton.

Write a long, beautiful, sad poem, telling the world your unhappy story. If it got published, it might help to cheer you up!

Ray Stiles (Mud)

I think you should try not to worry about it and go out and make new friends. Don't linger on the broken romance, make a big effort to find new friends. Who knows, you'll probably meet somebody better.

Sharon Mackenzie, Cambuslang, Lanarkshire.

The only real cure for a broken heart is time. But it's possible to speed up the cure by finding interesting things to do, so that time seems to pass more quickly.

Helen Boyd, Largs, Ayrshire.

The sea. Walking along the sands, or sitting quietly by myself, looking out over the water, always soothes me and makes me feel more philosophical about things. So does the rhythmic sound of the waves, and the beauty of a west coast sunset.

Diane Wilson, Huddersfield, Yorkshire.

The only time I was really heartbroken was when my old dog died, but we got a new puppy straight away. I know it sounds a bit hard, but we were so busy with the new puppy that we didn't have time to cry too much over the old dog, although we were very upset at the time.

Christine Compton, Salisbury, Wilts.

Just keep away from boys in future!

POP CROSSWORD SOLUTION

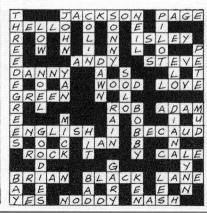

HEAD LINERS

A Jackie Special

YOU'VE asked for them! So here they are — the idols who've hit the headlines in the past year, for their looks, skill, determination and sheer ability to gain an admiring public!

Here's all the information on the kind of people they are; how they've achieved success, what they've done and what they want to do with their lives. So read on for everything you've always wanted to know!

John Conteh

JOHN CONTEH is 6 ft. tall, 12 st. 13 lbs, with a glistening body in the peak of condition — undeniably handsome, tough, dedicated and single-minded.

The boxing superstar from Liverpool was 24 on May 26. The fourth child of ten, he left school at 14, and he's boxed every evening since his father sent him to lessons at the age of 10, to keep him out of trouble!

John Conteh's earned himself a bit of a playboy reputation, though, with his cool self-assurance and his unashamed liking for the glamorous things in life. He's had a luxury house built in London's Hampstead. "I've made London my home and I love it," he says. He buys hand-made shoes and silk shirts as the fancy takes him, and has been known to order, in one week, six new suits at £150 each!

His interests range wide. He takes guitar lessons, watches films (goes in for war documentaries and cartoons) likes listening to soul, reggae and blues, and reads anything people tell him he should!

Nothing stops John Conteh. "I'm a positive thinker," he says. He also applies the rules of boxing to life. "Keep your head down and let nothing from the outside interfere with your target."

If success seems to have come easily, it's only because he's given himself to it, 100%. "There's nothing I won't do to get what I want," he explains. And that's how John Conteh's got so much of what he wants!

Michael Crawford

MICHAEL CRAWFORD'S the one who's taken 16 years to become an overnight sensation — he gets rediscovered with every new role!

He's 5 ft. 10½ ins. tall, weighing 9½ stone, with sandy brown hair and blue eyes. He was born in Salisbury, Wiltshire, on January 19, 1942, and spent most of his childhood in London and Kent, leaving school when he was 15.

Michael reckons that all in all he's had about 500 parts, including TV and radio, as an actor and singer!

His first London part was over 13 years ago. That was in something called "Come Blow Your Horn." Currently of course, "Billy" is the word that's been on everyone's lips!

Gradually, Michael Crawford's developing wider popular appeal, not only because of his success in musicals but also in TV, particularly with the hit comedy series "Some Mothers Do 'Ave 'Em!" where as the accident-prone Frank Spencer he's sailed unscathed through many stunts! People are always asking him whether the real Michael Crawford behaves like Frank Spencer — to which he answers emphatically, "No!"

His spare-time interests are reading (mostly paper-backs, anything from classics to detectives!), theatre (of course) and he also likes listening to pop records.

But more than anything, Michael Crawford's working hard to become accepted as a serious dramatic actor. And he's bound to make it with the next "discovery"!

Bjorn Borg

HIS father gave him a tennis racquet when he was nine, and he's never looked back since!

Swedish Bjorn Borg — 19 last June 6

— with a typically handsome Scandi[n]avian face and seemingly ice-co[ol] confidence, hit Wimbledon two yea[rs] ago, and as far as he's concerned, tenn[is] is his job and his life. He's got a straigh[t]forward approach to profession[al] tennis — and enormous drawing powe[r] as the girls who cheer him on and off th[e] courts agree!

But for a stubborn, tough, inte[r]national champion, Bjorn Borg leads [a] surprisingly unexciting life off th[e] courts. Tennis comes before ever[y]thing, so it's no late nights, no smokin[g,] no drinking — and "there's no way I'[m] going to become involved with wome[n.] If I were emotionally tied to a girl, I'd [be] finished as a top class tennis player[,"] he says.

He's travelling constantly ten month[s] of the year, but when he's not playing tournaments he gets out to discos and loves eating in restaurants.

The films he likes best are cowboy a[nd] war ones — preferably starring Cli[nt] Eastwood and Steve McQueen!

Long term ambitions? Bjorn's set [on] tennis for several years yet, but he'[s] always had ideas about teaching gy[m] when the tennis scene's worn out f[or] him — or when he's worn out everyo[ne] else!

And when he does have time for th[e] girl? "She must be honest; and, abov[e] all, enthusiastic about tennis!"

Roddy McDowall

RODDY McDOWALL was a child sta[r] in the "Lassie" films when h[e] was five, and since then he's had ov[er] 80 films to his credit!

Many of them have been British, an[d] in fact, it was the Academy Awar[d] winning, "How Green Was My Valley[,"] that first made him a star. After tha[t] Hollywood kept making him offers h[e] couldn't resist!

5 ft. 10 in. with brown hair and brown eyes, London born, Roddy McDowall now lives near Central Park, New York. Films still figure largely in his life. His very favourite occupation is watching movies, and he can sit through two or three a day (the highest figure he ever reached was six!). He's a talented photographer himself, and has published his own photo-illustrated book.

He's appeared in four "Planet Of The Apes" films to date, and for each one his face is insured for £400,000 against damage from the make-up, which takes three hours to apply!

Roddy loses weight easily while "Planet" is being filmed. Because of the thick make-up, all he can have is liquids through a straw, and those have to be cold, as anything hot would melt the ape-mask!

Robin Nedwell

TV'S handsome, competent doctor, Dr Duncan Waring, is in reality intelligent, extroverted Robin Nedwell.

Born in 1946 in Birmingham, he lived in Cardiff from the age of four, and it was there that he started his acting career — working as general dogsbody with the Welsh Theatre Company, for nothing but the love of it!

In 1966 he went to the Central School of Speech and Drama in London, and was offered his first part in the "Doctor" series before he'd even finished!

After he'd filmed the first series, he got more varied experience — including arranging the fights for the film of "Macbeth."

Fight arranging's quite a hobby with Robin. Sword fights fascinate him, and as he's really interested in Japanese culture, he's made a collection of Japanese swords.

All things Japanese interest him, in fact, including the women, though he says he certainly doesn't want to get married before he's 35. He's a happy bachelor, even doing his own housework, and his life of pubs and pals suits him fine!

He's also keen on reading science fiction, likes watching TV and prefers a game of darts and a chat with friends to extravagant nights out on the town. When it comes to acting, he admits he's not the dedicated type, but he'd like to try romantic parts. Otherwise, his main ambition is just to enjoy living!

Ben Murphy

AMERICAN BEN MURPHY bewitched the hearts of many when he became TV cowboy Thaddeus Jones. But in his real life, Ben leads a cosy bachelor existence in a small Hollywood flat, littered with books and sports equipment.

Born on March 6, 1942 (he's a Pisces!) in Arkansas, he "drifted his way" through more universities than he likes to remember, but eventually came out with *two* B.A. degrees!

He got into acting because he "felt the need to express himself." But I bet you couldn't spot him in his first film role — a one-line part in "The Graduate"!

He has little spare time, but whenever he does, it's taken up with tennis, playing guitar, reading, doing karate and ski-ing. He's a great fan of all sports, and likes travel, too. Another passion with him is health foods — he tries to eat only the "right" things. Even tea and coffee are out!

Ben's always learning, seeks inner peace, and is also looking for someone to love! Chief quality in any girl for him must be honesty, and it's important she's a very positive type.

Well, the 5 ft. 11 in. of blonde, blue-eyed heart-throb shouldn't find it difficult to get someone to love him!

Robert Redford

ROBERT REDFORD'S everybody's idea of rugged masculinity — and the private life of the 38-year-old Californian star bears out the legend.

He says he's been a rebel since his childhood: never bright at school, he went for art and sports and thought of becoming a baseball player when he left!

Instead, though, he took to painting. He left California, worked his way across the United States, often hitching and living very rough indeed. Then on to Europe — sketching in Paris — and over to Britain where he got as far as Scotland. He returned to the States depressed and unsettled, till he met Lola, the 17-year-old Mormon girl he married and has lived happily with for the last 17 years!

Between films, he and his family (there are three children now, Shauna, Jamie and Amy) take off and wander round Greece, Crete and the Aegean Islands. He's also built his own house, a retreat 8,000 ft. up in the mountains of Utah. There, in natural, rugged, unspoiled surroundings, Robert Redford can be himself. By nature he's aloof, controlled and completely independent. He loves to ride horses, ski and go off trekking and camping for weeks.

He doesn't neglect filming though; most recently he's made "The Way We Were," "The Great Gatsby," and "The Great Waldo Pepper." So it seems, whatever he does, Robert Redford's a winner!

Telly Savalas

CHEEKY, sarcastic Detective Lt. Theo Kojak's won everybody's heart. And Telly Savalas (the name's short for 'Aristotle'!) is himself natural, single-minded and involved a lot in public affairs.

Born in New York on January 21, he grew up in a large lively family and went to school in Connecticut and Long Island. He spent three years in the American army in the second world war, then went to Columbia University and got a degree in psychology. Then he worked for the Information Service of the State Department.

He started acting, when he couldn't find an actor for a theatrical agent who wanted a special European accent. Telly went to the audition and to his astonishment, got the part!

Telly Savalas had only appeared in three television shows when he was signed up for a role in the film 'Birdman of Alacatraz.' For that, he was nominated for an Academy Award as the best supporting actor of the year!

6ft. 1 in. Telly Savalas, brown-eyed and weighing 14 st 4 lbs., is a busy man between films and television. He plays golf and travels the world, often on goodwill missions on behalf of the State Department. He's kept almost as busy as Kojak!

YOUR LIFE IS IN YOUR HANDS

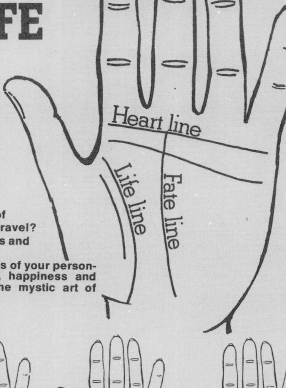

Heart line

Life line

Fate line

WILL I be lucky? What kind of romance will I have? Will I travel?

The answers to all these questions and many more are in your hand.

So read on to discover the secrets of your personality. We reveal the luck, health, happiness and romance in your life — through the mystic art of palmistry.

HEARTLINE —
Tells you most about your love life.

Starting Under First Finger
Luck in love will be yours.

Starting Under Middle Finger
You must try to be less selfish towards those you love!

Normal Length And Curved
You have a warm, pleasing, romantic nature.

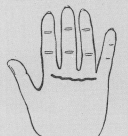

Short And Strong
You fall in love only once, but deeply.

Break
Break-up of big romance but you will eventually find happiness.

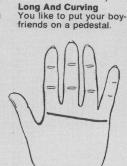

Starting High Up On Base Of Index Finger
A short romance and sudden marriage.

Long And Curving
You like to put your boy-friends on a pedestal.

Normal Length And Curved Upwards.
You're willing to sacrifice everything for love.

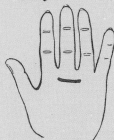

Wavy
You're a fickle, flirtatious girl!

Star
Happy marriage.

Starting Between Index And Middle Fingers
You give your heart away without thinking!

Long And Straight
Your heart controls your head.

Short And Thin
You have little interest in romance.

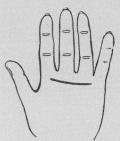

Faint
You have a faint heart in romantic matters!

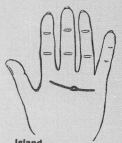

Island
An unhappy love affair!

Continued overleaf

190

YOUR LIFE IS IN YOUR HANDS

LIFE LINE —
Health, length of life, events affecting health and life.

Long and Clearly Marked
Good health, vitality, normal life span.

Short But Strong
Vitality, good chance of normal life span.

Short And Weak
Another person will control your life!

Doubled
A double dose of good health! A very lucky sign.

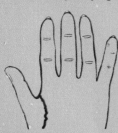

Weak and Wavy
Health problems and many changes in your life!

Swooping
Strong health.

Cramped
You're timid and shy especially in love!

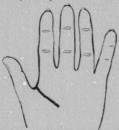

Sloping Towards Centre Of Palm
You will travel a great deal during your life.

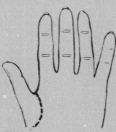

Chained
Many emotional problems! But you'll never be bored, you love adventure in life.

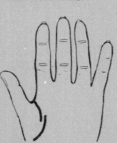

Break
Sudden change in life.

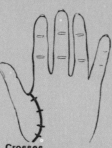

Crosses
Worries, but if the line is strong you are self-reliant and able to overcome setbacks.

Star
Crisis

FATE LINE-
The effect that other people and events have on shaping the course of your life — your destiny.

Strong And Deep
You'll have a very secure life with no money worries and you will make your name at whatever you choose to do. Fate will be kind to you.

Joined To Life Line At Start
To achieve what you desire in life you'll have to make many sacrifices at the beginning, but eventually you will have a very successful life.

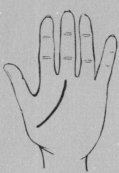

Starting On The Fleshy Pad Of The Thumb
Relatives will help you a great deal in reaching your goals in life.

Starting At The Heel Of The Palm
Destiny will bring you before the public. You will be a famous personality with a large following!

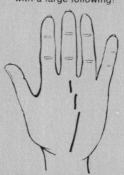

Breaks
Every break is a change of career or a big change in your life, such as emigration, a money windfall.

Branch From Fate Line To Heel Of Palm
A romance will influence your destiny for good or ill.

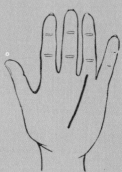

Fate Line Rising To Ring Finger
Success in your chosen career, probably something artistic.

Rising To Index Finger
Your career will place you in authority over others.

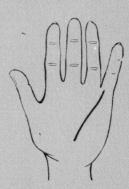

Rising To Little Finger
A career in some field of communication.

Star
Fame will come to you.

191

A Cathy & Claire Special on having that certain something....

REAL charm is a natural quality no-one can ignore, and some people can charm their way through life. People flock round them, and good fortune seems to come their way, almost as though they carry some sort of magic secret wherever they go.

Research has proved, for instance, that good-looking, charming children are more likely to do better at school than the ordinary and not-so-appealing kids.

The charmers may not be cleverer or more hardworking, it's just that they get more attention and more favoured treatment from teachers and examiners.

It seems awfully unfair, but people aren't even aware of favouring the charmed ones. It's just an automatic reaction.

Linda, aged 16, is one of the specially charmed people. All the boys fall for her, even though she's not always the most stunning girl at the party.

All the neighbours say what a lovely girl she is, although she's no more lovely than most girls.

She wasn't specially brilliant at school, yet she's just walked into a super job as P.A. to the boss of a small record company, where she was picked out from hundreds of applicants.

"I don't know why I got the job," she says modestly, "I think I'm very lucky that things usually seem to work out well for me. I must have been born under the right star, or something."

In fact, she was just born to be a charmer, and one of the ingredients of real charm is to be modest and natural with it.

People with natural charm are always noticed in a crowd. They seem to have some inner quality which shines out and spreads confidence.

People are magnetised by them and even insincere charm-power can be devastating till you see through it. How many women in history, and out of it, have given away fortunes to men who charmed them out of every penny?

BUT insincere charm can be very sickly indeed.

The cute kids who use insincere charm to get their own way are simply transparently calculating. You might be taken in by them at first, but you'll soon see through the act and realise that they're using their charm for selfish motives.

Sue, sixteen years old from Leeds, laughs when she recalls her early schooldays. At eight years old she had an angelic face, golden locks and large, beautiful blue eyes.

"I knew I was teacher's favourite," she says. "I knew how to get round grown-ups just with a smile. Well, I got rather fat when I was twelve and had my hair chopped off, and I found my charm didn't work on people any more.

"I guess it was a bit of a shock. I became very self-conscious because I felt I'd grown ugly and people didn't like me any more.

"It made me realise you can't go through life relying on being charming if you're not willing to put in the same work and effort as other people."

In fact, Sue's still very charming, it's just that she's stopped using her charm as a weapon. She realises that she is a far happier and more genuine person as a result.

If you're thinking you've missed out on all this beautiful charm, you can begin right now. Everyone has charm, it's just that most people don't develop it.

It has nothing to do with good looks, although good looking people find it easier to be charming because they usually have extra self-confidence.

Charm, you see, is really an attitude to life. If you feel good in yourself, you can be good to others.

The first important thing is to genuinely like other people, and take a real interest in what they are saying.

If you're always too busy worrying about the impression you are making on others, you can't be charming.

If you are suspicious and untrusting you can't be charming.

So charm begins by having sympathy for other people and being genuinely warm-hearted and open-natured.

SHYNESS is often an obstacle to charm.

Shy Sal envies the charmers and would like to be like them. She wants to talk and be friendly, but finds herself tongue-tied. She'd like to give a warm, sunny smile, but can't bring herself to commit herself for fear of being snubbed.

The will is there, and if Sal could control her shyness, she could be a real charmer.

It takes time and practice to overcome shyness, and the best thing to do is to practise little by little. Talk to people in shops and bus queues, talk to lonely old people and gradually build up to joining a club and getting on with boys and girls of your own age.

It's well-known that the less practice at meeting people you have, the more difficult it is to become at ease with people. And remember that if you really like people and want to get on with them, you'll manage it in the end.

Awkwardness in conversation is another problem. When you meet someone new you can make them feel at ease by talking about yourself and letting them know what sort of person you are. Then they will relax and begin to thaw through.

People with charm usually have to go more than half-way towards meeting others.

You don't have to make brilliant conversation to get along with people.

Even if you smile sweetly and embark on a boring description of the weather or the terrible 157A bus service, at least you're showing warmth and friendship, and others can't help responding.

The charming person has to have a strong enough personality to be able to cut across barriers of shyness and uncertainty.

A simple thing like a smile works wonders. Haven't you ever noticed that when someone smiles at you, it's almost impossible not to smile back?

Even when you're in a grumpy mood and you're walking down the street with a scowl on your face. Then a friend breezes up and gives you a glowing smile, and you suddenly find, quite without realising it, that you're grinning like a Cheshire cat.

So smiles and laughter are infectious and set a happy mood. **The charmers, above all, make others feel happy and at ease.**

MANY people cover their shyness by acting cool and casual. Instead of trying to overcome shyness they make it worse by refusing to admit it even to themselves and building up barriers between themselves and the rest of the world.

Wendy, aged 15, admitted being cool in self-defence against her shyness.

"I'm getting a bit better now," she said, "but a year ago I'd snub people at any opportunity. When someone spoke to me and tried to be friendly, I'd be as cool and off-hand as I could, just to show them that *I* was OK, and I didn't need *them*.

"Being honest, I was just petrified of being made to look foolish, in case I'd start stammering or blushing or something.

"So I pretended I didn't want friendship. Looking back I'm sure I hurt people often, specially shy people who needed courage to make the first move to be friendly."

Wendy discovered the secret of charm for herself, and she needed a lot of courage to drop her cool couldn't-care-less-act and show her real feelings for people.

The charmers are people who can show warm feelings towards others without fear of losing face.

Charmers have a good effect on other people. They never make people feel small or embarrassed. This means being easy-going and tactful, considering the other person's feelings and being sensitive to their moods.

Of course, natural courtesy and politeness are part of charm, but charm is often confused with social etiquette.

The rich young ladies who go to Charm Schools learn how to behave at a cocktail party, how to make small-talk at the races, and which cutlery to use for which course at a banquet. But that's not charm! You could be a charmless beast and still be an angel at a wedding party or a school open day!

Charm isn't an act. It's a way of life. We all have the natural charm there, and if we make a habit of using it more, we'd have lots more fun.

You can't learn it in a charm school; you just have to practise it in your everyday life. Don't go overboard on the fatal charm all at once, though. People won't know what's hit them!

Are you a real charmer?

CLEVER CLOTHES

PLANNING a wardrobe's a difficult job. You can end up with all sorts of colours that don't match and some things that you can't wear at all because they don't go with anything you've got!

We've divided you up into two groups . . . the casual 'jeans' look for those of you who love wearing trousers day and night and the dressier look for people who prefer skirts and dresses. There's a day-time look for each group and a night-time look, so there's something for everyone.

DAY-TIME THE DRESSED-UP LOOK

Some girls like to wear skirts and dresses, others have to for work where trousers may not be allowed. The secret of a useful 'everyday' wardrobe is simple . . . make sure that the basic colour is a plain, fairly dark one. You can always brighten it up with coloured shirts, jumpers and scarves so choose something like black, brown, dark green or the grey we've chosen here.

Our day-time wardrobe consists of a grey suit with A-line skirt, which is the most flattering kind for most shapes. The jacket is simple, too, shaped at the waist and single-breasted.

The cotton shirt is in a plain colour and has a tailored collar and long sleeves. The total look is smart without being over-dressed, it will take you anywhere and will last for ages, especially if you save up for a suit in good material that will wear — as it keeps its shape and lasts for ages.

Stage two shows a really useful wrapover cardigan, that's warm and flattering for most shapes and can be worn indoors or out on warmer days. It's really a second sort of jacket, not just a cardigan that needs another jacket over the top.

Next comes a pinafore in the same colour as the skirt and jacket. Wear it with the jacket on top and the shirt underneath and you've got a completely different look. We chose a simple v-necked style rather than a scoop neck, v-necks are much more versatile.

When it's chilly you can pop on a polo-neck under the pinafore or the suit, or under the cardigan.

Accessories like bags, belts and shoes should be plain, we chose black to go with the grey but choose brown ones if your basic colours are brown or green.

Scarves can be plain or patterned . . . it's nice to have some of each so you can ring the changes. Buy different shapes, too, some long and thin, some square so they all look different.

CLEVER YOU!

DAY-TIME THE JEANS LOOK

Jeans don't always have to be ragged and tatty, you know. We've chosen a very simple pair for our casual look, with two pockets and zip-up front. They're slightly flared and you can make them look how you want, very casual or dressier with smocks or jackets.

The first, everyday look we chose is made up from the jeans, plus a bright, plain shirt and a plain, round-necked navy wool jumper with long sleeves.

Buying a jacket the same colour as the jeans is a great idea, like this button-up bomber jacket which is warm but very casual. Pop it on over a sleeveless T-shirt like this scoop-necked one.

For a dressier look you could pop on a smock over a shirt, great for disguising unwanted layers around your hips and bottom! Buy a plain smock so you can brighten it up with patterned shirts, scarves etc.

The complete look is simple and very, very useful. Just jacket, jeans and a plain shirt, not at all fussy, but not tatty either.

Accessories should be simple . . . a pair of laced-up shoes and matching bag were our choice, plus one matching scarf and one other patterned.

The jeans look seems to have got itself a bad name, but there's no reason why you should keep it going by looking scruffy in yours.

Take care with accessories and always make sure that your clothes are clean with the right number of buttons, etc. and absolutely no hems hanging down!

NIGHT-TIME ALL DRESSED UP

Night time's always difficult when it comes to clothes, especially if you go to a regular club or disco every week. It's impossible to buy different things so how can you make what you've got go further?

Easy, invest in a really plain dress like this blue one that we've chosen. It's straight, but not too tight, sleeveless with a round neck that isn't plunging and isn't too high, either.

Now, the obvious thing to do next is to pop on a really super blouse underneath . . . this one's got a tie-neck and wide, floaty sleeves. These will cover up any extra flab on upper arms, should you have any!

Then there's always the over-shirt like this one that's got long sleeves and is nipped in at the waist. It can serve as a sort of evening jacket, too, to save you carting along a thick coat that doesn't go with the dress. Choose your colours carefully, though, plain colours will look smartest together.

A floaty smock looks great over the dress, too, and can disguise figure faults. This one's really floaty with short, wide sleeves and a round neck . . . remember it should be high enough to cover the top of the dress, though, otherwise it will all look awful!

Ring the changes with different evening accessories, black shoes and bag are best and you'll probably find that cheap 'silver' jewellery looks much nicer than cheap 'gold', so go for stainless steel bangles and chokers.

Buy scarves in all sorts of colours to tie round your neck, long silky ones look great. Invest in a shawl, too, to pop round your shoulders when evenings are chilly!

Sometimes you just can't get away with wearing your jeans to everything and you feel you have to try and dress up! No point in putting on a dress if you're going to feel silly in it, so invest in a really good pair of black trousers. Black's a flattering colour for heavyweights, too, so they're just right for everyone.

Grey and black look great, so we chose a soft grey bomber jacket in silky material with long sleeves. Put a shirt underneath or just wear it on its own, zipped up of course!

Really dressy is a super jacket, like this sequinned one we found, black velvet would be great, too. Buy a plain grey sleeveless T-shirt to go underneath, sew sequins on it one week if you want, your name on it the next.

Same jacket and trousers again, but this time with a plain shirt, with ties at the waist . . . just hang up your jacket when you're ready to dance!

Smocks are great for evening, in soft materials with wide sleeves. Make sure they're not so see-through that your bra shows through, though, and remember that a flesh-coloured bra won't be half as noticeable as a white one.

If you're going to a disco where they might have those ultra-violet lights that pick out everything white, don't wear knickers with a white lace trim if there's the slightest possibility of it being seen and check for white labels on the insides of things that might look very odd when picked out by those lights!

Black shoes and bags are best with black trousers, of course, and choose wide, shiny belts and pretty scarves to cheer everything up!

We haven't given you prices (because they change so quickly) or manufacturers' names as they can't guarantee that particular clothes will be in your area at the time you're reading this.

But these are the looks to aim for, so follow our fashion pages every week in Jackie and have fun shopping around!

NIGHT-TIME THE TROUSERS LOOK

what's your nature?

WHY does a storm excite some people, and frighten or depress others? Well, even without realising it, we all respond to nature, and the way in which we respond reveals a lot about our personality.

So study each of our illustrations carefully and decide which statement is closest to the way you feel. Then count up your score and turn to the conclusions to find out the hidden personality secrets you've revealed!

1. A light rain in the forest.
a) It makes you want to run barefoot in the grass.
c) You hope it stops soon so you can plan a picnic.
b) You want to walk beneath the dripping trees with the boy you love.
d) It's fabulous to stay at home with a good book.

2. Sunset on a south sea island.
a) You'd like to lie in the sand and let the surf lap over you.
d) You excitedly explore your surroundings.
c) You fall asleep lulled by the soft tropical breeze.
b) A suntanned boy plays a song specially written for you on his guitar.

3. Venice in the fog.
c) It depresses you and you imagine the city is closing in on you.
a) You feel a tremendous sense of excitement, mystery and suspense.
b) It is an ideal place to arrange a secret meeting with the boy you love.
d) You long to seek out all the most fascinating corners.

4. Storm over the city.
a) It makes you feel totally exhilarated.
b) You rush into the comfort of your boyfriend's arms.
d) You're glad because it will clear away the smog.
c) What a drag! All that rain.

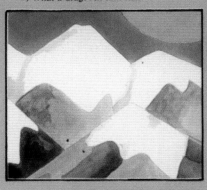

5. The sun shining on snow-covered mountains.
a) You cover your body with freshly fallen snow.
c) You feel bored.
b) You're enchanted and dazzled.
d) You take a brisk walk.

6. The moon over a desert oasis.
c) It makes you sleepy.
d) You feel like writing the most beautiful love poem ever.
b) A handsome sheik passes by and carries you off on his camel!
a) You lie down on the sand and bathe in the moon's rays.

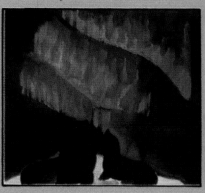

7. Light shining on the North Pole.
a) You shiver — not from cold but from intense excitement.
b) You feel amazed to be actually there.
d) You're interested in the reflection of the light on snow.
c) It doesn't particularly affect you.

CONCLUSIONS

If you had mostly (a):
You have a full appreciation of nature. You are sensitive, receptive and gifted with a passionate love of the city, fresh air and lush temperament. You can't stand the restrictions of open spaces, fresh air and lush countryside. You like to feel at one with nature because it frees you from everyday cares and liberty of open spaces.

If you had mostly (b):
You are a serious girl with acute and delicate. You don't have profound views on life. You are sensitive and you have a constant need love to be petted and caressed. You're inclined for company, to be alone and to use your imagination and you to dream, to try to escape from the real world.

If you had mostly (c):
You don't enjoy life to the fullest, and tend to be narrow in your outlook. You hate flights of fantasy, poetic abandon. You are doubtful of everything until you see yourself how it will materially benefit you. If you free yourself from this attitude, you'll find your life more complete.

If you had mostly (d):
You are gifted with acute powers of observation and with you, reason and emotion. But you also hate imagination and always look deeply into the superficiality and exploring your own motives and judging on a whim. In this way you sacrifice acting impulsively on a whim, but every sensation you feel, explore them. Look deeply into the do of experience makes a lasting impression on you.

G-AYIB

IT'S the sort of scene you've probably dreamed about. It's springtime, the sun's beating down, and you're alone in the country — alone, that is, except for the Bay City Rollers!

It all happened earlier this year when the Rollers were staying at a health farm deep in the heart of Hampshire. They came up to London for a day to record a spot for for "Top Of The Pops," and while I was chatting to them in their dressing room, they invited me to go down and visit them at the farm.

As you probably know, only four of the five members of the group went to the health farm. Les decided instead to go home to Edinburgh — for a very special reason!

"I'm taking flying lessons!" he told me. "I went down to see the people at Edinburgh Flying Club, and they've agreed to give me lessons. I've to go down to Edinburgh Airport tomorrow. I can't wait!

"I really want to learn to fly a helicopter, because they're more useful than planes. They can take off and land anywhere. But it takes ages to qualify as a pilot!"

In fact, Les turned out to have a natural flair for flying, and within a few months he was able to act as pilot for the rest of the group, and fly them from one town to another in the small private plane you see in the photo!

Although Les with his usual endless supply of energy, was spending his holiday racing about all over the place, the rest of the group were taking things much more quietly.

They told me that the health farm was the perfect place for them to relax and recover, away from the stresses and strains of the pop world. And when I arrived there the next morning, it was easy to see why they liked it!

To get to the farm itself, you have to turn off the road and drive for what seems miles up a drive which winds through thick woods. Then, just as you think you're never going to reach it, you turn a corner, and suddenly, there it is — a large, rambling building, with beautifully kept lawns leading down to a boating lake.

Driving round the edge of the lake, David the photographer, who'd given me a lift down to the farm, drove into the car park and parked our Mini between a Daimler and a Rolls Royce!

Then we went inside the building, where the receptionist told us to go straight up to the boys' bedrooms. They turned out to be right at the other end of the building, through a door marked "Men's Treatments" (ladies go through "Women's Treatments"!) which led into a corridor of rooms, all containing strange-looking machines that looked suspiciously like instruments of torture!

Then it was up a flight of stairs, past the sauna baths and the beauty salon, until at last we arrived at rooms 21 and 22 — the "Rollers' bedrooms!

JUST at that moment, th first door opened, an Derek looked out, smilin in his usual friendly wa

"Hello there," he said, "I thought I hear voices. Come on in!"

Inside the room, I discovered Eri kneeling on the floor, carefully ironing pair of jeans.

"Hi," he said. "You've come just in tim for lunch. We'll go down as soon as I'v finished this. I won't be long!"

While I was waiting, I sat down on one c the white-covered twin beds and looke round the room. It was big and airy with colour T V playing silently in one corne

"We're sharing this room," Derek said "and Alan and Woody are in the room nex door.

Just then, right on cue, Alan and Wood appeared. Like the others, they wer dressed in the health farr "uniform" — very smart, royal blu tracksuits.

They told me that, that afternoon everyone but Woody intended to g horse-riding.

"As you know, I'm allergic to horses," h told me. "They bring me out in a rash! It's real shame, because I love horse riding But it's just not worth it. I might enjoy it a the time, but I suffer for ages afterwards.

Instead, Woody was intending to tr out a very exotic skin treatment that he' seen advertised on the clinic's notic board.

"It's supposed to vacuum your skin an deep cleanse your pores — or somethin like that!" he laughed. "So you won recognise me when I come back, I'll be s sparkling and clean!"

By this time, Eric had finished hi ironing, so we all trooped down to th dining room for a lunch of delicious healthy salads.

As we ate, Eric and Woody took grea delight in leaning over the table and tellin us in whispers that the man at the nex table was a millionaire, and the old lad sitting by the window in dressing gow and slippers was a duchess!

AFTER lunch, the boys change into jeans, and saying good bye to Woody, everyone pile into our car and we set o to the stables, which were over the othe side of the lake.

"The man who runs the stables is friend of ours," Alan told me. "He used t run our local riding stable in Edinburg before he moved down here."

THE FARM...

At the stables, the stable boy, John introduced us to our horses. Mine was a nice quiet one (thank goodness!) called Pampiano, Derek and Alan were riding dark brown horses called Florinda and Senorita, and Eric was riding what he said was "the best horse of the lot," a very frisky grey called The Pickler.

When I remarked that these were quite uncommon names, Eric explained that that was because these were no ordinary horses!

"They're all very valuable," he told me, "because they've been specially trained as polo ponies. You'll soon discover that for yourself, actually. Be careful when you pull your horse up, because they're used to stopping dead in the middle of polo matches. If you're not careful, you find yourself bumping all over the place!"

As we rode out into the field, Derek told me that they often held polo matches at the stables.

"They're holding one this evening in fact," he said. "We might come down to watch!"

"We also have lots of shows here," added John, who'd come out to keep an eye on us! "On average, we have about three a week. And we get all sorts of famous people coming down for the shows — Princess Anne and Mark Phillips, for instance!"

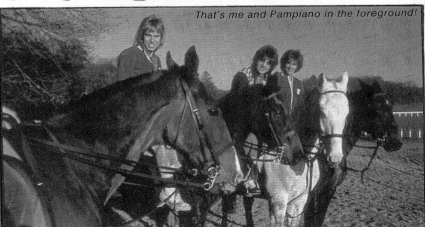
That's me and Pampiano in the foreground!

The Rollers decided to ride down to the lake, so the five of us set off together down the track, with poor old David following on foot!

The boys were all good riders, but out of the three, Alan seemed to be the most experienced.

"I've been riding for years now," he told me. "I used to look after the horses at our local dairy in Edinburgh, and I also used to go up to the common and ride the ponies that belonged to some gipsies who lived there.

"Of course, I don't have much time to go riding these days, but I still love horses."

Derek meanwhile, was impatient to let his pony canter. He obviously liked riding fast! When I suggested he should have been a cowboy instead of a pop star, he laughed and agreed.

"I would have loved to have seen the Wild West as it was in the olden days," he told me. "I love cowboy films. It must have been a great life!"

Eric, on the other hand, had ambitions to be a show jumper.

"I've done a bit of jumping," he said, "but I haven't had much time to practise. At one point, I was intending to buy myself a horse that I could jump, but I haven't had a chance to so far.

"Still, I'll maybe get round to it sometime. I'd love to have my own horse."

At the lake, the boys decided to take their horses into the water for a paddle. Senorita and Florinda splashed in happily, but The Pickler wasn't so sure. First of all, he wouldn't go in the water, and then, once Eric had persuaded him to go in, he wouldn't come out again!

Finally, everyone arrived safely back on dry land and despite all the splashing about that had been going on, nobody's jeans had even got damp.

"Now you know the real reason why we wear our trousers so short!" laughed Eric.

Going back through the woods towards the stables, Eric told me he was sorry we hadn't time for a longer ride.

"Sometimes we go off into the hills for two or three hours at a time," he told me. "You can ride right up to the top of the hill behind the farm. It's beautiful up there."

AT the stables, we put our horses back in their boxes, and then, waving goodbye to John, headed back up to the health farm.

At the door, we met Woody, all clean and glowing from his skin treatments!

"It was great!" he told us. "My skin feels really good."

The treatment also seemed to have given Woody an appetite!

"I'm starving!" he said. "Come on, let's go and have tea."

Tea consisted of slices of wholemeal bread and butter, a piece of the most delicious home-made fruit cake, and a choice of Indian or China tea —without sugar.

"That was a bit of a shock to us at first," said Alan, "because we all take sugar in our tea normally. But it's surprising how quickly you get used to the taste."

After tea, Derek went off to his daily yoga class, and Alan and Woody decided to go for a run in the woods. Eric, meanwhile, offered to show us round the games rooms.

First of all, he took us into the billiards room which was in a separate building across the drive.

"We spend a lot of time in here," he said. "We're getting quite good at it now. The other night, we got so involved in the game

that we forgot what time it was. And when we went back over to the main building, we discovered they'd locked us out!

"We'd to stand and bang on the door until someone came to let us in!"

Along the back wall of the billiards room was an amazing set of photos of stars who'd spent some time at the health farm. There were hundreds of film, T V and pop stars there — and every single photo had a signed message written on it, thanking the staff of the health farm for their help.

"We're going to get a photo of us and get it up on the wall as well," said Eric. "That'll be great, won't it?"

Then he took us upstairs to the exercise room which contained things like weight-lifting equipment, medicine balls and two cycling machines.

I had a go on one of the cycling machines but I have to admit, I didn't get very far! After pedalling for ages and ages, I'd still only managed to clock up three tenths of a mile on the metre!

"Oh, that's nothing!" said Eric. "We have to do at least 10 miles a day!"

As we strolled back across the drive, I asked Eric what he liked most about the health farm.

"Well," he said, quite seriously, "the main thing is that it's relaxing!"

Well, it may have been the Rollers' idea of relaxing, but it certainly wasn't mine! By this time, I was beginning to feel I'd done quite enough for one day.

So, leaving the Rollers to make their plans for the evening, I headed back up to London — feeling quite relieved to be getting back to some peace and quiet!

IT'S OUR CHRISTM

Princess Caroline of Monaco — because we're masochists — and because Alan fancies her!

Linda Lewis — because she's a super, fun, bubbly person — and because Alan fancies her!

Fanny Craddock — So she could do all the cooking, of course.

Princess Anne — Just to add a bit of class — and to make sure her brothers came along, too.

Pan's People — Well, we have to have some girls. And it would be nice to see them as they used to be on Top of the Pops.

Mae West — Because she's so witty and dynamic. And because she'd be able to tell us all the secrets of Hollywood in the Thirties . . .

John Curry — Who better to break the ice at a party?

Lee Majors — Because Dorothy fancies him — and she wants to see if he's really bionic . . .

Bing Crosby — Did you know that he's sold one million copies of "White Christmas?". It'd be nice if he could do it one more time just for us.

Jack Nicholson — Because we've always wanted to get our hands on an Oscar — and an Oscar winner!

Bryan Ferry — Because Nina's met him twice at parties before and she's hoping it'll be third time lucky!

Muhammad Ali — Well, we have to have a bouncer, and who better to get rid of unwanted gate-crashers?

Bianca Jagger — Alison would invite her, then tell Mohammed Ali she wasn't invited, so he'd throw her out.

Telly Savalas — Mary reckons he could provide the other blokes there with a lesson in how to treat a lady. Also, she fancies older men . . .

Stavros — He could cook delicious real American hamburgers for us. And Mary thinks he's cute and cuddly . . .

Gordon Jackson (Mr Hudson in "Upstairs, Downstairs") — Everyone in here's too lazy to go round all the other guests with crisps and peanuts and drinks and things . . .

Prince Andrew — Alison and Sandy agreed that if one of them gets off with Prince Charles, the other can chat up his young brother.

Tom Baker (Dr. Who) — If the party got boring, or if too many people turned up, he could whisk the bores and the extras to a different time zone where they couldn't bother us any more . . .

S PARTY!

And, as you can see, we've invited all (well, almost all) our favourite people. Our reasons for inviting them are all very personal (and very different!) and we didn't all agree on some of them! But, after a lot of argue . . . em . . . discussion, we finally decided that these guests would make any party go with a swing . . .

Leonard Nimoy (Mr Spock of Star Trek) — He can try the Vulcan mind probe on us any time!

Vincent Price — If things look like getting too hot, he can always chill our spines!

Robert Shaw (Captain Quint in "Jaws") — Can you imagine the size of turkey we'd need to feed all the people at this party? Quint's the only guy who'd dare take it on! Maybe they could film it and call it "Gobble" . . .

Paul Newman — Because we all want to stand and gaze into those incredibly blue, blue eyes . . .

Prince Charles — Because we all reckon that if he could only see us and talk to us, he'd fall instantly in love with us and then we could get to be Queen. Also, we all (at least, Alison and Sandy) think he's lovely!

Paul McCartney — Because he's lovely and everyone except Cheryl fancies him like mad, so while they were all chatting him up, Cheryl would be free to work on Prince Charles.

Dad's Army — We think they're all sweet (especially Godfrey) and since Mary fancies older men, there should be plenty here for her . . .

Les McKeown, Midge Ure of Slik, Yan from Kenny — To see if all three get on as well as the groups say they do. And if the record player broke down, we wouldn't be short of music.

The rest of the Rollers and Slik — Well, it wouldn't be a party without them, would it?

Brian May of Queen — Because Una, one of our artists, says she won't come unless he's there.

Mike Yarwood — In case nobody else turns up!

Mick Robertson — He's super and he's got such a fantastic voice. Jenny thinks it would be nice to have a quiet conversation with him (preferably in the broom cupboard) when she didn't feel like dancing.

Mick Jagger — So Alison could take him on a guided tour of the office buildings — including the filing cabinets . . .

Elton John — Because he's the star of any party — and he could bring along all his famous friends. We wouldn't mind a few extra people . . .

Robert Redford — Because . . . well, just because he's Robert Redford!

The Wombles — Everyone else is too lazy to clear all the mess up afterwards.

Fred Astaire — Because he's the best dancing partner anyone could possibly have!

HAVE YOU GOT WHAT IT TAKES?

WELL, have you? Do boys stop and stare when you bombshell by and generally stampede to get you under the mistletoe? If not, why not? Perhaps you're the original Ice-Maiden, all snowed-up inside, freezing them out, and leaving a trail of broken hearts behind you? To find out exactly what kind of appeal YOU have, answer our fun quiz and we'll tell you just how with it (or without it!) you are.

1. You're at a party and there are lots of lovely males around. What's your first reaction?
(a) Super! Which one shall I have first?
(c) That one over there looks nice.
(b) You fancy one in particular, but you aren't going to let him know it.
(d) So what?

2. Your long-lost cousin traps you under the mistletoe. He's very good looking. What would you do?
(b) Kiss him of course, but not by any means passionately.
(d) Give him a cousinly peck on the cheek.
(c) Keep still and let him do the kissing.
(a) Show him just how much you've learned about kissing!

3. What do you think about kissing in general?
(a) It's the best thing since nail varnish!
(c) Not sure yet — you'll have to get some more practice in!
(d) It has to be over-rated.
(b) Lovely — with the one and only boy for you.

4. How do boys usually react to you?
(b) They're very protective towards you.
(c) They don't know quite what to make of you.
(d) They're a tiny bit frightened of you.
(a) They hang about making suggestive suggestions!

5. You see that special boy walking along the street and you feel —
(b) amazingly, crazily, happy,
(d) all warm inside,
(a) like you're tingling from top to toe,
(c) half thrilled, half afraid.

6. A gang of workmen start to whistle at you. How do you feel?
(c) It depends on the workmen!
(d) Annoyed.
(b) A bit embarrassed.
(a) Delighted! At least they've noticed you.

7. What's most likely to be your favourite party outfit?
(b) A long floaty feminine dress.
(c) Something bright and beautiful.
(a) A figure hugging T-shirt dress in soft velour or velvet.
(d) An elegant and classic dress with a high neck and long sleeves.

8. Given the chance, who would you most like to change places with?
(c) Linda McCartney.
(a) Bianca Jagger
(b) Marie Osmond.
(d) Angie Bowie.

9. What's your favourite party game?
(a) Postman's knock.
(b) Sardines.
(c) Murder-in-the-dark.
(d) You don't have one. You think they're a bit silly actually.

10. What's the nicest thing he could possibly say to you?
(c) You're the most beautiful thing that ever happened to me.
(b) Marry me?
(d) I only want you for your mind!
(a) I think you're the sexiest thing on two legs!

11. What's your favourite bath routine?
(d) A sparkling shower and rub down with cologne.
(b) Lots of bubbles — and "Jackie" to read.
(a) A long, hot steam, with amber oil.
(c) A sauna.

12. What do you really think of boys. Are they —
(a) a lot of fun,
(c) some pleasure, some pain,
(d) a challenge,
(b) the ones who wear trousers *all* the time?

13. When he looks at your for the very first time, what's he most likely to notice?
(b) Your face.
(d) Your eyes.
(c) Your general expression.
(a) Your figure.

14. The lights go out at a party and suddenly someone grabs you! Do you —
(a) grab him right back,
(d) deliver a neat karate chop,
(b) scream (then giggle),
(c) just plain scream?

15. How much energy do you have?
(c) If you're happy, you've got tons; if not, none!
(a) You're always bubbling over with it.
(b) You mostly seem to have it when you need it.
(d) Basically, you're a bit lazy really.

QUIZ CONCLUSIONS

MOSTLY A
You've got it, all right! Tons of it — there's no doubt about that! Wherever there's fun to be had, you're generally there, too. Boys find your bubbling nature truly irresistible and usually they don't put up much resistance! Nor do you, if he's as easy-going and nice-to-be-near as you are yourself. But you can run into trouble when some boy mistakes your freewheeling attitude for something more serious.

You have to know how to say No, and nicely, without him thinking you really mean Yes! It's best to make it quite clear where your heart really is, as you're the kind of girl they used to fight duels over - and they could be back in fashion! So be very careful where you flutter your eyelashes — or you could be fighting them off on the doorstep!

MOSTLY B
Warm, cosy and lovable, that's you! You're everybody's pet person. You have the kind of appeal that makes a boy think about firesides and slippers and apple-pies. It might sound very old-fashioned, but get him as relaxed as that and you've got him well and truly hooked! You're the sort of girl who makes him feel comfortable, flattered and protective. He'll want to look after you almost from the start. You stand for all the nicest things about being a girl. He loves you because you're deeply romantic and truly affectionate, and because you care about people, about animals, and, most of all, about *him*. And so he should, he's a lucky guy! Just make certain he's the right one, and you have the best chance of all of living happily ever after!

MOSTLY C
Completely unpredictable, changeable as the ocean, broodingly moody and, occasionally, even mean - that's what they say about you! Boys find you absolutely fascinating because they haven't the faintest idea what you're really like. (Often, you haven't either, but that's your secret charm). You're a mystery, even to yourself.

If you say Yes today, it's likely to be No by tomorrow! You don't mean to be maddening; you just can't help it! Your feelings seem to go up and down like a yo-yo, and you never know whether the day will end in smiles or tears. Sometimes it's a bit difficult for you to know whether you really love or trust someone, but you're going to have to take the chance sooner or later, because you can't string him along forever!

MOSTLY D
Ice-cold princess, that's you! You have the enviable ability to scare the fellas stiff whenever you feel like it and only the bravest and best will take on the challenge. It'll be well worth it when someone does, though, because, although there's precious little sign of it on the surface, there's fire beneath that ice! The really intelligent ones (and that's the only kind that interest you) will bring their own want to be obtained!

You have the kind of attraction that enslaves forever; it's simply the amazing allure of the unobtainable! But sometimes, you're the one who misses out because, really, you actually want to be obtained!

So try to let a little of that hidden fire into your eyes and, show some more warmth and behave less like the Snow Queen. It could have interesting results!

<hr>

20 WAYS TO BE IRRESISTIBLE

1. Always look as if something wonderful is about to happen, and with any luck — it will.

2. Go out with a price ticket attached to the back of your coat or jacket. Nobody will be able to resist telling you about it — and it's a great way to start a conversation, especially if you make the ticket a nice big price.

3. Be fun to be with. Sing in the rain, yodel in the snow; if nobody laughs with you, someone's sure to laugh at you.

4. Become very rich. A wallet full of twenty pound notes makes anyone irresistible.

5. Cultivate becoming one of those people who always seem to say and do exactly the right things at exactly the right times!

6. Sit by yourself in a corner or on a park bench looking lost and tearful. No boy can resist a damsel in distress, even in this day and age.

7. Use musk–based scents, which are derived from the musk glands some musk deer use to attract their mates. It's supposed to work on human males too, only you'd best not visit the zoo at mating time — you might be in for a few surprises!

8. Try to be nice to everyone, and not just the people you care about.

9. Look dark and mysterious — if not irresistible, you'll certainly be interesting.

10. Find out as much as you can about anything you can think of. At least you'll be able to impress everyone with your conversation and general knowledge.

11. Find something nice about everyone.

12. Take a party of boys to the Hampton Court Maze, and hide yourself in the middle. They won't be able to get away from you — however hard they try, they'll keep coming back!

13. Work in a sweet shop. Sooner or later, everyone falls for something soft and sweet.

14. Soak yourself in expensive French perfume. (At least the chemist will love you.)

15. Enter, and win, the Miss World contest. That way you're sure to be irresistible to at least half the population of the world.

16. Start carrying a machine gun around with you. You'll find that people suddenly become very willing to obey your every command — whatever it might be.

17. Never take the power of a kiss for granted — develop your kiss into a deadly weapon, guaranteed to knock any boy flat on his back.

18. Smile a lot at everyone you meet. You'll often get a smile in return. (Don't smile *all* the time though, or someone's sure to come up to you and say, "All right, clever clogs, what's so funny!")

19. Impress everyone with your great sense of humour and sparkling personality. These often count much more than looks, so don't worry if you're not exactly a cross between Racquel Welch and Susan George.

20. Don't act as if you *are* irresistible!

ARE you one of life's beautiful dreamers, making quick getaways from the same boring old routines, faces and places to dreamy, faraway worlds of glamour, gaiety and glitter? Or are you one of those down-to-earth, hard-headed realists who have both feet always firmly planted on the ground? To find out the kind of stuff your daydreams are made of, and exactly what your daydreams reveal about your personality, follow our fascinating quiz . . .

HOW DREAMY ARE YOU?

1. When a boy hasn't looked at you, let alone smiled at you for a whole month, do you daydream that you're —
(d) Miss World,

(b) a fashion magazine cover-girl,
(c) sought after by legions of fanciable boys,
(a) the girlfriend of some handsome American millionaire?

2. You know for sure that the letter lying on the mat is just another bill for Dad, but in your daydreams it's —
(a) to tell you you've won the pools,
(d) to tell you a famous film producer wants to groom you for stardom,
(c) from an anonymous admirer to tell you how much he loves you,
(b) to tell you you've won a competition — and the prize is a night out at your local cinema with David Essex?

3. When you begin to wonder if you'll ever find someone to love, which situation seems dreamiest to you?
(a) To have a famous on-off relationship like Liz Taylor and Richard Burton.
(b) To be married five times.
(c) To have one glorious, steady love of a life-time.
(d) To have a tragic, secret and forbidden romance, full of heartache and joy.

4. When you feel you're just a nobody, do you dream of seeing yourself —
(a) on a 'wanted for bank robbery' poster,
(c) on a huge billboard with your name in flashing neon lights,
(b) on telly, advertising soap suds,

(d) immortalised by a famous portrait artist in the National Gallery?

5. When you go to deposit a few measly pounds in your post office savings account, do you dream of investing in —
(c) an Indian tea plantation,
(d) a chain of luxury hotels in Florida,
(b) a metal foundry in Huddersfield,
(a) a diamond mine in South Africa?

6. Waiting at a cold, dreary bus stop in the pouring rain, do you dream you're —

(a) lazing on a private beach in the South of France,
(b) eating chips on the prom at Bognor,
(d) eating scampi in New York,

(c) lying beneath the waving palm trees of a beautiful desert island?

7. When you've disgraced yourself, failing exams and getting rotten reports, which great honour do you dream of having bestowed upon you?
(b) To have a book written about you.
(a) To have a ship named after you.
(c) To have a song written to you.
(d) To have a street in your town named after you?

8. When you go to the disco and no-one asks you up to dance, do you daydream —
(a) that all the boys are queueing up to dance with you,
(d) that you look so beautiful and cool, none of the boys dare ask you,
(c) that a boy across the crowded room has fallen instantly and desperately in love with you,

(b) that none of the boys are good enough for you, and you've turned them all down anyway?

9. Listening to smoochy music, getting yourself all depressed and feeling lonely with just your radio for company, which dream boy do you imagine you're dancing with?
(a) A super-sophisticated boy who's in with the jet set.
(b) A particular real-life boy you've always fancied.
(d) Your favourite pop star.
(c) A mysterious, romantic stranger.

10. When you feel you must be the dullest, most ordinary person in the world, do you dream that —
(c) you're actually the nicest, most beautiful girl in the world, only you can't tell anyone in case they get nasty and jealous,
(d) you're actually related to the Royal Family and were found by gipsies when you were a baby,
(a) you're actually the richest person in the world, but you have to keep it a secret for your family's sake,
(b) you're a genius with an IQ of 250 but you can't let anyone know until you pass your O-levels?

11. It's Saturday night but you've nowhere to go and nothing to do. You're feeling a bit miserable. Do you start to dream that you've been invited —
(b) to a friend's birthday party rave-up,
(c) to a romantic dinner for two,
(a) to a private party on board a society yacht,
(d) to a mad round of jam-packed fun, first the speedway then the disco, and after that there's dawn sausage and mash at the all-night transport cafe?

12. When you look in the mirror and groan, do you dream you had the money/courage to —
(c) go platinum blonde,

(d) have extensive plastic surgery,
(a) go to an exclusive health and beauty farm for a month,
(b) buy and use the best, complete range of make-up on the market?

13. Everything goes wrong: you quarrel with your boyfriend; your friends gang up on you; mum nags you; no-one loves you, and you feel life just isn't fair. So you think everything would be so different if you were —
(b) Marie Osmond,
(c) Linda McCartney,
(d) Princess Anne,
(a) Aristotle Onassis's daughter.
Now count your score, mainly (a), (b), (c) or (d) and turn to the conclusions

how dreamy are you?

Quiz Conclusions Continued from page 70

Mostly (A)

You're the million dollar girl whose daydreams centre around money and the good life. Never mind if you haven't got a penny in the bank, your daydreams take you round all the rich, jet-set centres of the world — from luxury hotel, to casino, to millionaire's private beach and island.

You're a bit of a sophisticate: you have good taste and appreciate good things, and for you, money *does* buy happiness. You're a big spender at heart, though, which shows that you're basically an open-hearted and generous person.

You're extremely sociable and have a magnetic personality and few doubts about yourself, because you have a basic self-confidence and faith in yourself. You'd like to be at the centre of a sophisticated and fun-loving crowd of friends and you're motivated by a desire to impress other people. This goes with an ambitious nature — you want to get to the top of the ladder of success and you're not afraid of hard work if you think it will achieve your goals. You'll probably choose a fairly glamorous career and you won't be content with being second-best.

An ordinary type of existence isn't good enough for you — you want something a bit special. Basically, you want a life of comfort, ease and luxury, and really, you should have been born rich. If you weren't, well, never mind, because you've got the go and determination to get what you want and work to make your dreams come true.

Mostly (B)

Of all the dreamers, you're the one who's best able to face up to reality. Daydreaming's all right in its place, but you don't take it seriously — it's just a laugh for you. You don't believe in your daydreams partly because you just can't see all those fabulous things happening to little old you, and partly because real life is pretty nice anyway, so it doesn't matter much if your dreams fall on barren ground.

You're the type who makes the best of things as they are. You can accept things and enjoy life without wishing too much for the things you haven't got. You have the ability to be realistic about yourself, and you're mature enough to be able to come to terms with your faults as well as your good points. This gives you a strength which many other people lack. Because you're realistic about yourself, and you don't expect miracles, you cope much better than most.

You don't expect too much from life. Your attitudes are sane and practical; you can be quite tough when you have to be, and you have a clear-sighted view of your surroundings and your relationships. In fact, you're so well-adjusted to life, you hardly need to daydream at all — though it's relaxing when you're in the mood!

Mostly (C)

You're a romantic dreamer — all your daydreams are centred around love and romance, and your deep sensitivity of feeling. Your dreams are full of the most wonderful romantic situations, of deep relationships, and mad, passionate love affairs!

Everything in your dreams is centred around your emotions, and there isn't much room for ordinary feelings or any dull, routine happenings. How can real life possibly match up to your beautiful visions? You must guard against living in your dreams too much, though. Because you expect so much from life, disillusion may set in unless you ration the dreams a bit and come to terms with the hard unromantic world.

Basically, you're a loving sort of person, gentle and emotional. You're very aware and very sensitive to others — often too sensitive for your good. You feel everything very deeply and the most important things in your life are always to do with relationships with others. You have the ability to give a lot and to get a lot of satisfaction in return, and if you can find a boy who's as loving as you are, you'll have a wonderful relationship. But you must come to terms with the fact that not everyone in the world is as loving and genuine as you are, so be careful not to get hurt.

Mostly (D)

Your daydreams are wild, wonderful and far-fetched and you want the best of everything — riches, fame, beauty, adventure, excitement and all the best things life has to offer. You throw yourself into your daydreams and you really enjoy imagining yourself in the most romantic and glamorous situations, but deep down in your heart you know that the dreams are only stardust and are unlikely to come true.

So you cleverly have the best of both worlds — you can wallow in wonderful daydreams, and you can also face up to the harsh realities of everyday life! Basically, you're very outgoing and impulsive. You're great company and you have great energy and enthusiasm for life, coupled with a great sense of humour.

You don't brood over things for too long; instead you go into action, sometimes stirring things up and creating havoc. You have an open nature and a generous spirit. You look for adventure and excitement in your life and you tend to rush into situations without thinking what the consequences might be. You occasionally lack understanding in your relationships with others — this is because you often fail to realise how insecure other people are.

You have few doubts about yourself and it's difficult to appreciate other people's problems and panics when you're able to cope so well. You genuinely enjoy life. You get a kick out of your extravagant daydreams, and you get just as much pleasure and excitement from life itself. Aren't you lucky?

ALL OUT- IN STRIPES!

Warm up to winter in the brightest woollies around! Our stripy ribbed scarf, leg-warmers and matching drawstring bag are *the* things for winter, and the brighter the better! They're quick to knit and great to wear, so get out those needles and start knitting, right away!

OUR really simple pattern has been specially designed for Jackie by Gillian Green, with Sirdar Superwash DK wool, used double for quickness and extra warmth! We chose Gorse and Roman Pink from a huge range of 45 different shades which includes almost every shade and tone you can think of. You'll also need a pair of 6 mm (No. 4) needles, available from almost any wool shop.

STRIPED KNITTED SCARF, BAG AND LEG WARMERS

MATERIALS: Of Sirdar Superwash DK: **Scarf** — 7 (25 g) balls Gorse (shade 124) and 5 balls Roman Pink (shade 144); **Bag** — 3 balls Gorse and 3 balls Roman Pink; **Leg Warmers** — 9 balls Gorse and 5 balls Roman Pink. You'll need 18 balls Gorse and 12 balls Roman Pink for the complete set. Two 6 mm (No. 4) needles.

Sizes: Length of scarf, 180 cm (71 ins.); length of bag, 28 cm (11 ins.); length of leg warmers, 57 cm (22½ ins.).

Tension: 8 sts and 10 rows to 5 cm (2 ins.) with rib slightly stretched.

Abbreviations: K – knit; P – purl; sts – stitches; beg – beginning; rep – repeat; yrn – yarn round needle to make a loop stitch; tog – together; cont – continue; G – Gorse, RP – Roman Pink.

Note: USE YARN DOUBLE THROUGHOUT.

SCARF

TO MAKE: With 2 strands of G cast on 32 sts. Working in k2, p2 rib, work in stripes of: 12 rows G, 8 rows RP until 18th G stripe is completed. Cast off in rib (k2, p2). Sew in ends.

BAG

TO MAKE: With 2 strands of RP cast on 48 sts. Work 6 rows in k2, p2 rib.

Holes Row: (K2, yrn, p2 tog) to end. Work 1 row more in k2, p2 rib. Still working in rib, work (12 rows G, 8 rows RP) 4 times then 12 rows G again. Break off G and cont in RP only. Work 1 row in rib.

Holes Row: (K2 tog, yrn, p2) to end. Work 6 rows more in rib. Cast off in rib (k2, p2). Fold bag double and join side seams.

Cord: Cut 6 strands of RP 300 cm (118 ins) long and knot at each end. Place one end over a door handle and a pencil through other end. Spin pencil until the strands are very tightly twisted. Place ends tog and allow cord to twist itself. Smooth out cord and thread around holes at top of bag. Join ends of cord.

LEG WARMERS

TO MAKE: (Knit 2 alike). With 2 strands of G cast on 64 sts. Working in k2, p2 rib, work in stripes of: 12 rows G, 8 rows RP until 6th G stripe is completed. Cast off in rib (k2, p2). Join side seam.

Sirdar Superwash DK is available from wool shops and stockists throughout the country, but if you have problems send an s.a.e. to Direct Enquiries, Customer Relations, Sirdar Ltd., PE 31, Alverthorpe, Wakefield, WF2 9ND asking for the address of your nearest stockist.

EYE~OPENERS!

Who says blue eye colours don't go with brown eyes (or vice versa)? Model Vivienne says she can wear any colours she likes and she always matches up her eye colours with the clothes she's wearing. You can do the same thing too . . . so eyes down for the latest ways to make up *your* eyes, just like Vivienne!

Beauty Box

DON'T BE BROW-BEATEN!

BEFORE you begin to apply eye colours, you have to make sure that your eyebrows are neat and tidy and make a good frame for the whole eye area. Shaggy brows will spoil the whole look and you'll get the colours all mixed up with them!

Plucking your brows becomes a quick and simple habit after a while, although it can be a bit painful at first. The simplest way is to buy a good pair of tweezers with slanted edges and cover your eyebrows in cold cream so that the hairs will come out easier!

Never pluck away the straggly hairs from the tops of the brows because this will alter the shape completely and ruin the arch of your brows for ever!

If you do find plucking painful (even with cold cream) you could try dipping cotton wool into fairly hot water (*not* boiling) and holding it against the brow to be plucked for a few seconds. This opens the pores and allows the hairs to slip out quite easily!

Once you've neatened up your brows, you're ready for your eye make-up, but do decide what you're wearing *before* you choose your eye colours. You don't have to match up the colours with your clothes exactly, just make sure they tone nicely.

If you're wearing a patterned dress, or several colours at once, you can pick up two of them. Always choose colours that look good together and don't be afraid to try something really different and a bit daring.

Vivienne always uses powder shadows in basic, primary colours — they look good on their own or she can mix them to make more delicate and unusual shades.

WHAT YOU SHOULD CHOOSE

Vivienne's powder shadows are bright "primary" colours made up by Cosmetics A La Carte Ltd., 16 Motcomb Street, London SW1 8LB. They cost £1.50 each plus 20p for postage and packing, and come in clear pink, blue, rust, green, etc. You can find bright colours in your own town, too, from ranges such as Boots 17, Rimmel, Outdoor Girl, Miners, Evette, Maybelline, etc.

Powder shadows usually last longer on the eyes and look soft and pretty. **Eye Pencils** are simple to use and are great for shading small areas and drawing fine lines. **Cream**

shadows are easily applied with the fingers but may crease after a short while, unless you choose one that claims to be creaseproof!

Powder shadows are best applied with a small eye brush or sponge applicator if one is provided with the shadow you choose. Loose powder shadows are a good idea because they come in plastic bottles with sponge applicators set into the caps. Try Rimmel or Boots 17 mascaras, especially, and try Outdoor Girl Special Mascara Refill which you simply squeeze into the container you have already!

Don't make the mistake of getting stuck in a rut, using the same colours in the same way month after month. Take time off every now and then to sit in front of a good mirror and experiment with different colours used in different ways. You could be really surprised at the range of colours that will suit you!

PINKS AND BLUES

TAKE a look at Vivienne's pretty flowered top and you'll see that the main colours are green and pink! But clever Vivienne decided to pick up the pink and the little *blue* flowers for a really super look. Here's what she did.

1. Using a bright blue powder shadow, Vivienne started from the middle of the lid and coloured the outer section, sweeping the colour past the end of the lashes to the outer corners of each eye and also round the corner and underneath the first few lower lashes.

2. With the same blue, she then started from the inner corner and coloured the socket-line of each eye, taking the colour down to meet the blue at the outer corners.

3. Changing to a bright pink powder shadow,

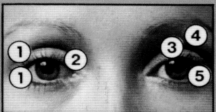

she coloured in the remaining space on the lid, from centre to inner corners.

4. Vivienne then used the pink to colour the final section from the middle of the brow-bone out to the end of

the brow, as shown.

5. Mascara came last, using navy blue swept *down* over top lashes, *up* under lower ones, then *up* under top lashes, *down* over bottom ones.

RUSTS AND BROWNS

BRIGHT yellow looks great on Vivienne, but bright yellow, green or blue eye colour would have looked all wrong. So, instead of matching her eye colours to her clothes exactly, she chose a pretty, clear rust as the main colour, with light brown to tone. Here's how she did it.

1. First of all, Vivienne used the rust powder shadow to colour lids from centre to outer corners just past the outer lashes, and round the corner just under the first few bottom lashes.

2. Using the same rust, she then coloured the brow-bones, shading quite lightly at the inner corners, heavier at the middle and outer corners for deeper colour.

3. Next came a light brown shadow, used on lids from middle to inner corners and just below lower lashes

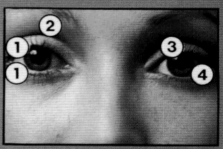

from middle to inside corners.

4. Finally, Vivienne

used black mascara applied as for the pink and blue eye make-up.

PARTY PIECES

It's those original touches that make you stand out from the crowd at any party! Here are some really stunning ideas . . . and they don't require a lot of effort!

Wear a cobwebby, lacey petticoat *over* a bright flouncy skirt. Search around jumble sales or second hand shops for a lacey petticoat. Sew pretty coloured ribbons to the top of the skirt and leave them trailing over the petticoat — (just like the lovely grass skirts of last summer!).

Make yourself a little rag doll, from odd scraps of wool and material. Attach it to a piece of plain cord and wear it round your neck.

Steal an idea from the chic French, who originated the idea of carrying perfume bottles around on cords! Tie your favourite perfume to a length of cord and wind it round your waist several times to make a really original belt. (He'll know which perfume to buy you as a present too!)

Carry your make-up around in a pretty drawstring bag.
We made ours from 18 rectangles of printed cotton (each 3 x 2 inches). Sew all the patches together, so that you have one large rectangle. With the wrong side facing you, turn down a small hem along one of the longer sides. Run a piece of cord through this, half an inch in from the top edge, sew on a Broderie Anglaise lace trim, fold the rectangle in half and (wrong side facing you) stitch together along the bottom and side, leaving the top end open.
Now you have a super drawstring bag, which is not only useful, but looks great hanging round your neck or dangling from your belt!

Wear tiny paper flowers in your hair. Cut yours from fairly stiff paper, then paint them in pretty colours. Stick the flowers to kirby grips, with a strong glue, such as Copydex (available from most large stores and stationers). Use them to pin your hair up . . . simply lovely!

This lovely peasanty apron is really cheap and easy to make.
You'll need three dishcloths — buy yours cheaply at any chain store (like Woolworth, Marks & Spencer or Fenwicks).
Cut one of the dishcloths in half and sew the halves to the other dishcloths, to make two large rectangles.
Sew four lengths of broad ribbon to each dishcloth — two for shoulder straps and two for ties at the waist. Try it on first, so that you get the waist ties in the right place.
Tie it on over cotton camisoles, and be a pretty peasant!

Carry the peasant look through, right down to your watchstrap! Buy a piece of embroidered braid, wide enough to fit your watch and sew snap fasteners on. Looks really original!

THEY'VE GOT STYLE!

MANY pop groups nowadays, such as the Bay City Rollers and Slik, as well as having their own individual sound, have also developed their own original look. And their distinctive gear helps to make them easily recognisable as well as giving them an instant impact onstage.

Pop stars have always appreciated that they need to look good and wear interesting, exciting, (and sometimes outrageous!) clothes and costumes, especially when performing live. And that's why the creative talents of top fashion designers are so much in demand.

Bambi Ballard, for instance, is currently working for a whole list of famous names, including the Bay City Rollers and Sweet.

"I enjoy working with the Rollers," she says. "At the moment I'm working on some new trousers for them and they know exactly what they want! Their basic look won't change, they just want to use better materials and feel more comfortable onstage.

"Andy Scott of the Sweet is also always full of good ideas. I did most of the band's clothes for their American tour and as they've had a complete change of image it was quite a challenge.

"They wanted to get right away from the high heels and glitter so their new wardrobe helps to mark them out as individuals and gives each of them a different look."

So, as you'll realise, thought, time and money are all important factors in the making of even the simplest clothes for a pop star!

Bambi thoroughly enjoys all the hard work she puts in though, especially when she gets the opportunity to see all her creations being worn by the stars.

"It's very satisfying when you see your clothes at a concert or on television. I always think that I could have done a better job, but I suppose that's natural!"

SLIK'S sensational look, too, baseball shirts and tight, drainpipe jeans, was their own idea and stemmed from the groups' interest in the music and style of the fifties. Those special

shirts were mainly designed by Glaswegian artist, Ed Smith.

"I've known Slik for a few years now as we share the same building in Glasgow," he said. "I have a studio on the top floor and they rehearse in the basement. The boys decided to design their own shirts, and the idea was that we should get together and pitch in ideas about the colouring of the shirts and the words that should go on them.

"Each shirt has different wording on it," said Ed. "For instance, Billy's has 'McIsaac Park' on the back, and one of the others says 'City Slikers', which I think is a great slogan!"

In contrast to Ed, Len Wilton, who works for Bespoke Tailoring in London, has been involved with show business fashion for quite some time now. He was the person responsible for the wonderful bump suits Kenny wore when their record, 'The Bump', was in the charts.

"The first suits we made were fairly dressy," Len says, "They looked fantastic but the boys found them a bit restricting onstage when they wanted to move around.

"Kenny like a loose cut but all the groups have different ideas. Slik, for example, want a completely opposite look to Kenny. We've just made some velvet trousers for them and they're very tight indeed!"

Another person who has a very distinctive style of dress is Bryan Ferry, who's well-known for being a very smooth, extremely dapper dresser. He has very definite ideas about his image and likes to discuss the design of all his stage clothes with designer Anthony Price.

He's been friends with Anthony for some time now and between them they come up with the looks that really appeal to Bryan.

For the suits he wears both on and off stage, Bryan goes to David Chambers.

David's another perfectionist and will spend ages getting the cut, the cloth and the colour just right — which is very important to Bryan!

ANOTHER person who sets a very high standard in the world of fashion is Tommy Nutter, who lives and works in London's Savile Row. He doesn't design many stage costumes for the stars but concentrates mainly on their private wardrobes.

Many of Tommy's clients have become personal friends and one of the closest is Elton John.

"I first met Elton about two years ago and he's always quite happy to leave the design of his suits entirely up to me," Tommy said.

"When he first came I did him some suits with padded shoulders, very wide Oxford Bag trousers and double-breasted jackets with no vent at the back. He ordered about eight suits at one time!"

Tommy has some very illustrious names on his client list, besides Elton. Gilbert O'Sullivan, Paul Simon, Paul McCartney and Mick Jagger are just a few of the more famous visitors to his shop.

Tommy's world is certainly very glamorous. He's forever buzzing about all over the world on business trips, especially to America and Paris. Obviously he's a very talented person who gets the most out of life but he also puts a terrific amount of hard work into his business, which is why it's so successful.

"It's not easy," he says. "Sometimes you can find yourself working till midnight. But I wouldn't give it up for anything — it's a wonderful life."

Tommy aims, and succeeds, at giving personal service and the same goes for well-known fashion designer Zandra Rhodes.

Zandra designs stage clothes for Queen and once managed to help them out of a right royal jam!

Queen were touring in the United States and Brian May lost the outfit Zandra had designed for him. He was terribly upset and immediately rang her up in London and asked if she could possibly send him a replacement. Unfortunately, the original designs had gone missing, but Zandra took the trouble to recreate her masterpiece, with the aid of a large photograph of Brian onstage.

And it's that kind of dedication and attention to detail that has got today's pop fashion designers where they are today.

So, the next time you see your favourite group all dressed up in their special onstage (and offstage!) clothes, just remember the people behind the scenes, who've helped make them look the way they are today!

fashion do's & don'ts

1. Wrong Short, skirt, strappy shoes pale tights all make fat legs look fatter.
Right Skirt just below the knee, darker tights, plain shoes help to camouflage.

2. Wrong Single-breasted jacket with side pockets makes thin girl look even more stick-like.
Right Double-breasted jacket with wide collar and deep pockets takes away that skin-and bones look.

4. Wrong Calf length skirts, coloured tights and huge shoes with no fronts make legs and ankles look like sticks.
Right Skirt just below the knee and pale tights help to accentuate fattest part of the leg, shoes with high fronts make legs look more substantial.

5. Wrong Short legs look ridiculous in calf-length skirts and ankle-strap shoes.

The right choice of clothes can make all the difference to your figure and help disguise faults. We take a look at some of the most common problems and how to cope with them.

3.Wrong Opposite of No. 2. Double-breasted jacket makes broad girl look vast. Padded shoulders make the whole thing even worse.
Right Slimming single-breasted jacket in a dark colour gives the impression of length instead of width.

Right Knee-length skirt and plain, uncluttered shoes give the impression of length.

6. Wrong Dumpy girl looks podgier when jacket breaks her up at the waist and patterns draw attention to it.
Right Longer, plain jacket is slimming and gives the impression of height.

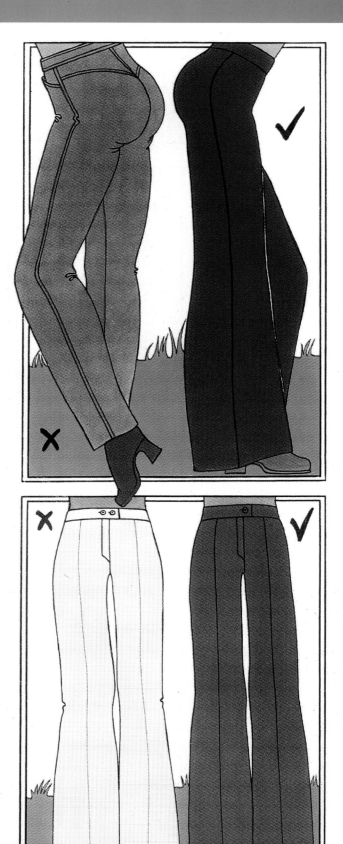

7. Wrong Big bottom looks really grotesque in tight jeans which are straight or tapered.
Right Trousers that fit well and are the right size are the only answer, preferably with flared or wide legs.

8. Wrong Being short from waist to neck isn't helped by high-waisted trousers which make the gap even smaller.
Right Trousers with a thin waist-band, or none at all, give more length to body.

9. Wrong Short legs look even shorter when trousers have large turn-ups.
Right No turn-ups help give a long, slim look.

AND NOW FOR SOME QUICKIES

10. Horizontal stripes make fatties look wider than ever.

11. Fussy prints, buttons, frills and bows make fatties look bitty and lumpy.

12. Scoop-neck T-shirts and tops accentuate skinny shoulders and lumpy collarbone.

13. Tight waists make large hips and bottom look worse.

14. Short skirts make busty figure really top-heavy.

15. High-heeled, dressy shoes rarely look sexy with tight jeans.

16. Wide expanses of back, unless brown and beautiful, look horrid, especially if there's any flab about.

17. Spot the difference! No prizes for guessing that the clean, tidy girl looks better than the dirty, sloppy one.

EVER wanted to find out what your boyfriend is really thinking? Well, you can quite easily become clairvoyant, read his mind like a book, discover his very deepest thoughts and exactly how he feels about you. How? Merely by getting him to sit down, and then studying the way he arranges his feet/drapes his legs/and, altogether, occupies the chair. For the way he sits tells you all you need to know to truly understand your boy . . .

The way this boy is sitting speaks louder than volumes of words. He's poised on the verge of flight and is ready to spring into action at any moment. His feet are ready to run and he looks restless, as though he feels confined just sitting in a chair.

A boy who sits like this is not giving *you* his full attention, as he's so full of pent-up energy that he longs for freedom. It might be that he's thinking of leaving you to search out new adventures and experiences, and even if he doesn't do anything about getting up and going, be warned, because it's in his mind.

When you see your boy's in this mood, it's up to you to interest and stimulate him — suggest some exciting excursion, even take him for a run round the block — anything to keep him occupied and to dampen his restlessness.

If this is his most usual sitting position, you've got trouble on your hands. This boy is very lively-minded and aware, and he needs constant excitement in his life. He's the type who gets really enthusiastic over something, but very quickly loses interest and latches on to something else. He's very sociable, he loves parties and being with lots of people, but he's also a bit of a flirt.

He's not easy to pin down as he hates any form of set routine. It's up to you to be so fascinating that he'll never lose interest and his desire for freedom will take second place to you. He's a wild character so good luck to you if you think you can tame him!

This way of sitting suggests that the boy is a bit arrogant, and likes to be in complete control of a situation. If your boy sits like this he's definitely intrigued by you, but although he's keen to get to know you better, he's not going to go overboard — not yet, anyway.

He likes to play it cool and to preserve his independence as long as he can. He doesn't like the idea of being tied down to a steady relationship on anything but *his* terms. He's a bit wary of what you want from him so the best thing to do is not to rush your fences but let him take his time. Show him that he's the boss all right, and that you're just an adorable weak female.

If this is your boy's most usual sitting position you can be sure that he's very self-confident and knows exactly what he wants from life. He does tend to be a bit critical though and his ideal girl

would really have to be nothing less than perfect. He's strong-willed but he's fair — he always weighs up a situation very carefully before committing himself.

He also wants to be proud of you and for you to feel proud of him. The best way of catching this boy and holding his attention is to be subtle, and pander to his every need, but don't appear too weak or he'll walk all over you!

Poor little boy, he's scared! Look at the way he's sitting, with his knees together and his feet turned inward, as though he's petrified that you're going to eat him alive! When a boy sits like this, he's feeling very insecure and lost.

All his self-confidence has drained away and he just doesn't know what to do. His sitting position is a kind of cry for help. He desperately wants your love, but is frightened of being rejected: he desperately wants to confide in you, but is scared about what your response will be.

When he's in this kind of mood try and put him out of his misery by mothering him and telling him what a marvellous person he is. Be kind to him, coax him and, above all, flatter him, so that his faith in himself is utterly restored. Give him all the love and comfort he needs and you'll have a man, and not a mouse!

If this is his most usual sitting position, he's a bit unsure of himself and finds it very difficult to express his feelings. In fact, he's got plenty of feelings, the trouble is that they're all hidden away inside. Underneath he's generally very kind and understanding and, if you can help to put him in the right mood, he'll be very sympathetic and romantic. But he's a shy type and finds relationships difficult.

It takes time and patience to get to know him properly, but once he really trusts you, you'll find he's a very warm person with a lot to give. Make him feel manly and appreciated and he'll soon come out of his withdrawn moods. You can be sure of one thing — this boy really needs you, so don't let him down!

Arrrgh! What a wreck! This boy looks permanently as though he's just crawled out from under a stone after a very hard night on the town — either that, or he looks like he's about to go down with some deadly disease. But it's far more likely that he's out of his mind with worry — he carries all the problems and burdens of the world on his own shoulders.

When he sits like this you can be sure he's a very worried boy. Perhaps you've done something to upset him; maybe he's worried about his relationship with you and would like to talk about it, but doesn't know where to begin. Or it could be that he's so wrapped up in his own problems he probably wouldn't notice you even if you pranced about in front of him wearing nothing but a grass skirt and a few flowers!

However, you can soon get him out of this state of mind if you persevere. First of all, try to make him talk about all his worries and tell you what's getting him down. Once he's got it all off his chest and out in the open he should feel much better and start being human again.

If this is his usual sitting position, he's frankly well on the way to worrying his life away. He takes life and himself extremely seriously and consequently reads far too much into everyday situations and takes little things much too much to heart. He succeeds in complicating everything around him and is very liable to get his love-life hopelessly tied up in knots. He's an over-emotional

REALLY LIKE?

type and, all in all, he sounds rather a dead loss, but he does have a saving grace — he's a very clever bloke. He's the intellectual type who's hopeless on relationships but utterly brilliant on Einstein's Theory of Relativity. In fact, he's mentally alive and interesting, and if only you could stop him worrying, he'd be a terrific boyfriend to have around!

You only have to glance at this boy to see that he's all tensed up, with every nerve in his body on edge and anxiety oozing out of every pore. When he sits like this, you immediately know that he's not happy about the situation he's in.

His way of sitting reveals that there's something wrong with your relationship, and, to help put his mind at rest, it would be best to get it sorted out right away. He's withdrawn into himself and unless you can establish contact with him again, this could well be the end of your beautiful friendship. What you've got to do is to have a real heart-to-heart and, hopefully, start watching those tortured limbs untwisting!

If this is his most usual sitting position, he's a naturally tense, shy sort of person who's very sensitive and easily hurt. He feels he has no control over his life and goes in for a great deal of soul-searching in an attempt to find out just where his destiny lies. He hasn't really "found himself" yet and, because of this, is inclined to get very depressed.

He needs lots of patience and understanding, but at the same time be careful not to pander to his moods too much as he does tend to be selfish. He's got to learn that it's up to him to make the effort to unbend and relax. He's an emotional type, and you could have a great relationship with him if only you can make him loosen up and enjoy life more. He may need dynamite to get him going but it'll be worth it!

Sunshine boy himself! A boy who sits like this is feeling incredibly happy and relaxed, amazingly lazy and he hasn't a care in the world, as life has never looked so good before. For this optimist everything is permanently coming up roses and things always seem to work out well for him.

He's enjoying your company, he's completely happy about your relationship and he also feels very sure of the situation. You've got the knack of making him feel utterly at home and at ease and although he's not in an incredibly romantic or passionate mood, he's feeling very warm towards you and is probably very fond of you indeed.

If this is his most usual sitting position he's a very out-going, sociable person who finds it easy to get along with others and is always pleased to meet new people and take up new interests. He has a happy nature, usually very con-

tented and relaxed, and life holds no problems for him.

He's a confident person who doesn't like compli-

cation so he does make an effort to keep things running smoothly. He's also understanding and considerate, although he doesn't really enjoy deep, soul-searching discussions about your relationship too much. He's got a very open and natural personality and he'll always be popular.

If all this sounds too good to be true then we have to admit that he does have one slight drawback — he's such a natural charmer that you'll have to keep a close eye on him as every girl for miles around is almost bound to fall for him, too!

When a boy sits like this, legs spread out in abandon, feet firmly touching the ground, he's feeling in top form. He loves you and wants to express his feelings for you. All his reserve is gone and he's extremely happy.

To him, every word you utter is a gem and he's watching you with rapt attention. He feels emotionally warm and close to you, and he has a great deal of faith in your relationship as he regards you as a very special person.

If this is his most usual sitting position, it shows that he's a very active, masculine type with bags of energy and always on the go. He enjoys outdoor activities — rugged, masculine sports like rugby, football, climbing etc.

He's fairly ambitious and usually succeeds at anything he puts his hand to. He's sociable too, and he really enjoys being "one of the boys." He'll always be a good sport and whatever activity he happens to be engaged in, he puts his heart and soul into it.

Altogether, he's a great guy, with lots of personality. He makes you feel very feminine and secure and wherever he goes he seems

to inspire confidence and admiration, in other people as well as in you.

He's kind-hearted, too, especially to anyone he feels is a bit of an under-dog and he's generous, particularly to those he's fond of. So if this boy's yours, hang on to him — he's too good to let go!

Any boy who sits like this, with his legs stretched out and his feet curled round, is a real humorist. He finds practically the whole of life one big, excruciatingly funny joke! He has a wonderful sense of freedom and well-being and usually feels incredibly pleased with himself.

He may have just ended a longstanding, tiresome relationship and is busy congratulating himself; perhaps he's achieved some astounding exam results or been given promotion at work, or maybe some other equally marvellous and fantastic thing has happened to him.

It could be though, that he's just looking pleased with himself because you make him feel good. In this mood, he's marvellous company and a terrific friend to have around.

If he usually sits like this, he's a real character, full of fun and frivolity and never giving himself time to be serious over anything.

His sense of humour dominates his every action, thought and word. He'll never brood for long over problems and difficulties, but will float happily along always seeing the funny side when things go wrong. He does tend to be a bit reckless, though, and is inclined to be over-impulsive in some things. But he doesn't demand a great deal — just so long as you laugh at his jokes and keep cheerful, life will be wildly hilarious for both of you!

DO YOU MEAN WHAT YOU SAY?

Are you one of those nice girls whose every word rings sincere and true? If you are then you shouldn't be reading this! But probably, like most of us, you quite often say one thing and mean another. It's the kind of technique that comes in very handy for settling old scores, as you are able to be downright rude with a sugary smile on your face!

So here's our Jackie Guide to What People Actually Say and *What They Really Mean . . .* and if they come out with any of these little gems — beware!

YOUR HOME

What a cosy house.
Boy, what a poky place you live in.

How nice! Everyone has matching specs.
Eye trouble must run in the family.

Your kid brother/sister's a real bundle of fun.
Spoiled brat!

You must come back to my house for tea sometime.
I'll put it off as long as I can.

See you.
Not if I see you first though.

You know, it's funny, I've never had liver and bacon for tea before.
Liver brings me out in spots! And I can't stand bacon—specially the way your mum cooks it.

Gosh, isn't your room bright?
Wow! She must be colour blind!

It's really nice and quiet round here, isn't it?
How can you stand it?

Your mum/dad/brother's not at all like I expected.
Whatever happened to the Paul Newman, Debbie Reynolds and David Essex I was led to expect?

YOUR BOYFRIEND

You seem to be crazy about him.
You must be mad!

He seems a really nice boy.
But . . .

Don't you ever wonder what John does on Wednesday nights?
He's seeing Stephanie.

You're always so trusting.
He's playing around with every girl in town.

He's got a really unusual face.
Must have modelled as the original gargoyle.

He's crazy about you.
He always is – for the first week.

You're meant for each other.
Nobody else would have you.

I don't think Simon's as shy as you say he is.
You should have seen him under the table with Susie at Belinda's party!

Has he got a skin problem?
It's lucky nobody dies of acne.

I bet your mum likes him.
He's REALLY boring.

But nobody trains five nights a week.
He's trying to tell you something!

We were surprised to see you without Steve the other night.
So the rumours about you breaking up are true!

Didn't your boyfriend and Lesley get on well at the party?
How embarrassing for you – he was all over her!

It must be nice to have such a popular boyfriend.
What a flirt – I'd kill him!

I wouldn't tell you this if I weren't so fond of you.
So I will, 'cos I'm not!

Anyone can see you're mad about each other.
Which is just as well for everyone else!

It's funny you're still just friends.
He wouldn't fancy you in a million years!

You've done really well for yourself.
I fancied him!

YOUR FUTURE

You're sure to get a good, steady job.
You're so predictable and boring.

Don't suppose we'll be seeing you around for a while.
Thank goodness.

Why don't you travel?
They tell me the Gobi Desert is quite nice!

You should be a model or in films.
She'll believe anything.

I wonder what you'll make of your life?
Not much.

You'll always do O K for yourself.
You're so selfish.

Oh, you'll do O K, you've got a fantastic personality.
Pity you missed out on the brains, though.

Well anyway, good luck and see you around.
Around the year 2000, I hope.

YOUR APPEARANCE

Are you feeling O K? You look tired.
You look terrible! Like death warmed up.

Bet you're looking forward to your holiday.
You look ghastly.

I wish I was always neat and tidy like you.
You're so boring it's not true.

Those jeans are a really good fit.
But not when you've got 40 inch hips!

I've always liked you in that dress.
You're not going to wear it for yet another year, are you?

You've had your coat cleaned!
At last!

That dress is really sexy.
So long as you like looking like a barmaid.

Freckles can be very attractive.
Not in your case, though.

You look very sophisticated in that dress.
Must be a relic from the Boer War.

What an unusual hairstyle, it's really different.
Different, yes – like a haystack set with spray starch.

You must have been a beautiful baby.
Pity you didn't stay that way!

I remember you as the prettiest girl at primary school.
What happened?

You really take a lot of care with your appearance.
You've got to!

YOUR PERSONALITY

You're so sensitive.
Oh no, she's off again! Where are the tissues?

We must seem right nutters to you.
You're so creepy and boring. What are you doing hanging around with us?

It must have taken you ages.
What a waste of time.

You do have a very serious outlook on life.
No sense of humour, that's your trouble!

I wonder what you're dreaming about now?
Dope, you've never got the faintest idea of what's going on!

You're so much more responsible and mature than I am.
But all the boys fancy me!

Your mum must be proud of you.
She's the only one!

Good for you!
But only average for anyone else.

You really know a lot about make up/cooking/parrots.
And you really go on about it too!

You're bound to be successful!
At scrubbing floors.

You always seem to be meeting boys.
So how come no-one ever sees them?

You're too deep for me.
I can never understand a word you're saying.

When did you last read a book?
Thickie!

It wouldn't be a party without you there!
Loud-mouthed exhibitionist, wonder what you'll get up to this time?

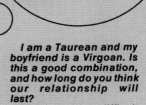

Star Quest

Could you tell me how romance is starred between a Scorpio girl and a Taurus boy?

A relationship between a Scorpio girl and a Taurus boy should have a lot going for it. There are two factors you'll have to watch — your jealousy and his stubborness.

The Taurus boy is very loving and easy going-on the surface, that is! Don't make the mistake many girls do and think you can treat him just as you please, because you're in for a terrible shock. If he gets *really* upset he'll make mincemeat of you.

Many Scorpio girls treat their boyfriends with about as much respect as a bundle of last week's washing — and they get away with it! But not with a Taurus boy.

Apart from that you are both people who enjoy a steady relationshop and you are both very loyal. If you treat your Taurus boy well, you've got it made.

My friend is a Virgo girl and I'm a Sagittarian. The problem is, we both like an Aries boy. Could you tell us which one of us would get on with him better – or doesn't he like either of us?

It's unfortunate that you and your Virgo mate both fancy the same Aries boy, but it often happens that way. Being born under Sagittarius, you are far more compatible with Aries than your Virgo friend could ever be.

Both Aries and Sagittarius are fire signs — made for each other, you might say! This is a case where two sensible girls should get together and talk the situation out. I don't think you'll have much trouble, as your Virgo friend is too much of a realist to want this boy for herself when she realises that he can be very selfish and unreliable.

But don't let that put you off him, as Sagittarians are very adaptable. You know what they say: "People in glass houses shouldn't throw stones!" If you don't expect too much, you two could have a great time together.

I am a Taurean and my boyfriend is a Virgoan. Is this a good combination, and how long do you think our relationship will last?

It's always very difficult to predict how long a relationship will last, because there are always so many unknown quantities which should be taken into account.

Certainly a Taurus girl and Virgo boy should have a lot in common, as you are both earth signs. It's basic to both your natures to want a steady relationship — nothing spectacular, just nice and comfortable, going out together, doing things together. I think you'll find that you share lots of interests, and very often these are the things which make for a happy and lasting relationship.

I'm a Pisces girl, and I wonder if you could explain something to me. Why is it that an Aries boy brings out a devilish side of my nature, while a Capricorn boy makes me act and feel like a saint?

It's no puzzle to me that an Aries boys bring out the devil in you, and a Capricorn boy makes you act and feel like a saint. It's exactly what I would expect of a Pisces girl like you.

You see, you are so sensitively attuned to what is going on around you that you naturally adapt to any situation. Your Aries boy is probably a wild and likeable boy who is game to have a go at anything, and sensing this, you immediately play the same role.

Your Capricorn boy, on the other hand, is quiet, serious, possibly even a bit of a stick in the mud, and almost without realising what is happening you put on your saint-like image.

UN JOUR AVEC DAVID À PARIS!

DAVID ESSEX is a Cockney, born and brought up in the heart of London. And although he's now an international star, travelling all over the world, he hasn't forgotten his origins. As far as he's concerned, England's the greatest!

But his love for his own country doesn't stop David enjoying the other places he visits. France for instance, is a great favourite of his — and Paris in particular.

"I love Paris," he told me. "It's a beautiful city. I've been there about ten times now, and the more I see of it, the more I like it!

"The funny thing was that the first time I went there, one or two things went wrong, and it wasn't a very nice trip. I came home feeling a bit disappointed, because I didn't like it as much as I'd expected.

"But the second time I went, it was completely different. Everything went really well for me, and I just fell in love with the city!"

When it comes to the music world, the French people tend to stick to their own stars. Very few British or American singers are successful over there — which means it's all the nicer for the few, like David, who are!

David's single "America" was one of the most popular foreign records ever released over there, selling over 400,000 copies, and he's appeared several times on French television shows with stars like Mireille Matthieu and Sacha Distel.

"I really enjoy doing French TV," he told me, "but it's quite strange for me, since I can only speak about a dozen words of French! I can never understand what everyone around me's talking about!

"But luckily, the French people don't seem to mind. In fact they tease me and make jokes about it! One time I was on television they kept asking me long complicated questions that they knew I wouldn't understand! So, to get my own back, I answered every one with one of the only French words I know — 'L'amour'!"

The only thing that David regrets about his popularity in France is that it means most of his visits to Paris are working ones, so he doesn't often get the chance to be a tourist and go sightseeing.

"I get recognised in the streets," he said, "so it's not all that easy to walk about. I've never been on the Metro either because I usually travel by car.

"But, when I have the chance, I like wandering up and down the quieter boulevards, and maybe stopping at a pavement cafe for a cup of coffee. I find that really relaxing."

David also likes wandering round the shops of Paris — but he admits he prefers window-shopping to actually buying anything!

"Most of my clothes are British," he said, "but I do buy the occasional thing in Paris. I've bought quite a few French jackets, for instance. I like them because they're always so beautifully cut.

"But most of the clothes over there are very expensive. In fact everything in Paris is expensive."

ALTHOUGH David hasn't had much time for sightseeing in Paris, he has managed to visit most of the famous tourist attractions.

"The Champs Elyseés is one of my favourite places," he told me. "I always try to spend some time there when I'm in Paris. I haven't managed to visit the Louvre, and I haven't been to the top of the Eiffel Tower, but I hope to do both some day.

"I have been up the Arc de Triomphe, though of course that's not so big! I went to Versailles the last time I was there, and I thought that was really impressive. I also went up to Montmartre, and that was lovely.

"But my favourite part of all is the Latin quarter, where all the students live. I've spent a lot of time down there, and I love it."

Apart from its beautiful buildings, there's another thing Paris is famed for — its beautiful food! David admits he's a big fan of French cooking.

"Paris has some really good restaurants," he said. "I must admit I don't eat snails, but I'll try anything else! I adore French onion soup — that's one of the nicest things you can get. But really, I just like French cooking in general.

"So if I have an evening off, I'll spend it at a restaurant having a nice meal — or maybe I'll go to a nightclub.

"I've discovered a fantastic night-club called the Alcazar. It has a clever show, which has a bit of everything in it — comedy, singing, impersonations — all sorts of things. I found it entrancing.

"And the nice thing about it was that when I went there, they spotted me in the audience, and so they kept mentioning me in the show!

"That was a super night out. I'm definitely looking forward to going back there. In fact I'm definitely looking forward to going back to Paris again!"

FACE UP TO HIM!

DID you know that just looking at the boy you fancy gives you the power to discover his hidden characteristics? No? Well, it's perfectly possible with the help of the ancient art of face-reading! Face-reading helps you to find out if he really is as nice as he looks — and it can also tell you exactly how to act with him . . .

The first sign to look for is the shape of his face. So take a long, hard look at the boy you think is for you and decide whether his face is:

BROAD:
He's confident, very sure of himself and likes to be the boss. By nature he thinks big and seldom "chickens out" of awkward or difficult situations. He's a very strong character and has a high opinion of his own abilities!

HOW TO ACT WITH HIM:
Don't start something with this self-confident boy that you can't finish. He's a very determined type so don't let him browbeat you too much either, as you'll soon find that he's a really determined character!

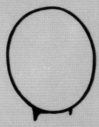

ROUND:
This boy makes the most of life as he's very friendly and out-going. He loves entertaining and keeping everybody around him happy and comfortable, including you! He's always organised but he does love his home comforts and expects you to provide them.

HOW TO ACT WITH HIM:
Make him feel at home, cook like his mum and volunteer to darn his socks. Don't let him get too cosy and comfy though, as he does tend to be a bit lazy at times.

NARROW:
This boy needs a boost to his ego. He's just as talented as anyone else, and often more gifted, but his own opinion of himself is low. He's continually surprised to find he can do really well if he puts his mind to something.

HOW TO ACT WITH HIM:
Encourage him all the way and don't be over-critical. He won't believe you love him unless you make it pretty obvious, so reassure him that he's the most marvellous person in the world, then he will be!

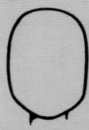

SQUARE:
He's determined to change the face of the earth! This boy is born to build and dig and fight. He's always on the move, but inclined to get so wrapped-up in his latest project that he could forget all about you.

HOW TO ACT WITH HIM:
Keep him interested, spring new ideas, new aspects of your personality on him — all the time. Otherwise he'll soon get bored, and to him there's nothing worse!

Now take a look at his *EYES* and decide whether they're:

SMALL:
Don't expect a great show of affection from this boy. He's got feelings all right but he finds it very hard to express them. In fact he's extremely wary of letting his emotions show through at all.

HOW TO ACT WITH HIM:
He needs a lot of patience and understanding to help him tell you exactly how he feels about you. Show him *you* care and he'll return your feelings.

UPPER EYELID PLAIN TO SEE:
This boy likes to take direct action, he likes to get straight to the heart of the matter — whatever it is. Everything is in black and white to him and he can't be bothered with girls who play around.

HOW TO ACT WITH HIM:
Always answer his questions with a direct yes or no, don't drive him mad by saying "maybe," or "I don't know." Be as decisive as he is but be careful not to get too aggressive.

SMALL IRIS:
These are known as melancholy eyes, so don't expect this boy to be light-hearted and cheerful. He always seems a bit miserable, as though he has a lot of unsolved problems weighing on his mind.

HOW TO ACT WITH HIM:
If you get this boy to one side and hear him out as someone who's genuinely interested in him, he'll open up and pour out his worries to you. Wait for the right moment and he'll soon start feeling happier when he realises that somebody cares about him.

EYES THAT SLANT DOWNWARDS:
This boy is highly critical, he's never satisfied unless everything is perfect. To live up to these high standards you need to be a very special kind of girl.

HOW TO ACT WITH HIM:
Don't let him trample all over you. Try to show him that this critical trait in his nature, if not controlled, could get in the way of love — of which he definitely has a lot to give. He'll be loyal and passionate — with the right girl.

Now to move on to his _EYEBROWS_. Are they:

HIGH: He's the kind of boy who's rather hard to get to know. He seems detached and aloof at first but once he gets to know you he could be your warmest and truest friend. Most people will think he's a show-off and a know-all but underneath that cool exterior he has a very warm heart.

HOW TO ACT WITH HIM: It'll be up to you to open the conversation and show, in a friendly way, that you've noticed him. Take the lead in a subtle way but be careful not to be too pushy.

LOW: A boy with eyebrows that sit down on the eyes is easy to get on with and enjoys a good laugh. Nobody's a stranger to him. When he first meets you, he'll act as if you're an old friend he's just met up with again.

HOW TO ACT WITH HIM: Respond by being just as friendly, even if you are a little taken aback by his openness. Otherwise he could well get the idea that you're rather cool and reserved and not relaxed enough for him!

EYEBROWS WHICH FLARE UP AT THE ENDS: This boy is a dramatic exhibitionist who loves being the life and soul of the party. He's a great mimic and shifts easily from one role to another, so don't take all he says and does as being completely true to nature.

HOW TO ACT WITH HIM: Try to calm him down a little if he seems to be getting too carried away, but show that you appreciate all his carefully managed exits and entrances. If you're a good audience and laugh at all his jokes and listen attentively to his stories — he'll love you (madly!).

STRAIGHT: This boy is sensitive and very artistic with a strong romantic streak in his make-up. He loves beauty and harmony so don't let him catch you cutting your toe-nails or, Heaven forbid, squeezing a spot!

HOW TO ACT WITH HIM: Give him the elegant atmosphere he craves — be serene, romantic and beautiful, light your perfumed candles and play soft, soothing music.

Now, are his _LIPS_:

THIN: "Nice day" is a long sentence for him so expect this boy to be brief and to the point. Unless he's talking about his favourite subject, he won't have much to say for himself. He's also very efficient and hates waste in any form.

HOW TO ACT WITH HIM: Don't be hurt by his abrupt manner. He just has a short way of doing and saying things. Find out about his favourite subject, (apart from you!), and show a real interest in it. Try to bring a bit of humour into his life but be careful not to overdo it!

FULL: In contrast, the full-lipped boy is generous with time, words and love. He's lavish with money but has no idea about time. He's almost bound to be late everytime you meet him but he'll make up for it when he does arrive!

HOW TO ACT WITH HIM: Be spontaneous, don't analyse your relationship too much. One thing's for sure, if he's on time for your dates, he's really interested in you!

TURNED DOWN AT THE CORNERS: Just as you'd expect, this boy is a bit of a pessimist and generally not much fun to have around. The muscles which are supposed to lift the corners of his mouth in a smile have become weak because he doesn't use them enough!

HOW TO ACT WITH HIM: Fortunately this condition needn't be permanent. Make him laugh and smile by talking about good times and places. He'll lose that "sour-puss" look eventually, but be patient as it could take some time.

UPTURNED CORNERS: This shows the opposite type of boy, he's a true optimist. He likes to look on the bright side and is easy-going with a great sense of humour. He's always smiling or laughing, and looks like he's having a good time and usually he is!

HOW TO ACT WITH HIM: Enjoy yourself!

What's his _NOSE_ like? Is it:

ROMAN: This boy is business-like and likes to get a job done. He has a strong sense of duty and his tendency to always put business before pleasure can be a bit irritating.

HOW TO ACT WITH HIM: Don't let him get too serious, make him see that there's more to life than work. Try to broaden his outlook and his interests and bring out the light-hearted side of his nature more.

UPTURNED: This boy is really kind and helpful, he has a great desire to be of service to other people. Human beings are all that matter to him, but he may be so busy worrying about other people and the state of the world, that it'll take him a while to get round to you!

HOW TO ACT WITH HIM: Always ask him for his advice and assistance, make him feel that _you_ need him just as much as the rest of humanity does.

STRAIGHT: Very romantic, this boy, but he's also impractical, idealistic, sensitive and poetic. He's usually up on Cloud 9 and can be annoyingly vague.

HOW TO ACT WITH HIM: Don't try to force him to be someone he's not, but appreciate his gentle, loving qualities. If you nag him too much, he'll gently float out of your life.

SNUB: This boy is an optimist. He's easy going but he also has a strong practical streak in his nature. He's a bit of an extrovert, a joker and you'll always know when he's around!

HOW TO ACT WITH HIM: He can't bear miseries, life's too short, so if you want to attract this boy, show him you can be as fun-loving as he is!

So there you are, now you know how to read your boy's face like a book! But remember, exactly the same is true for you. So take a piece of paper and make a list of your facial features, then you, too, can discover what you're really like.

Now, from your list, you'll be able to find out the qualities that draw other people to you, such as magnetism, generosity, optimism, humour, helpfulness and affection. If you find that from your facial features you tend to be critical, unemotional or a bit miserable, then decide to do something positive about it! Face up to yourself, and you can't go wrong!

Do you believe in ghosts? Do you shiver with fear every time an owl hoots or something goes bump in the night? Or are you the fearless type who isn't worried by anything — least of all a few strange noises in the dark?
To find out how you really feel about the supernatural, just follow our eerie ghost story. Choose the alternatives you think fit in best, and we'll reveal your innermost fears, and some secrets of your personality which may surprise even you!

ARE YOU SCARED TO D

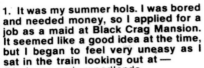

1. It was my summer hols. I was bored and needed money, so I applied for a job as a maid at Black Crag Mansion. It seemed like a good idea at the time, but I began to feel very uneasy as I sat in the train looking out at —
(b) dense eerie woodlands,
(c) open moorland, grey and empty,
(d) soulless suburbs, seeming to stretch into infinity,
(a) jagged cliffs and turbulent seas.

2. Suddenly the train stopped at a tiny country station. "All passengers for Black Crag change here," announced the guard, and I shivered as I realised I was the only passenger for Black Crag. It was dusk, and the place had a dead feel to it with strange noises of —
(c) wind whistling and echoing across the platform,
(a) the persistent hooting of owls, like a strange cry of warning,
(b) bats, swooping under the eaves of the platform shelter, like a premonition of evil,
(d) the rain splattering down on my coat collar.

3. At last a small old-fashioned steam train appeared, and I cautiously stepped into a deserted compartment. The doors of the train shut instantly, and I suddenly felt horribly, inexplicably trapped.
(c) I told myself I was being silly, and tried to dismiss my fears.
(d) Interesting! I began to suspect that there was more to this job than met the eye.
(a) My stomach turned to jelly, and I wished with all my heart that I could turn round and go home.
(b) I knew I had to cope with strange forces I couldn't begin to understand.

4. Eventually I got out at Black Crag, and my suspicions that something peculiar was happening were confirmed when the station master said —
(b) "You're the first person I've seen off that train in the past twelve years."
(a) "Sorry, Miss, you startled me — I I thought you were a ghost for a minute."
(d) "Well you won't need your return ticket, Miss — there's no return from Black Crag."
(c) "I don't mean to pry, Miss, but are you sure you really wanted to come to Black Crag?"

5. Mystified by what he had said, I steeled myself and walked away from the station. After walking down a wide track past a few cottages, I suddenly realised I was lost, so I knocked on a cottage door and asked an old lady for directions.
(c) She said she had never heard of Black Crag Mansion.
(d) She gave me directions with a sly smile on her face.
(b) She looked at me with large frightened eyes, and begged me not to go near it.
(a) She fainted on the doorstep!

6. At last, Black Crag Mansion came into view. It was —
(d) an old style villa surrounded by barbed wire.
(b) a stark stone building like a prison with tiny windows.
(a) an elaborate castle with turrets against a black sky.
(c) a crumbling Georgian mansion.

7. At the gate I saw —
(a) a sinister-looking guard in a black cloak.
(d) an electric alarm system.
(c) a huge Alsatian dog.
(b) two enormous stone dragons.

8. I walked fearfully up the driveway, and rang the bell. There was the sound of clanking chains and creaking wood, and the butler opened the door. He was —
(c) young and handsome but with a steely look in his eyes.
(d) a deaf mute who looked more like a bodyguard than a butler.
(b) a tall thin man who looked as though he'd been carved out of wax.
(a) an old, bald cripple with shuffling feet.

ATH?

9. He got a footman to show me to my room, up winding stone staircases, through a maze of rooms and corridors to the east wing. My room was like a prison cell, and sitting alone I could hear —

(b) loud breathing behind me wherever I turned.

(c) tapping on my window.

(a) strange high-pitched moaning and wailing through the wall.

(d) the scuffling of rats in the dark corners of the room.

10. I tried the door and realised with horror that I was locked in.

(c) I banged at the door, yelling and screaming to be let out.

(a) I sat and waited and prayed.

(b) I looked frantically for a way of escape.

(d) I sat and played "I Spy" with myself out of the window while I waited.

11. After terrible hours of waiting in the cold, damp room, the footman led me downstairs, and told me I was going to meet the master of the house. I told him I'd changed my mind about taking the job, but he grasped my arm and pushed me into a room —

(a) like a graveyard with weird stone statues, lit by a ghostly green light,

(d) like a weird space laboratory, with machines and strange mobiles hanging from the ceiling,

(c) like a room in a stately home, but everything was faded and covered in dust,

(b) like a jungle with weird flowering cacti, and huge rubber plants.

12. "Come here, young lady," echoed a voice all around the room, but I could see no-one.

(c) My mind was in total confusion, and I was too stunned even to feel frightened.

(b) I took a deep breath to brace myself for what was to happen next.

(a) My heart thumped like a steam engine, and I thought I'd faint on the spot.

(d) I suddenly became intrigued with the situation, and determined to get to the bottom of it.

13. "Who is it? What are you playing at?" I called out, trembling in every limb. There was silence, and then —

(b) a black cat leapt from nowhere on to my shoulder, digging its claws into my flesh,

(c) a blinding light suddenly beamed on to my face,

(d) the sound of ghoulish laugher rang in my ears,

(a) a current of cold air froze me to the spot.

14. Suddenly, to my horror, a panel in the wall opened out, and the master

of the house appeared before me, wearing a mask so I couldn't see his face.

(c) "Congratulations," he said, "You have passed the first test — now I will tell you the reason you are here."

(b) "You have come at my command as I knew you would," he said. "Now you are in my power."

(a) "I have searched the earth for you for a hundred years," he said. "Now at last I have found you!"

(d) "Ha, ha," he said. "You fell for my trick hook, line and sinker, and walked right into my trap!"

15. For a moment I was too shocked to fathom out the meaning of all this, but as the master of the house went on talking, it gradually dawned on me that —

(a) he was a ghost,

(c) the whole thing might be a clever cover for an organisation dealing in top secret government work,

(d) the whole thing must be an elaborate practical joke,

(b) the master of the house was an exponent of Black Magic, with a warped, evil mind.

Now count your scores, mainly (a), (b), (c) or (d) and turn to the conclusions on page 91.

225

WANTED - SUPERCOPS

ONE thing's for sure, some of the most popular TV series in the past year have been those with detectives in them. These cool, handsome hunks have kept us gripped to the edges of our seats as they sort out the baddies, and had us heaving sighs of relief as they made everything work out right in the end!

What is it that makes detectives so appealing? Well, it could be something to do with that combination of mystery, courage, insight and super-calm that makes them so riveting! Here are some favourites who've definitely got it all!

Kevin Dobson's got everyone's dream job — as Crocker, he's Kojak's assistant in one of the most popular television 'tec series of all time! And we think he's lovely!

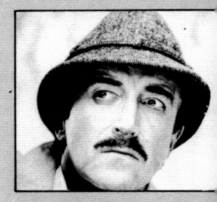

Peter Sellers is his usual hilarious self — but even more so, as Inspector Clouseau.

Lovely Ben Murphy stars in "Griff" with Lorne Green, whom you may remember from "Bonanza." Ben himself, of course, was also a star of that memorable series, "Alias Smith and Jones."

Mike Douglas is Steve, the good-looking assistant to top 'tec Karl Malden in "The Streets of San Francisco." Wouldn't you guess he's the son of that famous and distinctive-looking actor, Kirk Douglas?

Dustin Hoffman and Robert Redford aren't really detectives, but they are investigators in the exciting film, "All The President's Men." And even though they're not cops, we think they're lovely anyway!

Peter Falk plays Columbo — he looks slow and shabby, but don't be fooled — he's one of the sharpest detectives around!

You'll probably remember Robert Wagner from the exciting TV series "Colditz." Detective fans will also have lapped up "Switch," in which he starred with Eddie Albert.

One of the first-ever detectives to be shown on the screen, film star Humphrey Bogart, who appeared in lots of exciting films. His ever-popular pictures are now being re-made and up-dated!

James Garner's already a famous film star — now he's a star of the television series, "The Rockford Files."

The rough, tough 'tec in Thames Television's "The Sweeney" is played by lean, blond Denis Waterman.

Handsome heart-throb George Peppard, star of many films in the past, now stars in the title-role of the television detective series, "Banacek."

Everybody's favourite — he doesn't even need introducing! Telly Savalas, as big, calm, soft-hearted Theo Kojak!

David Soul (left) and Paul Michael Glaser are "Starsky and Hutch" — Dave Starsky and Ken Hutchinson, the young, tough and dedicated undercover police officers.

QUIZ CONCLUSIONS

Continued from page 77

Continued from page 77

Mostly (a)

You're a great believer in ghosts, ghouls and things that go bump in the night, and you enjoy being terrified. You feel a pull towards the unknown, towards the occult, and spend a lot of time thinking about the meaning of life. You're an extra-sensitive person. Earthly things are only superficial to you and you're very curious about the world beyond. However, your fear stops you from delving too deeply.

You are sincere and easily hurt as a person, and rather prone to the influence of others. You take yourself very seriously, and love and romance are important and serious, too. You have sound intuition about friendship and romance, and you often manage to sum people up quite accurately by instinct. However, very often your rich imagination gets mixed up with your intuition and you can make mistakes.

Guard against depression, and against your tendency to brood on morbid thoughts. Ghosts are OK for a laugh, but try not to take them too seriously.

Mostly (b)

You can certainly cope with ghostly apparitions and sinister situations. You're drawn towards the unusual and the bizarre, and have an excellent awareness of the unknown. This highly developed sense of awareness makes you very alert and helps you to see through situations in general.

You're very curious about the occult, but deep in your heart you have to admit you're not a serious believer. Ghosts and ghouls give you a thrill, but they're not for real. You have great faith in the power of the human mind, and perhaps even feel you're rather psychic or telepathic. However, you don't altogether agree that these are evidence of a world beyond.

You are a thinking person, living very much in your mind, and for this reason you're good at analysing people and situations. Although you tend to dramatise yourself and life around you, and are prone to emotional ups and downs — underneath you're far more level-headed than you might think. You have a great deal of faith in yourself, and although you're often influenced by people and circumstances, you have basic good sense which will keep you out of danger.

Mostly (c)

You have mixed feelings about ghosts, ghouls and the occult in general. Your common sense tells you it's nonsense, yet your emotions seem to contradict you. Perhaps you're more psychic than you realise, and only a fear of the world beyond has stopped you from believing in it.

Basically you live in *this* world, and enjoy all the good things it has to offer. You're a sophisticated and ambitious person who enjoys comfort, and likes to make a good impression on others.

Your head tends to rule your instincts and although you cope with life very well in general, you are thrown by the unusual or the bizarre.

You demand a lot from life and relationships and in general you get on well with people and tend to be rather a leader. There is a tough, cool side to your nature which doesn't often appear, but which is very useful indeed in many situations. Carry on avoiding the lure of the occult — you are far too vital and busy in this world to have time for the world beyond.

Mostly (d)

You can stand up to ghosts and ghouls and occult happenings any day, because you have the knack of dismissing them entirely and overcoming any difficulty by sheer force of personality.

You are a brave, active, adventurous person. Being basically practical, you can cope with situations and people without getting into emotional tangles. You cut your way through life in such a decisive manner that you usually end up getting your own way. You are determined and single-minded, and your mind is usually occupied with what is in front of you. You haven't much time for wondering and soul-searching and, as far as you're concerned the world beyond can go back where it came from!

You are a strong person with strong feelings and opinions, and are never likely to be worried by ghouls and phantoms — in fact, the poor, innocent spirits don't stand a ghost of a chance with you around!

I WAS SO SURE I'D LANDED A DREAM JOB

LOOKING back now on the time I spent working for Louise, I can hardly believe it happened. It's like a nightmare, strange and unreal.

When I first got the job, though, it was more like a dream. Companion/help to a 22-year-old disabled girl, living right in the centre of London in a luxury flat.

Since I was a kid I've had this dream of being independent, getting away from our quiet little town to somewhere alive and exciting. When I read the newspaper ad and then actually landed the job, I was walking on air.

I knew my mother was a bit worried. I'd never been anywhere without the family before. But she knew how much I wanted to go, and she never tried to stop me. She and Gran insisted on coming down to London with me to see me settled; and though they didn't say as much, to meet the girl I was going to work for and see if she was OK.

I hadn't met Louise either till that day. Her mother, who was very posh and lived in a big house with a heated swimming pool and servants all over the place, had taken me on. Louise seemed nice. She was very quiet, and I thought that, like me, she probably felt a bit shy with strangers.

Four years before, her car had been in a head-on collision with a lorry, and she had spent a year in hospital. Now she was confined to a wheelchair and would never walk. But she insisted on living her own life away from her wealthy family, and she had just taken this flat. She even did a part-time job as a telephonist, driving to work in an invalid car.

She didn't tell me all this, her mother did. I thought she must be very brave, and my mother did too. If a crippled girl could leave home and manage alone, I ought to be ashamed of myself for being nervous at leaving the nest.

When Mum left, she hugged me and said something about promising to come home if I wasn't happy. I laughed it off, I was determined to make a go of the job, and being unhappy didn't seem likely.

HOW wrong can you be? In the first week, any illusions I'd had about having time off to see the sights and enjoy myself, went up in smoke. Louise had to be helped with everything, including having a bath every day, and I found I was working seventeen hours a day. I was on duty seven days one week, and five the next — but by the time my weekend off came round, I was too exhausted to do anything except sleep.

Maybe the work wouldn't have mattered if Louise had turned out to be nice as I'd thought, or even bearable. Her quietness certainly wasn't shyness, more a feeling that she was my employer and I was her servant, and talking to me was beneath her.

She acted like a queen, shouting for me every few minutes, to put a book back on the shelf or take a speck of dust off the carpet. Even being in the bath was no excuse for me not rushing immediately.

I had to eat my breakfast standing up in the kitchen, washing tea-towels, and if she had friends in, I was banished to the kitchen and not allowed to come out till they had gone.

At night, when she got back from work, she would check the cutlery and

crockery and the contents of the fridge. In case I was stealing the silver or eating more than I should, I suppose.

I tried to make excuses for her. She'd been brought up with servants. She was used to being waited on. Things would change when we got to know each other. You have to make allowances for how frustrated and unhappy she must be, being in a wheelchair. I was much more fortunate than her really — even if I was poor and miserable and homesick, and she'd inherited a fortune from her grandparents.

But all the brainwashing I could manage didn't help when the workmen

came in to do a few jobs, and she made me hide the towels in case they used them, and instructed me to charge them 2p for coffee. At night I'd lie awake, thinking of my nice family who hadn't any money to spare but would give anyone anything.

I thought of Mum, worrying maybe that I was out too late, living it up. I never told them the true story when I wrote. A few times I almost did, but I ripped up the letters. Once I even packed my suitcase, but I couldn't crawl home and admit I'd failed, especially when my family had told everyone back home what a great job I had.

ONE day, pushing her round the supermarket, I thought the breakthrough had finally happened, she wanted to be friends. She asked me if I liked cheesecake, and when I said yes, she bought two pieces. Back home she had me cut one piece in half and handed me half, while she ate all the rest herself. She watched me all the time to see how I took it, and I almost threw my piece in her smug face.

Shortly after that came the night I had my "funny turn." I got violent pains in my stomach and had to be taken to hospital, where I was examined and questioned by a doctor for two hours. It was my nerves, he told me. I needed to do less work, or I was heading for a nervous breakdown.

I didn't even mention the diagnosis to Louise, who didn't look worried anyway. Things just carried on where they left off, and I suppose I might have had a breakdown if it hadn't been for Dave, who came to mend the phone, and succeeded in making me see sense.

He was so nice and friendly and it had been so long since I had talked, really talked, to anyone, that I poured out the whole story. I even made him a cup of coffee.

"You must be mad," he said. "Why don't you just walk out?" Then, without waiting for an answer, "I suppose you're ashamed to go home and admit the streets of London weren't paved with gold after all. Everyone fails sometimes, love. It's not your fault. Nobody will love you less."

I laughed. I'd almost forgotton how. "There's something else, though," I said seriously. "I don't like Louise, but I feel responsible for her. She depends on me. What would she do without me?"

"Find someone else, maybe someone who suits her better. Having a girl your age around must be a constant reminder of what her life was like before the accident. I expect she's jealous of you."

IT seemed incredible that Louise could envy me. But then I hadn't really thought much about her feelings. I'd been too busy hating her and trying to hang on to my sanity. I'd never got through to her. Maybe some of it was my fault. I hadn't that much patience and understanding. Someone older might have. Just telling someone about it made it a bit better. I wished I'd done that before.

My next weekend off, I left for good, the coward's way, I'm afraid. I knew Louise's mother was coming for her, so I left a note saying I wouldn't be back and slipped away.

I'm in my new job now, looking after a lovely little girl, still in London, and I love it. I'm relaxed and not neurotic about making a "success" of it. I know now I don't have to prove anything to anyone. Dave was right. People don't love you less just because you can't work miracles.

But I often think about Louise and I hope she is happier. I wish I could have helped her. I only hope someone else can.

THE MOST BEAUTIFUL MAN IN THE WORLD (see page 18)

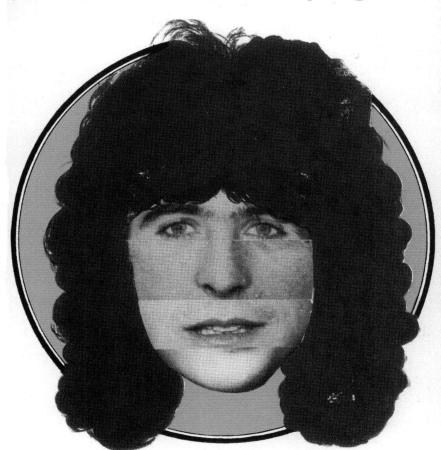

Well . . . maybe we'll just settle for them the way they are!

RUSSELL MAEL

DAVID ESSEX

DAVID BOWIE

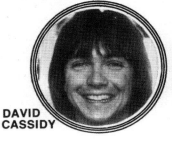

DAVID CASSIDY

DONNY OSMOND

229

Are You A HUMAN DUSTBIN ?

AVOID . . .

Butter or margarine: 266 calories per oz.

½ pint white sauce: 527 calories

Salad cream: approx. 100 calories per tablespoon

Large slice of bread: 105 calories

Cream of tomato soup, 1 portion: 111 calories

Egg Mayonnaise: 280 calories

Cheddar cheese: 120 calories per oz.

Cream cheese: 180 calories per oz.

Cod, fried in breadcrumbs, 1 portion: 583 calories

Mackerel, 3 oz can: 240 calories

Roast beef, 3 oz portion: 327 calories

Chips, average portion: 250 calories

Carton of coleslaw: 320 calories

Large banana: 80 calories

Tinned fruit salad, 1 portion: 140 calories

Strawberry fruit fool, carton: 213 calories

Apple pie, average portion: 300 calories

Chocolate pudding and sauce, 4 oz portion: 661 calories

Danish pastry: 473 calories

Scone with butter, jam and cream: 515 calories

Chocolates, toffees, fudge: 160 calories per oz.

Glass of milk (½ pint): 190 calories

Coca Cola, 1 glass: 80 calories

INSTEAD . . .

Outline: 110 calories per oz.

Sauce made with Outline, low fat milk: 255 calories

Waistline: 40 calories per tablespoon. Or dressing made from vinegar (no calories) or lemon juice (no calories) with dried herbs (experiment yourself!)

Crispbread: approx. 26 calories per slice

Kidney soup, 1 portion: 67 calories

Boiled egg: 80 calories

Edam cheese: 88 calories per oz.

Cottage cheese: 33 calories per oz.

Cod, grilled, 1 portion: 188 calories

Sardines in tomato, 3: 120 calories

Roast chicken, 3 oz portion: 162 calories

Potatoes, boiled, average portion: 115 calories. (If you can substitute green vegetables, so much the better. Average portion of cabbage — only 12 calories!)

Own salad made from grated carrots, shredded cabbage and onions with vinegar dressing: 24 calories

Medium apple: 40 calories

1 orange: 60 calories

Plain low fat yoghurt, carton: 60-90 calories (depending on make)

Baked apple: 150 calories

Chocolate swiss roll, 1 slice: 82 calories

Piece of sponge cake: 150 calories

Cream meringue: 150 calories

Boiled sweets and pastilles: 100 calories per oz. Liquorice: 84 calories per oz.

Glass of skimmed milk, or made up dried low-fat milk powder (½ pint): 100 calories

Low calorie drink, per glass: 8 calories

EVERYBODY knows the only way to get slim is to cut down on what you eat. That means consuming less calories — a calorie being a unit by which the "fattening" value of food is measured.

So you probably know a cheese salad is far less fattening than a Wimpy and chips (because it contains a lot less calories), and you'd be better off munching an apple for your mid afternoon break than a bar of chocolate.

But that's often about as far as it goes. Unless you go around with a complete calorie list in your hand and swot it up before every morsel goes into your mouth, you'll probably find it pretty hard to remember what's good and what's not so good, out of the hundreds of things you consume every day.

And that's where would-be slimmers meet their doom! It's easy enough to stick to ideas like "cakes and biscuits are fattening" and "cheese and meat are good for you," but you *could* be kidding yourself along all the while. You see, if you cut out those couple of plain biscuits you usually eat when you get home but fill up with Cheddar cheese, you might well be a few hundred calories worse off!

There are dozens of things you just get used to eating, without imagining what they're doing to your calorie intake. That all-milk bedtime drink for instance; a couple of buttery scrambled eggs on toast, a toffee or two.

So, what we're going to do is tell you how to be your own calorie counter — *without* remembering loads of figures.

without having to follow a rigid, boring diet.

First, then, here's your own magic no-diet diet! Once you've got the basic rules in your head, you'll be able to eat sensibly and slimly for as long as you like! All you've got to remember is: **IT'S BAD IF**

There's a lot of oil in it.

It's very buttery.

It's a combination of sugar, fat and flour (e.g. pastry!)

It's heavy and solid rather than watery or airy (e.g. fruit cakes are much higher in calories than light sponges).

It's anything in or on pastry.

It's processed and tinned (most of these foods have added sugar or fat) — unless specially for slimmers!

And **IT'S GOOD IF**

It's grilled or boiled.

It's in its natural state.

It's specifically labelled "low fat."

It's a vegetable cooked without any fat.

Remember, these are general rules; but to put you right about the foods you're most likely to eat, read on! We're *not* telling you the obvious and the boring, like "Have a stick of celery instead of a cream bun." Of course that's the ideal, but if you've *got* to have something sweet, and nothing else will do, you'll see you *can* indulge yourself. So we're suggesting realistic alternatives, not torture-yourself ones!

You'll find lots of surprises here — a few foods you never thought of as fattening, but which can be disastrous; and some that are allowable, rather than a far worse alternative!

And these are all things that may give you a big surprise, so — watch out!

Cheese and biscuits (average portion): 306

Cheesecake (one slice): 606

Milky bedtime drink: 322

Scrambled eggs on toast: 527

Nuts: 170 per oz.

Chocolate brazil, 1: 65

1 square of chocolate: 40

1 crisp: 5 calories

1 chip: 31 calories

Pastry, shortcrust: 157 calories per oz.

1 peanut: 6 calories

1 walnut: 18 calories

Remember, if you're planning to lose weight, 1,200-1,500 calories a day — and no more! — are what you should aim for.

Real dangers to diets, then, are things that are: FRIED, FATTY, SUGARY, HEAVY or PROCESSED.

Dieting's difficult, but it's going to be a lot easier now you know the basics!

WATCH OUT

Here's an "annual" look at our TV favourites! It's a very special selection of people whom we think made really good TV viewing! We'd like to give them all a Watch Out award — and here are a few reasons why . . .

Good old **NOEL EDMONDS** must be one of the busiest men around, but in his role of host on "Swapshop" he never let the action flag, and he keeps us laughing!

How could we miss the most famous frog of them all! **KERMIT** has a tough job keeping those Muppets in order. He definitely has something to be able to emerge unscathed from Miss Piggy's attacks!

Here's someone who's come from down under to up top — lovely Australian, **JEFF PHILLIPS**. We'd like to give him a special award for always looking as if he's really enjoying himself!

Someone with a real talent for comedy — **PAULINE QUIRKE**. In her TV appearances, she shows that she's a born comedienne and deserves to go far.

ROBIN ELLIS as the dashing Captain Ross Poldark captured all our hearts. It must be the way he copes with major disasters without batting an eyelid. Added to the fact that he's very handsome, of course, and looks marvellous in his 18th century costumes!

Whatever show he's in, **RICHARD O'SULLIVAN** always seems to be cooking up something good!

CHARLIE'S ANGELS brought a great deal of glamour and fun to our screens, and we thought it was great the way they solved all those crimes so effortlessly. Of course, Farrah has left the series now but with her looks we think she'll be a successful "fallen angel."

For sheer smoothness we couldn't ignore lovely **GARETH HUNT** and his smooth acting in "The New Avengers"!

Here's someone frightfully smart — it's **ANTHONY VALENTINE** in his role of "Raffles." Whatever happened to him, he always remained cool and calm, showing that a successful jewel thief and safecracker can be a perfect gentleman, too!

ROBERT POWELL must have one of the most beautiful pairs of eyes ever, and those, coupled with his superb acting, made "Jesus of Nazareth" compelling viewing.

Blimey, guv, we couldn't forget this geezer! **DENNIS WATERMAN** isn't just a talented actor, though, he's turning his attentions to singing and songwriting — quite a change from Detective-Sergeant Carter's hobbies!

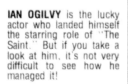

IAN OGILVY is the lucky actor who landed himself the starring role of "The Saint." But if you take a look at him, it's not very difficult to see how he managed it!

We all *had* to stay in to watch "Rich Man, Poor Man" and we hold **JAMES CARROLL JORDAN** in his role of Billy Abbott personally responsible for completely changing our Saturday night routines!

ARE YOU A SPACE-AGE STAR ?

COULD you be a fearless space explorer, travelling through time and space to uncharted planets and unknown dangers? Find out if you really fit into the Space Age by whizzing through our special quiz journey. Travel round the Universe with us, and when your trip's over there'll be some home truths waiting for you!

1. You need a bit of a break, and rush to the Galaxy Travel Bureau to book a trip round the Universe — well, it's a change from Bognor Regis, anyway. You hire a space-craft called —
   (d) Eagle-Ray,
   (a) Endeavour,
   (b) Bertie,
   (c) Queen of the Skies.

2. The friendly old moon is your first stop, where you're booked into —
   (a) The Sea of Tranquillity Retreat,
   (c) The Man-in-the-Moon Motel,
   (d) The Lunar Hilton,
   (b) Habitation 23rd Crater West Central.

3. You bounce about happily on the moon for a few days, but it's rather crowded and you keep bumping into people, so you shoot on to Mars. A young Martian falls madly in love with you and follows you around everywhere. The only trouble is —
   (d) these holiday romances never seem to work out,
   (b) you don't really fancy kissing someone with an emerald green face and a TV aerial sticking out of the top of their head,
   (a) you haven't really got a great deal in common with each other,
   (c) you don't want to be disloyal to your boyfriend back home?

4. So you decide to breeze off along the planetary tourist trail, but something seems to have gone wrong. Jupiter and Saturn go whizzing by and you seem to be hurtling through —
   (b) a remote, unmapped cluster of bright young stars,
   (a) a weird echoing black void into infinity,
   (c) a star-spangled fairyland swathed in a floating gaseous blue mist,
   (d) a fiery furnace of angry sky, with glowing burnt-out suns, and black smoke clouds.

5. Well, you wanted to get away from it all but this is ridiculous! You fight with the controls as you're carried further and further off course. Suddenly a strange object comes towards you. You can't quite make it out, but —
   (c) it seems to be a flock of giant golden birds, their wings shimmering and their beaks bared,
   (b) it's only a common or garden exploding meteor, that's all!
   (d) it's a hostile space-ship with menacing arrow-heads and huge ungodly black metal claws,
   (a) it's like some kind of ectoplasm, a ghost cloud changing shape, now a human form, now a monster . . .

6. You plunge on —
   (d) through magnetic storms and hurtling comets,
   (a) beyond the hideous, wailing caverns of darkest Pluto,
   (b) through solar systems and galaxies,
   (c) into the timeless heavens of no return.

7. **You realise you are hopelessly lost. What's your reaction when the awful thought strikes you that you may never see the dear old planet Earth again?**
   (a) I'll just have to find a new kind of spiritual existence, and develop a new character to cope with a solitary life in space.
   (c) Oh no, please God, it's too terrible! Never to see my family and friends again. I'm lonely and homesick. I can't even send Mum a postcard!
   (d) Never see planet Earth again? Don't be silly, of course I will. I'll fight with everything in my power to get back again.
   (b) Oh well, at least I'll get out of the end of term exams, won't I?

8. **Suddenly you are pulled by a magnetic force onto an unknown planet. You peer hesitantly out of the window to see —**
   (d) a time-switched scene of ancient Greek palaces, golden harps and magnificent warriors on horseback,
   (c) a snow-covered wilderness with the strange sound of the wind across the ice, a silver palace in the distance,
   (b) a civilisation so advanced it makes your mind boggle,
   (a) a network of rumbling caves with unearthly reptiles and weird music echoing from within.

9. **Terrified, you step out of the space-craft to be greeted by a handsome boy, who says his name is Damian Jones and he's —**
   (c) a flying doctor on a mercy mission,
   (a) a space artist and photographer on a magazine assignment,
   (b) Dr Who's trainee assistant, out to get the Time Lords,
   (d) on a secret mission for the Foreign Office.

10. **You think Damian is the most amazing person you've ever met because —**
    (d) he's wearing a black velvet cape and is carrying a weird-looking briefcase,
    (b) he obviously knew how to get here — so surely he can get you back home,
    (a) he has the most fascinating eyes you've ever gazed into,
    (c) he looks just like Robert Redford.

11. **It's love at first sight and as you stand hand in hand gazing out over the starry skies, he tells you —**
    (b) he'd love you madly even if you *weren't* the only girl around for fifty billion light years,
    (c) he wants to do something in-credibly old-fashioned like taking you back to Earth and marrying you,

(d) he's been around in Space for a long time with a girlfriend on every planet, but he's never met anyone like you!
(a) it can't just be coincidence, it must be fate meeting him in this desolate place.

12. **Clever Damian gets you both back to earth simply by —**
    (d) swallowing a time capsule,
    (c) borrowing a magic carpet,
    (a) using his psychic powers of auto-suggestion,
    (b) phoning the inter-space rocket taxi service.

13. **So there you are safe in your lovely earth-bound home, with your cosy bed, your Starsky and Hutch pin-ups and your hot cocoa. What's your verdict as you think back over your "holiday?"**
    (c) It was a long way to go to meet a new boyfriend, but it was worth it!
    (a) It was a wonderful, enriching spiritual experience.
    (d) Never mind spiritual enrichment, I'll sell my story to the highest bidder.
    (b) I think I'll stick to Bognor Regis next year!

Count your score, mainly (a), (b), (c) or (d) and turn to the conclusions below.

Conclusions

Mostly (a)

Your planet is Uranus, that mysterious far away planet shrouded in the secrecy of the unknown. This is because your questing mind is always fascinated by the strange and mysterious. You are also rather a private sort of person, with your own thoughts and feelings at life. You're introverted and thoughtful, good at sensing atmospheres and using your instincts. You're also self-sufficient, with a quiet, inner confidence in yourself. And this makes you very adaptable. Therefore you could cope with life on Uranus, without feeling lonely and isolated. You need a few really good close friends around you, that's all, and a super boy who is as aware and sensitive as you are. As for life on the planet Earth, you tend to find some people shallow, and daily routine a bit boring. You're rather an idealist and would like to create your own beautiful world around you. You're good at that - but remember to come down to earth occasionally, won't you?

Mostly (b)

Your planet is Mars, the planet of action, sometimes warlike, sometimes friendly, but always strong and practical. You have a great deal of confidence in yourself, and although you're generally easy-going, you also have a hot temper and a will of your own. You can cope with life and look after yourself and you're also sociable and extrovert, with a great sense of humour. You have faith in yourself, and courage, and this means that you could cope with life in Space as well as you cope with life on Earth. You have a lot of energy and drive, and a sense of adventure and a hard-headed attitude to life. You're seldom worried by doubt and your positive approach usually guarantees you success in whatever you set out to achieve. You seem to be doing very well on Earth, so you might as well explore this world to the full before you go blasting off to Mars!

Mostly (c)

Your planet is Venus, the planet of love, beauty and sensitivity. You're a sensitive sort of person, living on your emotions, and your relationships are the most important part of your life. You tend to romanticise people and situations, sometimes reading too much into people's actions and motives. You're a very imaginative person with a genuine appreciation of nature and beautiful things. You're not very practical, but your feminine intuition usually leads you to the right judgments and decisions. You are honest and sympathetic, a loyal friend who respects confidences and can be trusted with secrets. You're nostalgic and sentimental by nature, you get very attached to people and places, so you're not a very good candidate for becoming an astronaut of the future. You love the world you live in, so why waste time whizzing about in Space? You want to find beautiful places and beautiful relationships as near to home as possible.

Mostly (d)

Your planet is Jupiter, most powerful and magnificent of all the planets! You're a dramatic person, with change-able moods. You love the limelight and hate being second best. You want to be a special person, with special powers and talents so that others admire you and look up to you. People perhaps think you're a bit conceited sometimes, and that you sulk if you don't get your own way. It's simply that you have a very strong personality and perhaps haven't learnt to cope with yourself yet. You sometimes find self-control difficult. But the sky's the limit as far as you're concerned; you're ambitious and dynamic with a magnetic charm. Although you're not afraid of Space, you're a worldly sort of person who wants all the best things the planet Earth can provide. You'd be happy wherever you could carve out some space for yourself – and where you weren't alone.

WILL HE BE YOUR PRINCE CHARMING?

— or will he be your Toad of Toad Hall? Find out with our fun panto guide to boys!

WINTER'S the time for pantomimes, when all the Principal Boys take the stage. And could some of those Principal Boys be appearing in your life this winter? Some of them are super enough to be top of the bill, but others deserve to be booed out of sight. So read on and see how to get (and get rid of!) your Principal Boys!

PETER PAN

You remember, he's the one with the secret of eternal youth. You *must* know some boys like this. They just can't grow up.

COSTUME: Jeans, sneakers, and horrible sweaters with Donald Duck motifs knitted by their adoring grans.

ACT: To prove he has the secret of eternal youth, Peter Pan will be full of boyish pranks. When it snows, you'll get hit in the face by a snowball. When it's frosty, you'll be pushed over on the ice. All this is just to show his affection, of course!

If he's *really* beginning to grow up, he might ask you out . . . fishing! Which means sitting on a freezing riverbank for hours while he boasts about his maggots. Don't let him see how disgusted you are, or he might shove a few down your back!

HOW TO GET RID OF HIM Talk non-stop at the top of your voice so you frighten the fish away.

KING RAT

The leader of the pack. The evil one. His very presence casts a chill and yet some girls (yes, even you) might be attracted by his air of sinister mystery.

COSTUME: Could be leathers, could be football supporter's gear; depends on whether he's into deafening people or flattening them!

ACT: King Rat doesn't believe in charm. With him it's the strong-arm approach. He'll expect you to fetch his crisps at break, let him copy your homework, and buy his fags for him — and to show his contempt for pain, he'll stub out the fags on the palm of your hand. To King Rat a girl is there just to be impressed.

So your job's to sit around and look enthusiastic as he bullies people, revs his motorbike, and punches walls to show how hard he is. If this sort of life appeals to you . . . keep quiet about it, for goodness' sake! And if not . . .

HOW TO GET RID OF HIM Get a cat (try Dick Whittington) or call in the Rodent Exterminating Officer.

BUTTONS

The boy-next-door, the brotherly type who's always there to put his arm round you (and that's all!) when things are going badly. When things are going well, of course, you're off like a shot (nearly breaking his arm as you go!).

COSTUME: The ordinary boy-next-door gear of jeans, sweater and anorak. But don't forget the BUTTONS; usually lapel buttons saying things like, *IF YOU CAN READ THIS YOU ARE STANDING TOO CLOSE* or, *WATCH OUT, I BITE!* (Actually, of course he doesn't bite; he's totally harmless, but you can't go round wearing a lapel-badge saying, *I'M TOTALLY HARMLESS,* can you?)

ACT: Being a Nice Guy to everybody. He's even nice to your little brother, which takes a bit of doing. Buttons will do your nasty jobs for you (such as pumping up your bicycle tyres on freezing mornings). If an old lady slips up on the icy pavement, he'll be out there in a flash with bandages, blankets, and kind words.

If there's any trouble at school, he'll own up right away — even if he hasn't done it! And he always remembers everybody's birthday, even the maths teacher's! Of course, he *adores* you, and has done for years. Which is why he's just the slightest bit of a bore.

HOW TO GET RID OF HIM Give him a lapel-button which says, *PRESS BUTTON TO RELEASE . . .*

Winter brings out all Dandini's love of finery and entertainment. It's the season for parties, and Dandini knows where they all are — and if there aren't any, he'll throw one himself.

COSTUME: Velvet trousers, three-piece suits, cashmere sweaters, posh fur coats, leather boots . . . etc.

ACT: Prepare to play second fiddle, because as far as Dandini is concerned, you're just a fancy accessory and not *quite* as attractive as his Indian silk scarf!

He'll want to parade up and down the High Street on Saturday mornings, and he'll always be eager to show his clothes off at the disco that night, so if you like window-shopping and bopping, he's great. But if not . . .

HOW TO GET RID OF HIM Greet him one day with, "Hello, you look scruffy!" Or borrow his best coat and fall down in the mud.

PRINCE CHARMING

He doesn't have to be a real prince — there aren't enough of them to go round, nowadays! But there are a few Prince Charmings lurking in even the most ordinary streets.

COSTUME: Prince Charming has good taste and whatever he wears looks good on him — even if it's a grey wig, white tights and high-heeled shoes!

ACT: Prince Charming is aptly named. If it's freezing cold, he'll insist on putting his coat around your shoulders. If it's pouring with rain, he'll put down his coat for you to walk over puddles. (In fact, he seems to want to get rid of that coat!) He's a real old-fashioned gentleman. If anyone tells a rude joke, he'll raise his eyebrows and look disgusted. (Maybe he laughs about it alone, afterwards.) He's totally enchanting to all ladies — even your mum. In fact, it's when you realise that Mum likes him that you begin to think something might be wrong . . .

HOW TO GET RID OF HIM Say, "Cor · coo o mi GAWD BLIMEY***" and wipe your nose on the back of your hand.

ALADDIN

Remember him? The boy from the laundry who loved exploring? And got rich with the help of his genie?

COSTUME: This is a rags-to-riches story, so he wears rags or at least, raggy jeans. (Still, everybody wears raggy jeans nowadays, so he may be difficult to recognise.)

ACT: Aladdin likes exploring, so prepare yourself to be taken up hills (draughty), down dales (boggy), and across moors (bare, boggy and draughty). Snow and ice will not deter him. In fact, it'll spur him on, so make sure you have at least three jerseys (get him to lend you some from the laundry).

As for his other interest — doing magic tricks and giving people expensive presents . . . well, it's a bit suspect nowadays. So if he gives you a brand-new transistor radio and says it's from his genie, be suspicious! It might well have fallen off the back of a lorry — and what judge is going to believe that story about a genie?

HOW TO GET RID OF HIM Have a word with his genie. He might be able to arrange something.

TOAD OF TOAD HALL

The main thing about Toad is that he's always boasting about his gadgets. And they're always new and expensive. You know the type of thing.

COSTUME: He may have goggly eyes and be covered in warts, but we all have our problems, don't we?

ACT: You can hear Toad coming: "I'm getting this Honda 125 with chrome crash bars and . . ." He'll try to impress you with details of his calculator (hyper-bionic and technicolour with a built-in cassette deck), his fountain pen (centrally-heated for comfort during November exams), and his pushbike (with new hovercraft attachments).

If you're technologically inclined, Toad can be fun, but if you're not, it can get quite a lot like a Consumer's Report from the 21st century!

HOW TO GET RID OF HIM Borrow one of his gadgets and flush it down the lavatory.

Write for the present!

Did you know that just by looking at your boyfriend's signature, you can tell an awful lot about him? And, at Christmas you might wonder what he's like when it comes to the present stakes — will he give you one for a start, and if he does, how will he give it? Will he press it into your hands and run away blushing or organise a presentation in front of all your friends? Well, take a good look at our special guide and it'll tell you a lot about the boy in your life at the "present" time!

If his signature is large and flamboyant with lots of flourishes and twirls to it, then he's friendly and extrovert. He'll buy you the biggest bunch of flowers, the largest box of chocolates — yes, he's a bit showy! — and he'll shower you with kisses when he hands them over, too.

If his signature is small and has a left slant you could be in for a nice surprise. He isn't going to reveal his affections for all the world to see, but he'll have good taste and go searching for something that's just you. If he genuinely likes you — you're in luck!

If his signature is the same size as the rest of his script he doesn't put on any act, he's just what he seems to be — reliable and sincere. He's loyal and you'll know where you are with him. His present will be practical and something you want. He'll make no bones about handing it over and expect a friendly kiss in return.

If his signature is threadlike — tapering off with thin strokes at the end, or like Steven's with a straight line in the middle of his name, then he knows how to handle people. He will know exactly what to buy to please you. The only thing is, he might not remember to get the present, since he's not always very reliable.

The small signature writer will demonstrate his slight secretiveness and wrap his present carefully. He's very cautious and if he does put a message with his present, it could be a very brief one. It's because he's shy and thoughtful, but he does mean what he says.

Watch the writer who underlines his name — he's full of himself and a bit of a show-off. He'll want to make an impression in his own style. He's determined, ambitious and sure of himself and he could be pushy. He might give you something that looks impressive, but isn't very useful!

If his signature is tall and narrow — watch it! — he could be quite mean when it comes to gifts. He's not really keen on going out and when he does he might even expect you to pay for yourself. He's likely to be mean about presents because privately he thinks they're a waste of money.

A large rounded signature denotes a fun-loving personality, even if he's a bit lazy — he's not very dishy, but that's just the way he is! His present could be useless or a piece of nonsense, but one that will give you a laugh anyway!

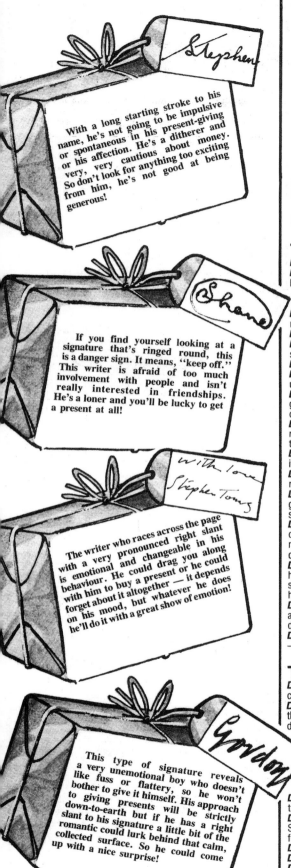

With a long starting stroke to his name, he's not going to be impulsive or spontaneous in his present-giving or his affection. He's a ditherer and very, very cautious about money. So don't look for anything too exciting from him, he's not good at being generous!

If you find yourself looking at a signature that's ringed round, this is a danger sign. It means, "keep off." This writer is afraid of too much involvement with people and isn't really interested in friendships. He's a loner and you'll be lucky to get a present at all!

The writer who races across the page with a very pronounced right slant is emotional and changeable in his behaviour. He could drag you along with him to buy a present or he could forget about it altogether — it depends on his mood, but whatever he does he'll do it with a great show of emotion!

This type of signature reveals a very unemotional boy who doesn't like fuss or flattery, so he won't bother to give it himself. His approach to giving presents will be strictly down-to-earth but if he has a right slant to his signature a little bit of the romantic could lurk behind that calm, collected surface. So he could come up with a nice surprise!

SURVIVAL GUIDE TO PARTIES

It's the season of parties — well, what else is there to do when the weather turns nasty? But if the thought of parties makes you feel quite weak, here's a few tips to help you through — and to make sure it really *is* the season of goodwill!

Here's how to cope with:

THE OFFICE PARTY

Do make sure you get there on time.
Don't take your coat off until there are at least six other people between you and the office Romeo!
Do wish your boss a Happy Christmas.
Don't go and meet him in the Post Room at midnight as he suggested!
Do offer to serve the drinks round.
Don't let the Office Manager mix you a special Gin Fizz!
Do wear your new dress.
Don't experiment with low necklines — unless you intend to keep your cardigan on!
Do try and look as though you're having a great time, even when everyone around you is doing the Hokey-Cokey for the fifth time.
Don't imagine it's a good time to ask for a rise — even if the cleaner does earn more than you.
Do have a go at dancing, just once, even if it's only with the pimply creep in the corner.
Don't ask the DJ to play the Stranglers' new record when everyone else is waltzing.
Do keep a clear head — it doesn't look good to fall on the floor after only two shandies.
Don't bother about causing a scene when the dumb blonde secretary on the dance floor makes eyes at your fella — go out there and quietly tread on those twinkling toes of hers.
Do avoid the smoothie young executive when he comes round with the mistletoe for the sixth time — he's got no plans for getting you home on time!
Don't believe that kiss and cuddle with the advertising clerk goes unnoticed — it doesn't!
Do get to work on time the next morning — otherwise tongues will wag!

THE FAMILY PARTY

Do help get things ready — even though you can't stand Uncle Bert and Auntie Ivy.
Don't tell your mum you refuse to go — though the thought of hearing Uncle Jack's dirty jokes for the third year running makes you cringe.
Do some of the food preparations — if they're good, perhaps everyone will eat too much and go home early.
Don't be spiteful and sprinkle salt over the Christmas pudding.
Do put all the presents round the Christmas tree.
Don't let Grandad get hold of your brother's Sex Maniac's Diary, a special present from you.
Do set place-names on the dining-table.
Don't put Granny too near the brandy butter.
Do offer everyone a festive drink.
Don't let Uncle Arthur near Dad's whisky — he drank the lot last year!

Do pull the crackers — but not too near the cat.
Don't encourage your younger brother to practise his party tricks on Auntie Ethel — he lost her false teeth last Christmas!
Do remember to hang up the mistletoe.
Don't get caught by Uncle George like last year — he counted the number of berries then insisted on the same number of kisses!
Do play party games like Charades and Chinese Whispers.
Don't encourage cousin Bertha's request for a game of Monopoly using real money.
Do invite your friends over to join in the fun.
Don't ask the boy you fancy — if you want to see him again!
Do wish everyone goodnight — if you can stay awake long enough.
Don't stop to think what fun it'll be next year, when the party starts all over again!

A FRIEND'S PARTY

Do take your coat upstairs to her room.
Don't get pinned against the wall by the first eager beaver you meet on the stairs.
Do circulate — it keeps the eager beavers on their toes!
Don't get trapped in a corner with the guy who reckons he's the life and soul of the party.
Do look like you're enjoying yourself.
Don't spend too much time in the kitchen if the strip-lighting makes you look like a puffy peach.
Do remember to eat some food — you don't want to keel over after a glass of fizzy orange.
Don't get carried away and pile your plate with too much — it'll only end up in someone's lap.
Do make sure you've got a glass in your hand — you never know who'll come along and fill it up!
Don't go to the wrong cupboard and take one of their best cut-glass goblets by mistake.
Do experiment with some new make-up.
Don't go mad and risk the sparkly sort if there's any chance it'll bring you out in boils.
Do go along to the hairdresser and have your hair done.
Don't listen when they say everyone's having their hair sprayed silver for Yule-tide.
Do flirt a little — it's Christmas after all!
Don't let your boyfriend catch you.
Do stand near the mistletoe — just in case.
Don't go and get off with your best friend's bloke because *he* was standing near the mistletoe!
Do go home with the guy who brought you.
Don't expect an invitation next year if you were the belle of the ball!

And since (hopefully) you're going to be spending eight hours a day, five days a week of your life in some sort of job, it's only natural that you want an interesting, worthwhile one that's suited to your own, unique talents.

So whether you're still at school and don't have much idea of what you want to do, or are still looking for a job, or maybe already have a job but don't like it much, we're going to help you take a fresh look at your problems and show you the first practical steps to take to put things right. After all, it's *your* life — and you don't want to waste a minute of it in work that's pointless, boring or just plain hateful!

> **6 6** *I just haven't any idea what I want to do when I leave school. My parents tell me I should try for one thing, my Careers teacher says I should try something else — and I'm just stuck, very undecided and confused, in the middle.* **9 9**

If this is your problem, the first thing you should do is — *leave as many options open as you can.*

This means that if, for instance, you're trying to choose a course to follow at school, university, polytechnic, training college or whatever, but have no very definite career in mind, don't choose a narrow course, but get the widest one you can, which leads to the most career possibilities later.

If you're job-hunting and can't find exactly what you have in mind, don't throw the whole thing up in despair. Try, instead, to get into some job that has links with the career you've got in mind.

For instance, if you have ambitions towards writing, in journalism or advertising or anything similar, but prospects are dim, don't throw away your dreams and head for the nearest factory — take secretarial work in a firm with strong connections with advertising, public relations, magazines or publishing.

There may be ways of edging your way towards that dream career, and in any case secretarial work is always helpful to a would-be writer!

> **6 6** *I've just started a course to help me towards my future career — but I've been in it two months now, and I hate it!* **9 9**

If this is your problem, we'd say that you really should try never to leave a course unfinished.

Dropping out halfway through or (worse still!) at the very beginning, is going to damage your self-confidence and it won't look good on your record. So you have absolutely nothing to gain by dropping out. On the other hand, if you finish the course, you have a very great deal to gain.

If you put your mind to it and pass the course, you don't *have* to use it in a follow-up career, but the very fact that you have qualifications of ANY kind shows prospective employers that you have intelligence and perseverance, all good points to have on your side in these days of high unemployment.

Also, you may be able to use the qualification in a way you haven't realised — specialist training like nursing, or O levels in maths and science subjects, have wide application in many jobs.

And even if you do fail to obtain a pass or other qualification at the end of your course, it can still be a help to you. For one thing, there are degrees of failure, and a near-miss can be looked on favourably by many employers — it's certainly better for your record than not having taken the subject at all!

Of course, if you've embarked on a course and you really have given it every chance, but realise that you'll never, ever, make a nurse, hairdresser, dental assistant or whatever, you really ought to have a word with your parents and your teachers at college. They may be able to reassure you that you're not doing quite as badly as you thought you were — or they may advise you to change courses.

A change of course, like this, though, should never be embarked on without a lot of thought and without a lot of discussion with parents and teachers alike. If you start to make a habit of chopping and changing from one course to another, you may end up with no qualifications at all — *and* a record of indecision which won't look good to *any* prospective employer!

> **6 6** *I don't have enough O or A levels to get any sort of decent job. But, since I've already left school, I can't see me taking them now.* **9 9**

If this is your problem, remember, it's *never* too late to re-take an exam if you want to.

If you have left school and have since realised that you could be in a better job, with more interesting work and brighter prospects if only you had one or more O or A levels, you can still take them and improve your career.

Get advice from your Careers Officer at the local Education Authority, or by asking at your nearest Careers Service office, or by consulting the Adult Education Department in your area. Yo can take evening classes to get these and A levels, or study with the Ope University, or possibly get your employ to put you on a Day Release course.

If, though, you're worried about th year's exams and regret time wasted, it still not too late to make sure you get tho vital passes. Speak to your teachers even if you've been a lazy or bad stude if you're willing to work even at this la date, something can be done.

You might not be able to make u missed work in a few weeks, but yo teachers can advise you which are th most likely areas to be covered by exa questions, and you can concentrate those.

And in your local paper, you can fi people willing to give additional, priva tuition for particular O and A level especially maths and english.

You can also contact the university bo setting the O and A levels for your schoo and buy copies of old exam papers. The are usually two years old by the tim they're issued, but are good practice ar show how the examiners' minds work!

They normally cost around 50p f one subject. Your staff at school ca tell you where to write or telephone, ar may even have papers you can borrow

> **6 6** *I already have a job — and hate it! I thought I'd like doing thi type of work, but it hasn't turned ou at all as I expected. What am supposed to do now?* **9 9**

If this is your problem, there just may n be all that much you *can* do about Especially if things are tough at home.

Your family may quite likely discoura you from job-hunting if they really ne

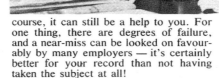

e money your wage-packet brings,
d you may feel guilty if you know your
her is out of work, or his job is on short-
ne or hanging in the balance.

If you are miserable in the work you're
ing, though, there are still steps you
n take to make life more enjoyable,
thout putting anything at risk. The
lden rule these days, though, is NOT to
row up the job you have until you are
ally quite certain you have a better job to
to!

When job-hunting it is best, sometimes,
keep it absolutely quiet, and don't let
e fact get whispered round the offices of
ur present employers, or you might find
u get the boot before you're ready!

Also, if your employers learn you are
ssatisfied, you're not likely to be offered
ances of promotion or improvement.

So, look around for something
itable — but do it tactfully. Secondly,
o it with common sense.

There's not much point yearning to be a
ain-surgeon or film star if you don't have
e qualifications, whatever they may be!
nd if your main complaint about your
esent job is that it's boring, you
ould be practical and realise that most
ork is fairly routine.

You get your enjoyment from liking
e people you work with, the satisfaction
doing the work well, and the fun of
ending your money at the end of the
eek! So don't set your aims too high.

In fact, the change you need might be
lot closer to hand than you realise.
ry to discover why you feel so dissatis-
ed.

It may be because you don't have
ough to do, or feel you could cope
ith more challenging work, or don't get
n with the people you work with. In any
these situations, it is possible there's a
b you'll like a lot better inside the
rganisation you're currently working for.

Don't be afraid, in this case, to ask
ound. Take the line, "I like this firm,
it I think I'm ready for more challenging
ork" — and then nobody will take
fence. Even if there isn't a vacancy
ght away, you could be ear-marked for
mething better quite soon.

Most organisations much prefer to
ove staff up from the inside, rather than
ke on new people, so by looking around

inside your present firm, you stand a
better chance of a change of job, than by
approaching outsiders.

If you really feel you simply *must*
change your job before you go totally mad,
though, go back to your local Careers
Service or Job Centre, explain your
problem to them and you'll find them very
sympathetic and helpful.

> ❝*I left school ages ago, and I
> still haven't found a job. What's
> wrong with me? Why don't people
> want to employ me? I'm beginning
> to think I must be a failure at
> everything.*❞

**If this is your problem, don't, for
goodness sake, think that not being able to
find a job is some sort of judgment on you
and your abilities.**

Thousands of good men and women are
unable to find work, and it's mainly due
to the economic situation. So don't write
yourself off as a failure.

Instead, be positive about your predica-
ment. First, check that you really are
doing everything possible to find work.
Don't expect Careers staff to do it all!

You should be regularly checking
employment vacancies in local papers, at
agencies and employment bureaux, at your
nearest Job Centre and on notice-boards
at large local organisations. If you have a
definite career in mind, don't wait for
notices of vacancies to appear — try
writing to the Personnel Officer of the
organisation concerned, stating your
qualifications and asking about possible
future vacancies.

Quite often the large organisations have
lists of possible candidates for future
employment, and you could be put on a
short list for inverview in a few months'
time.

Also, use the free time you have now —
it's an advantage, and you should make
full use of it. You may be able to improve
your qualifications by home study.

You can make yourself a more useful
person, too, simply by widening the scope
of your local knowledge — get to know
your home town, find out all that the local
libraries have to offer, discover how many
different types of work are carried on
locally, take an interest in your local paper,
town hall, community centre, etc.

If you keep an alert and lively mind,
life becomes more interesting, you have
more chance of noticing an opportunity for
a job, and you develop the kind of personality that makes employers want to give you
a job when you do go for an interview!

You can also use the time to practise
things like writing letters for jobs, short-
hand (try taking down the between-record
comments of disc jockeys) and type-
writing (you can buy a second-hand
machine very cheaply). You can also make
life more interesting and save money by
learning to make your own clothes,
teaching yourself a language (ask at the
library for books and records), or by
learning to type or cook.

And don't despise part-time employment! Naturally, if you are hoping to get a
job some day as a teacher, a dental
receptionist, a laboratory technician or
whatever, you don't want to have to admit
defeat by working full-time as a loo cleaner!

But a variety of part-time jobs adds
enjoyment to life, gives you the independence of a little earned income, and
can also be surprisingly useful in giving
valuable experience of what a working
life is really like. Look for part-time work
like jobs in canteens, pubs, shops,
offices — you'll find them in local papers,
on cards at newsagents and stationers, and
on notice-boards of large organisations.

Also, be prepared to do a full-time job
for a few weeks only now and then,
working at something you maybe wouldn't
care to do for the rest of your life. You'll
be surprised how much even the most
boring-sounding job can teach you about
work, life and people — and all this will
come in useful later.

But don't fall into the trap of being side-
tracked. Keep looking all the time for the
real career you want. Your ideas may
change as you go along, but you should
gradually find out more about what you're
looking for.

Keep that ideal in mind, keep looking —
and keep trying to improve your qualifications or abilities, so that when a
chance comes along, you're the ideal
person and *must* get chosen for the job!

---

*If you have career problems don't forget
that you can get a lot of information about
training, qualifications, pay and
prospects by reading one of the excellent
Career Guides put out by the Employment
Service Agency. They cost from 8p to 45p
each.*

*You can get a catalogue of all the
careers booklets, with an order form,
from H.M.S.O., 49 High Holborn,
London WC1V 6HB (enclose an s.a.e.)
and you can often read any of the
leaflets free, at your public library. There
are over 40 leaflets available and,
to give some idea of the variety, new titles
added to the list include Forestry,
Road and Rail, Home Economics,
Remedial Professions, Advertising and
Speech Therapy!*

So go to it – and good luck!

TREE OF LOVE

Like to try your arm in the love stakes? Well, our tree of love game is ready and waiting for you to climb it, from the tricky lower branches of meeting and having that extra special first date with your dream boy, up through the dangerous boughs where you meet his mum and dad, to the dizzy height at the very top of the tree where you find true love! Happy climbing!

Branch 7
HE SAYS HE LOVES YOU. Would you —
a) simply say, "I love you, too".
b) go all red and pretend you hadn't heard,
c) wish your friends could hear him say it,
d) reply, "Oh, you're just saying that"?

Branch 5
YOU MEET HIS FRIENDS and want to convince them you're the greatest thing since Farrah Fawcett-Majors. Would you —
a) give every one of them a great big kiss,
b) wear your sexiest dress,
c) laugh like a drain at all their jokes,
d) try to be one of the boys?

Branch 6
YOUR FIRST QUARREL. This could be the beginning of the end unless you —
a) drive him back into your arms by having a great time with other boys . . .
b) "accidentally" bump into him and act as if you've never fallen out,
c) beg him to take you back,
d) get a friend to tell him how much you miss him.

Branch 4
YOU MEET HIS PARENTS FOR TEA. Alone with his mum, do you —
a) ask if she thinks apricot is a pretty colour for bridesmaids,
b) ask for her plum cake recipe,
c) leave her to get on with the washing

240

You can play the love game on your own, with friends, or — if you really want to live dangerously — with your boyfriend! All you need is a dice. Throw a six to start and climb on to the first branch. Answer the question you'll find there and then look at the base of the tree to see if you're romantically correct! If you're wrong, you'll be given a penalty before you can start climbing again. So think carefully — and good luck!

Branch 1
YOUR FIRST GLIMPSE: You see him at a party. You fancy him like mad! Would you —

a) flirt with someone else to make him jealous and desperate to get to know you,
b) talk to him, saying you don't know a soul at the party,
c) give him a big smile,
d) offer him a crisp?

you —
a) gaze deeply into his eyes.
b) ask where you can park your chewing gum.
c) throw your arms around him.
d) hope he doesn't smudge your lipstick?

Branch 2
IT'S YOUR FIRST DATE, and he seems nervous and shy. Would you —

a) chatter on about this and that,
b) suggest going to see a film,
c) gently ask him about himself,
d) tell a long joke?

Branch 1
SCORE. If you chose a, you can't move on until you've thrown a six, because he'll think you're not interested in him! If you chose c or d, miss a turn, because although either move would do for starters, they're not as direct or half as effective as b. So, if you chose b, move on to the second branch without delay!

Branch 2
SCORE. If you answered a, b or d, don't move till you've thrown a five, because all these moves would only make him feel even more self-conscious and inadequate. But if you chose c, you'd be right, because this would encourage him and give him more confidence! So move on to branch 3 . . .

Branch 3
SCORE. If you chose c or d, you can't move on until you've thrown a six, because you were either too cool or too keen! If you chose a, move on to branch 4!

Branch 4
SCORE. If you score a or b, don't move on until you've thrown a three. You see, your boy's mum would regard these questions as potential threats. If you chose c, throw six twice before moving on. This is a cardinal sin.

If you chose d, you've realised that the corny moves are often the best. Every Mum loves drooling over her little treasure (if only she knew!). So now move on to branch 5.

Branch 5
SCORE. If you chose a, b or d, don't move on until you've thrown a three. If you chose c, then you've found the easiest way of flattering your boy's friends, without annoying him! So now move on to branch 6.

Branch 6
SCORE. If you chose a, c or d, don't move on until you've thrown a four. These moves all present too many dangers; he might: a — believe you really are having a great time without him, c — treat you like dirt because you're so obviously vulnerable, d — go off with your best friend! If you chose b, though, you've allowed both of you to save face (sensible girl!). So now you can move on to branch 7.

Branch 7
SCORE. If you chose b, c or d, then you're not ready yet for the love of your life! So go straight back to branch 1 immediately and start climbing the tree of love all over again (but full marks for being honest!).

If, though, you chose a, then lucky you, you've reached the top of the tree and can now pluck the fruit of true love!

I KNEW HE WAS MARRIED~BUT I DIDN'T CARE!

THE Newberrys are fairly new to our small country town. They came down from London about six years ago, when their daughter Kerry was two years old.

She was a pretty kid with little bunches of hair behind each ear and great big blue eyes. She and I took to each other straight away.

Her mum was very young — only about four years older than me, in fact, and her dad wasn't much more. They lived a couple of streets away from us, so I used to see her out walking with Kerry quite a lot.

One day she asked if I could look after the little girl for an hour or two while she and Brian — her husband — went out for a drink. It was their wedding anniversary. Of course, I said yes.

I liked going to their house, so I was quite happy to go a second time, and a third. Brian was one of those really funny guys — you know the type — that keep egging you on and teasing you and well, a bit sort of flirty, I suppose.

We all used to have a good laugh — Brian, Kit and me. Of course, I knew everything didn't always go well for them. They had rows.

You could often, well, *sense* an atmosphere although they'd put on a front when anyone came, like me. I suspected that most of their arguments were over money.

The only thing that bothered me slightly was that whenever they had had a fight, Brian used to be extra nice to me. It was as if he was trying to make Kit even madder by sitting chatting to me for ages, both before they went out and after they got back and Kit had gone to bed.

One evening he even said, "You know, Elaine, I'm really glad you're baby-sitting for us. We get along so well. You ought to drop round more often, just for a chat."

I can't remember what I replied then, but I do remember that, when I told Mum about it later, she made some stupid comment like, "You seem to be pretty friendly with Brian Newberry. Doesn't Kit mind?"

Why *should* she mind? I kept telling myself that there was absolutely nothing suspicious about Brian. He was probably nice to everyone.

Things went on like that for a few weeks more, although I noticed Kit was looking quite upset whenever I went round. She never said anything so I tried to ignore it. It was none of my business, anyway.

Until the Saturday when Brian came over to my house and asked if I could sit with Kerry that night. He seemed in such a good mood that I couldn't help asking him what he was so pleased about.

And he showed me the two tickets he'd got for the Bryan Ferry concert.

Well, they were like gold-dust in our town.

"Kit must be really excited about going!" I told him.

"Well, actually, I haven't said anything to her yet," he said. "It's to be a surprise.

"They were a bit expensive," he said. His face clouded just for a minute. "Tell you the truth, I had to borrow the cash off a bloke at work.

"Still," he said cheerfully, "we don't go out all that much. What's money, after all? Can you be at our place at six?"

JUST as I reached their back door that evening, I heard the shouting. A real humdinger of a row. I couldn't make out the words, and after a few seconds there was the awful sound of sobbing, and then a slam.

I waited a few seconds, then rang the bell. The door opened almost straight away. Brian stood there, a bit red in the face but obviously ready for the concert because he looked really good.

He stared at me for a minute as if he didn't know me, then pulled himself together and said:

"Oh, Elaine, hello."

"I've come to baby-sit," I reminded him.

"Yes. Well." He shrugged his shoulders. Then he put out a hand and touched my arm. It felt — well — nice. Sort of friendly.

"Kit doesn't want to go. She — er — she isn't feeling well. Look, Elaine, I suppose you don't want to?"

"Want to what?" I asked, bewildered.

"Go to see Bryan Ferry. It seems a pity to waste the other ticket. Actually, Kit sort of suggested it."

"*Kit* did?" I found that surprising, and deep inside me, although I pushed the thought away, I knew it wasn't true.

"Oh, OK," I added, suddenly making up my mind and feeling as if I really was doing something — well — exciting. "OK, I'll come."

"Great!" The old Brian broke through, his smile lighting up his face. He grabbed me round the waist, and pulled the door to behind him. "That's my girl! Let's go!"

I had a great time. Really super. Bryan Ferry was fantastic. So was the whole evening.

"We must do this again, Elaine," Brian said, holding my arm and helping me into the car. "I haven't enjoyed myself so much for ages.

"Tell you what. Let's just have one drink to celebrate before I take you home."

We called in at the Nag's Head, which is only a few yards from my house. Brian had told me some sort of silly joke just before we went in, and we were clutching each other and giggling like crazy.

I didn't notice straight away who was at the bar, not until they spoke.

It was Mum and Dad.

"I thought you were baby-sitting," Mum said. She looked at me so accusingly that I felt like a criminal. She didn't speak to Brian at all, and neither did Dad.

"I was," I said, feeling stupid.

"It looks like it," Mum went on, drily. "I don't think you've even *seen* Kerry tonight at all. Have you?"

I shook my head.

"Look here, Mrs Minster, I can explain," Brian began. He looked a bit sheepish, like you do when you've been caught doing something you shouldn't.

"You've no need to explain to me, lad," Mum told him. "Save it for your wife. She rang earlier to speak to me."

"Oh." Brian sounded deflated. He didn't seem to know what to do, and then he suddenly seemed to decide. "'Bye, Elaine," he said to me. "See you around."

And he went off, whistling as if he didn't care, as if we hardly knew each other and hadn't shared such a great evening together.

DAD bought me a Coke, and then we all went home. Mum was kind of quiet, and thoughtful. When we got in, she told me to go into the sitting room because she wanted a word with me.

"No lectures, Mum, please!" I pleaded. "I haven't done anything wrong."

"No, maybe not yet," she said. "But without meaning to, you just *might* be making a mistake you're going to regret. You like Brian Newberry, don't you?"

I nodded. "Of course. He's fun."

"He's also married." Mum sounded grim. "And it's time he grew up and faced his responsibilities.

"Kit rang me tonight in an awful state. She said you'd gone out with Brian. Oh, she guessed where you were going all right."

"He said she wanted me to go with him," I muttered.

"You knew that wasn't true," Mum said. She looked at me so hard that I had to turn away to avoid meeting her eyes.

"You knew what he was like really. You just sort of — fancied the idea, didn't you?"

I could feel myself blushing right up to the tips of my ears.

"He's *married*, Elaine," Mum repeated. "He should have stopped playing around ages ago. Think of it from Kit's point of view.

"For a start, she won't ask you to sit with Kerry again because she'll feel she can't trust you where Brian's concerned. Brian's the sort of person who's never really accepted he's married.

"He's been seen around with quite a few girls, you know. Kit's got quite a lot of work on her hands trying to keep the family together. There's Kerry to consider too, remember."

"Well, that's Kit's problem," I grumbled. "It's nothing to do with me."

"But Elaine, can't you see? You're part of that problem and you're adding to the trouble between Kit and Brian. Don't you care about upsetting other people's lives?"

"It's just a silly fuss about nothing. It's never meant anything." I muttered. But I knew I didn't really believe that.

"No, it isn't," Mum persisted. "And you know it."

Oh yes, I knew it all right. Deep inside. And Mum was right.

Kit hasn't asked me to baby-sit for her again. She sees me as a threat, and you can't really blame her. If I think about it, I suppose I did encourage Brian. It seemed fun flirting with him, knowing it wasn't serious.

I knew it was wrong, of course. And I know Mum's right about him. I won't see him again.

But — I can't help wondering — if she and Dad hadn't happened to be in the pub that night, well, who knows what might have happened . . . ?

TEST YOUR EYE·Q!

If you think you've got an eye on the pop people of today, see how you get on with our eye-Q test. We're sure you'll get them all — no matter how far away you are. But if your eyesight's poor, the answers are on page 108. . .

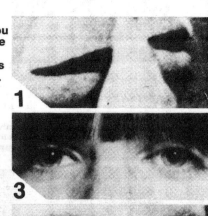

1

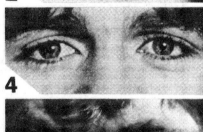

2

3

4

5

6

7

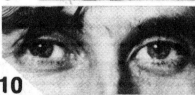

8

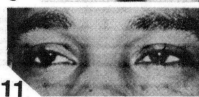

9

10

11

12

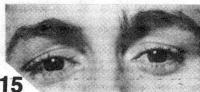

13

14

15

Getting Him Into Shape...

WHAT type of boy do you go for? The strong well-built guy who looks as if he's the King Kong of the building trade, or the tall skinny boy who looks as if a good gust of wind would have you helping him to his feet?

Well, whichever male shape turns you on — or off — reveals an awful lot about you.

Recent research carried out by a team of American psychologists revealed that quite apart from being inspired by a boy's personality, conversation and brains, different girls are attracted to different physical types. (If only they'd asked, we could have told them that a long time ago!)

So now, just for fun, test yourself according to their findings. Choose from the boys below, the one that is closest to your ideal — or nearest to the boy(s) you've been dating recently. Then read on to find out something about the shape *you're* in!

If you go for boys with thin arms, chest, shoulders, waist, hips and legs . . .

You're sensitive and emotional. You're concerned about your appearance and how your friends rate you. On the other hand, you tend to be rebellious, refusing to accept other people's opinions and determined to try out everything for yourself.

You've got a lot of nervous energy and can't stand being bored. You value your freedom and tend to be very independent, so you refuse to tolerate boys who act as if they own you.

On the whole, you're ambitious and able to stand on your own two feet.

If you're attracted to a boy with medium-weight shoulders, waist and hips with solid arms and legs . . .

According to the psychologists you're a conventional, indoor-type girl who comes from a traditional home. You're steady and reliable, so you go for a boy who looks comfortable and relaxing — rather than madly exciting. He'll be readily accepted by your parents as he obviously poses no threat. In fact, your mum might feel driven to give him the highest praise and say, "He looks exactly like your dad did when he was young!"

On the whole, people trust you and like you and you probably have lots of friends.

If you go for boys with wide shoulders, sturdy arms and legs, slim waist and hips . . .

Extrovert girls like this shape. You're probably cheerful and outgoing with few emotional problems or hang-ups.

You tend to be unsophisticated, athletic and country-loving. You probably enjoy tennis and swimming and dislike smoking. You and your boyfriend would definitely enjoy keeping-fit together! You're also very feminine and like the idea of your boyfriend being strong enough to protect you and to keep you safe from harm!

On the whole, you're fun to be with — people think you're a good sport.

If you go for a boy with hefty arms, legs, shoulders, waist and hips . . .

You're the maternal type. You like to "baby" your boyfriend and run after him.

You prefer to stick with things you know and sometimes it takes you ages to accept a new fashion, usually just as everyone else drops it!

You like to read a lot — usually romances — and aren't too keen on sport or anything energetic. It could well be that you're a little overweight yourself.

Generally, though, you're very sympathetic and soft-hearted — the kind of girl others lean on!

So there you are! Of course, it's not as simple and straightforward as that. For instance, the psychologists discovered that the girls they interviewed were rather unscientific and claimed that their favourite boy of the moment had their favourite body shape, even if this wasn't strictly true!

In fact, nowadays the V-shaped boy with wide shoulders and slim hips and thighs is considered the most fanciable. So if this is the type that you go for, it doesn't really reveal much about you, just that you go for the ideal shape that's fashionable at the moment.

The psychologists summed it up this way . . .

Girls who are feminine and rather conservative, like strong, tough, musclemen to protect them from the nasty old world.

More liberated, independent girls who think they can take care of themselves, tend to go for the slim-line look.

Big girls like big boys!

In fact, on the whole, girls tend to fancy boys who have similar physical characteristics to their own.

The one shape, though, that really handicaps the potential Romeo is a small chest with big hips. Sadly, most girls find the pear-shaped boy the ultimate turn-off!

So next time you see a boy and size him up, it could just be that he'll reveal the psychological shape you're in!

HOW TO HAVE THE LAST LAUGH...

Nobody likes being laughed at. Well, not unless you're attempting to be a second Morecambe and Wise, you don't! For most of us, though, there's nothing worse than suddenly finding everyone laughing themselves stupid only to discover that it's *you* they're laughing at. Being made a joke of is one of the things we dread most, along with having a spider run up our leg and eating spinach, that is!

So here's our special Jackie guide to help you through those awful times. There are lots of useful phrases for various occasions — just to make sure it's *you* who has the last laugh!

LAUGHTER is a lovely emotion and having a good laugh *with* other people is one of the best ways of making you feel good. The trouble is that laughing *at* other people is one of the most common of human failings.

There's a very basic bit of sneakiness in all of us that quite likes to see other people embarrassed and uncomfortable. And the strongest feeling you get when you're laughing at others is, "Thank goodness it isn't me!"

Everyone gets laughed at once in a while and often it's because of something silly they've done. Other people's clumsiness makes people laugh.

Some people make a living out of it, like Charlie Chaplin did. But one thing he always managed to do was turn the tables and get the last laugh. And that's the hardest thing of all.

But if you know you're quite likely to do something silly, then build up a few useful phrases so that people end up laughing with you and not at you.

Having a sense of humour and using it can bring you out on top so that people don't remember so much the daft thing you did, as the funny way you got out of it.

If you storm off in a sulky huff you'll end up the loser all round. So if you find yourself in any of the fairly common situations below, make sure you get the last laugh:

1. Hurtling home from school on your bike, you wave to your friends, wobble a lot and end up in a heap under the handlebars.

Try saying: "I think it's about time I went in for a service."

Or: "How come the Queen manages to wave to the crowd — and she's on a horse!"

Or: "Throw me a lifebelt, I'm sinking!"

2. You've knocked your own, or somebody else's, lunch into your lap.

Try saying: "I've heard of quick snacks but this is ridiculous!"

Or: "What's for pudding?"

Or: "I've always liked tossed salad."

3. You've leapt for the vaulting horse in the gym with gay abandon — and got stuck in the middle.

Try saying: "Is there a doctor in the house?"

Or: "I think I'll take a smaller size."

Or: "I never could stand heights."

4. You've tripped up. That happens all the time, but usually when it matters.

Try saying: "What a silly place to put a pavement."

Or: "I knew I shouldn't have had that last glass of cherryade."

Or: "That ant must be at least nine stone!"

THERE'S another reason why you might get laughed at, at some time, and that's due not so much to something you've done, as to a much more unpleasant need some people have to put others down.

It usually means that they pick on others because they haven't got much confidence themselves.

Fortunately, it doesn't happen too often but again, humour is the best way out of it or, if you can manage it, in some cases, a snooty "put down" phrase which puts you in control of the situation and makes them look very silly, childish and spiteful.

It's not the easiest thing to cope with, but now and then it happens to everyone in a crowd and if you can, try very hard to cope with it so that you're not picked on again.

If you blush and stammer and look uncomfortable, the jokers in your crowd will soon get to know you're an easy target. But it's not hard, with a bit of preparation, to find a quick answer for some of the situations that might arise!

1. You're at the swimming pool and somehow last year's bikini doesn't seem too roomy. Someone in your crowd calls you "fattie."

Try saying in a confidential whisper: "Well, you know what they say about thin people, don't you?" (It doesn't matter if they know or not — they're not going to ask!)

Or: "Yes, I really must ask my mum not to give me strawberries and cream *every* night."

Or: "Yes, I've tried counting calories but I haven't seen any yet."

2. You've told a joke which you know is funny but everyone is standing around looking deadpan.

Try saying: "Oh, well, I thought you wouldn't be able to understand it."

Or: "My brother warned me I should only tell that joke to an intellectual audience."

Or: "Now don't applaud, just throw money."

3. Someone's played a practical joke on you. They've left some pretty strong cheese in your desk at school or work.

Try saying: "Dr Watson, come here quickly, I've found a clue!"

Or: "If I'd cleared my desk out more often this would never have happened."

Or: Sniff and say, "Funny, I could have sworn Angela Drummond (or whoever) was walking past."

4. You've appeared at the youth club with a new hairstyle or a new dress. A few people start to giggle.

Try saying: "It's the newest style for winter but I don't expect your barber would know about it, Sharon."

Or: "There are a few fellas I want to shake off, so I thought I'd change my image."

Or: "The lady in the shop said you had to have the right face and figure for it, so at least no-one will copy me."

Don't be surprised if after you've managed to get yourself out of a difficult situation a few times, you actually begin to enjoy it and start playing for laughs most of the time.

"He who laughs last has only just seen the joke" might be true if you're a comedian but "He who laughs last, laughs longest" could become *your* motto — even if the joke started out being on you!

WILL YOU LIVE HAPPILY EVER AFTER?

Well, what are your chances of living happily ever after? Find out by answering our very special fairytale quiz, designed to reveal your secret hopes and fears, and what you can expect from life.

Are you sitting comfortably? Then we'll begin!

1. When you were very young, which of the four following fairytale heroines was your favourite?
(a) Goldilocks.
(b) Rapunzel.

(c) Cinderella.
(d) Red Riding Hood.

2. Which of these fairytale heroes did you most admire?
(a) Aladdin.
(b) Prince Charming.
(c) Jack and the Beanstalk.
(d) The Frog Prince.

3. Which of the four following girls did you like best?
(a) The Little Match Girl.
(b) Alice in Wonderland.
(c) Snow White.
(d) The Little Mermaid.

4. And which of the following male characters, from this mixed bunch?
(a) Pinnochio.
❤ (b) Robinson Crusoe.

(c) Dick Whittington.
(d) The Little Tin Soldier.

5. Which "Magic Roundabout" character was — and probably still is — your favourite from the following four?
(a) Zebedee.
(b) Dougal.
(c) Florence.
(d) Brian.

6. When you were a little older, which of these four was your choice for a bedtime book?
(a) Grimm's Fairytales.
(b) Alice in Wonderland.
(c) The Arabian Nights.

(d) Hans Andersen's Fairytales.

7. Lots of nursery rhymes had "baddies". Which one of the following did you *hate* most?
(a) Wee Willie Winkie.
(b) Humpty Dumpty.
(c) Tom, Tom the Piper's Son.
(d) Little Jack Horner.

8. Which nursery rhyme character would *you* most like to have been?
(a) The lady who went riding to Banbury Cross.
(b) Goldilocks.
(c) The girl who had a little nut tree.
(d) Mary (the one who had a little lamb).

9. Even in nursery rhymes, people had problems! Which of these four did you have most sympathy for?
(a) Polly Flinders.
(b) The Old Woman Who Lived in a Shoe.
(c) Simple Simon.
(d) Bo Peep.

10. Which do you consider the perfect friendship from among the following twosomes?
(a) Jack and Jill.
(b) Tweedledum and Tweedledee.
(c) Jack Spratt and his wife.
(d) The Owl and the Pussycat.

CONCLUSIONS

Mostly (a) answers

YOU definitely have star quality, and, although you may appear to be quiet on the surface, you secretly long for admiration and fame.

Almost certainly, your career will be full of interesting ups and downs — but the blazes of glory, however brief, will more than make up for any hard knocks you have to take — and there may be quite a lot of these, because you love to dice with danger! Your eagerness for excitement may lead you into situations you can't handle. Then you'll have to run for safety, like Goldilocks did! Probably you've already escaped from some tight corners, but don't push your luck! The day may come when you can't make a getaway fast enough, and trouble catches up with you.

The thing you hate and fear most is authority. In a job where you can do things your way, you will work hard and shoot to the top surprisingly quickly, but a fusspot boss who is a stickler for punctuality, will really bring out the rebel in you. You would probably be happiest as a journalist, actress, or working for the sort of charitable organisation where you are expected to turn your hand to anything, and live on a few pounds a week pocket money. For starters, you could always get a temporary job at a holiday camp, or looking after children in a nursery.

Only three things could sour your non-stop love affair with life. One is working for a big organisation, where the bosses are faceless, and the workers are simply numbers on a time sheet. However, there's little chance of this quenching your bright spirit, because nothing, not even a wage of £100 a week, would induce you to stay there for long.

The second thing you must guard against is rebelling against *all* authority, that of parents included. They are only doing their job, which is to protect you to the best of their ability, and see you don't come to harm.

Thirdly, it would be very easy for you to get into bad company. You are the kind who will always spring to the defence of her friends, but be careful that you don't follow them into folly!

Your adventurous nature, courage, and ability to live for today instead of worrying about what tomorrow may bring will ensure that you live happily, especially if you cultivate your talents in every way possible. You should also keep some emergency money on hand and always tell some really responsible person where you are going before setting out to seek your fortune!

Mostly (b) answers

You're the type who never, ever loses her cool, which must put you well on the way to living happily ever after!

The thing you hate and despise is weakness. You respect people who are trying to cope with a difficult situation, like the Old Woman who lived in a shoe and found it hard to handle her big family and housing problem! But you have no sympathy at all for hopeless, helpless, Humpty Dumpty types.

Being caught in an embarrassing situation is something which happens to other people; never to you. Of course you have your secret doubts and fears like everyone else, but you've learned already that nothing succeeds like success, and if you *look* confident people will be prepared to give you the opportunities you need to show you can do lots of things very well!

Probably you've already been given responsibilities, perhaps as a school prefect or sports team leader, and in the job market what you look for is a situation which offers lots of "oportunities for advancement." You seem ideally suited to become a nurse, or a secretary, but really, whatever career you decide on you are almost certain to receive speedy promotion!

As you make definite goals in life for yourself, and work hard to reach them, you *ought* to live happily ever after, but if you don't seem to be getting as far as you would like as fast as you should, this is probably because there are people whose sole ambition seems to be trying — usually unsuccessfully — to take you down a peg. You are not so self-sufficient as you seem, and it hurts to be called "Miss Know-All," and "Granny" by people you are only trying to help.

You must resist the temptation to outsmart everyone; they won't like you being always right; or at least acting as if you are. Many of your friendships are sure to be love-hate affairs, like that of Tweedledum and Tweedledee, but the important thing is that you're always loyal to your friends when they are in trouble, or anyone else dares to criticise them — and usually they show the same loyalty to you, because they respect you.

You are one of life's winners, but can only live happily ever after when there are others to share your triumphs. They'll be glad to share your troubles too, if you give them the chance to advise *you*; just for a change!

Mostly (c) answers

You tend to gain your own ends by fair means, which includes soft, flattering words and playing the role of damsel in distress; something you can do very well! You like to live in harmony with everyone, and this makes you quick to stop quarrels springing up amongst your friends.

Extravagance is likely to be a problem with you, because you love luxury. Money burns a hole in your pocket, and you can't resist fast-talking door to door salesmen, and the like! Your wardrobe is full of clothes you hardly ever wear! In fact, you are what's known as a "soft sell."

If you can't beat the sales staff, you can always join them! Working in a shop selling luxury goods would suit you ideally, and most store managers welcome you with open arms, because of your even temper, patience, winning smile, and genuine enthusiasm for the beautiful things surrounding you. You'd be a good demonstrator too, or maybe even a model. Other work possibilities are as a receptionist, or working with children, old people or animals.

As you find it easy to observe rules and regulations, realising that they usually help things run more smoothly and benefit everyone, you have no sympathy for rebels.

Despite your gentle, easy-going nature you admire success very much, and the kind of boy who is industrious and hard-working as well as capable of taking risks, would be just right for you. However, you get along well with practically everybody, because you believe in compromise, so your friendships are as trouble-free as the partnership of Jack Spratt and his wife who agreed so happily to differ!

Unless one of those friends lets you loose with a mail order catalogue that is! Just tell yourself firmly that people are much more important than possessions, and don't even *look* at it!

Mostly (d) answers

You really don't expect to live happily ever after, and you're certainly not one to wail "Why did this happen to me?" when things go wrong. Yet, because you are never short of the three essentials — trust, hope and a cheerful smile, life is bound to hold a lot of joy for you.

Like the princess who was so kind to a humble frog that it was able to shake off an evil spell and become a handsome prince again, you bring out the best in people. Of course, some of your friends take you for granted, and treat you carelessly, but how they value your loyalty. In fact, it may be because they feel so safe in your friendship, and know you would never wittingly hurt anyone, that they don't try to conceal their moods and are occasionally rather off-hand with you.

However, there are several things which could make life more bitter than sweet, unless you can bring yourself to be firm with people. You're far too ready to accept every hard luck story, not necessarily because you believe it (you're no fool), but because you are sorry for people who find it necessary to tell lies!

Also, you allow people to take advantage of you. So don't always be the one to volunteer for the background jobs which aren't much fun, like spending parties seeing that everyone gets plenty to eat, or listening to the non-stop nattering of some self-centred bore.

You do tend to wallow a bit in feelings of unrequited love. You could become a martyr if you set your sights on someone who couldn't care less about you!

Social work appeals to you, and jobs such as that of speech-therapist, assistant in a childrens' home, teacher of handicapped children. Your career possibilities are endless, but you must feel you are helping people, otherwise you'd practically pine away. Although you set high standards for yourself, you can sympathise with inadequate people like dozy Bo Peep!

Most of us get what we work for and deserve but do remember that people are only human, yourself included. Instead of trying hard to behave like an angel *all* the time, see what a dash of devilment can do for you, now and again!

247

TAKE TWO GUYS!

Two of the most exciting — and successful — groups to have made a stand in the charts this year are Generation X and the Boomtown Rats — and we talked to their two lovely lead singers, Billy Idol and Bob Geldof . . .

Beat Rat!

BOB GELDOF can't believe what a tremendous year he's h
"This time last year the Boomtown Rats were celebrating th first hit, 'Looking After Number One,' and since then we have looked back!" he said.

Not only has every single they've put out been a massive hit, this year Bob and the rest of the group have recorded their sec album in Holland and completed a successful British tour, too. can't beat this bunch for working hard!

The Boomtown Rats deserve every single ounce of success t achieve — never before have we met a more genuine bunch of re nice guys. They work hard, they produce some amazing music, an doesn't matter how tired they are — they've always time to talk to

"It's about two and a half years since we formed," Bob told "and the reason we did was because we were so bored of hear country-rock, funk-rock, jazz-rock — anything but *real* ro We knew that we could make it if we tried, and, as we were unemplo at the time, there was nothing to stop us trying!

"I always wanted to be a star, and there's no point denying th enjoy all the fame we have gained. When I was eleven I wanted to like Mick Jagger of the Rolling Stones; at twelve I wanted to be J Lennon of the Beatles and after that I wanted to be Pete Townsh of the Who. Now I'm glad to be me!

"We played the music we wanted to play and now it's paid o Bob went on. "We have a great time when we're touring and so do audiences.

"At one concert we did in Scotland everybody was on their clapping and dancing and generally having a fantastic time. Afte had finished the manager of the hall came backstage and told us he'd never seen anything like it in his life.

"He'd never seen so many people enjoying themselves and managing to behave. Apparently not one seat had been broken, wh was pretty unusual.

"But that's what the Boomtown Rats are all about," Bob explain "Having fun. We certainly enjoy ourselves — and we like to think audiences do, too!"

WHEN we talked to him, Christmas was very much to the fore in the thoughts of Billy Idol of Generation X!

"I don't see my mum and dad very often because I live in London, but they always invite me over for Christmas Day and to be honest, I'd be surprised and upset if they didn't bother to ask me!" Billy told us.

"Although I wouldn't feel guilty about not spending Christmas Day at home with them, I know it would upset my mum if I didn't join in," Billy went on. "I know the family will be there with the tree and the presents, so just to show I care about them, I take part, too. But I don't get totally caught up in the Christmas spirit because I think a lot of it's silly.

"Christmas only means something to people who have to work from nine till five, five days a week, because they really look forward to having a holiday. I don't have holidays.

"Just as every day's a holiday, every day's a work day," he explained. "I don't know what they mean by celebrating each New Year either as I'm never aware of a new year or seasons — I don't even know what month it is! I don't know today's date. I'm not aware of things like that.

"But when people want to create fun, I suppose Christmas provides the perfect excuse!

"To me, the actual occasion of Christmas is just going home for a day, like any other normal day, except all the shops are closed," Billy explained. "But to my parents it's **Christmas** and much more, so I enjoy being with them.

"I like seeing my sister, and my cousin, too. My family try to make it like a traditional Christmas and we all have to wear hats round the table when we eat our Christmas dinner," Billy went on. "Once I upset everyone by taking mine off!

"Apart from my cousin, we don't have relatives coming over to see us on Christmas Day, thank goodness! We're not like that and I'm glad because I can't stand all that family business.

"I think it's a shame when relatives meet and no-one's got anything to say to each other, and they come to family gatherings because it's more like an obligation.

"I've always felt like that. Relatives just pretend to each other all the time and say it's wonderful to see you when they don't mean it, and **you** know it!

"I know I play a sort of game at Christmas time," Billy admitted. "I mean, I like Christmas but it's not all that special to me, but if I told my parents I didn't think Christmas was important, just imagine how they would react to that!"

Billy's Our Idol!

Now turn to page 128 to find out all about two of our favourite gi stars!

L. to R. – back: Simon, Bob, Gerry
front: Johnny, Pete, Garry.

L. to R. – Billy, Mark, Bob, Tony.

249

A JACKIE QUIZ

Which Is The Season For You?

ARE you a sunny summertime girl, or a winter wonder girl? Each season has its own very special character — autumn's changeable and unpredictable, while summer's full of fun and carefree! But which one are you? Which season of the year reflects your personality? Answer our fun quiz truthfully and find out! You might be in for a few surprises!

1. If you could change your name to something which suits your character more, which of the following would you choose?
(c) Charity.
(a) Felicity.
(d) Faith.
(b) Verity.

2. Which do you think would make you look most interesting?
(a) A long, sweeping black velvet cloak.
(d) A misty lace veil, which hints at your beauty underneath.
(b) A sparkling diamond and pearl tiara.
(c) A zany, shocking pink paper party hat.

3. If you were to take up a thrilling new hobby, would it be —
(a) athletics,
(b) fortune-telling,
(d) horse-riding,
(c) writing poetry?

4. Is your favourite colour —
(d) lively red,
(a) sizzling yellow,
(c) romantic pink,
(b) glowing orange?

5. Where would you most like to go for a swim?
(a) In warm, sky blue seas, tinged with the pink of coral, and filled with rainbow-coloured tropical fish.
(d) In sparkling crystal clear water, ruffled by tiny lacy waves as it hits golden sands.
(b) In a rocky, craggy cove where you can dive into the murky green depths of the sea.
(c) In brilliant turquoise sea at the edge of miles and miles of white sand glittering in the sunlight.

6. If you suddenly won a fortune, would you invest in —
(c) a 16th century cottage in deepest rural Somerset,
(b) a mansion on the Yorkshire moors,
(a) a villa on the coast of Cornwall,
(d) a castle in the Highlands?

7. Would you rather be the proud owner of —
(c) your very own strawberry garden,
(d) a thoroughbred racing stable,
(a) your own disco,
(b) a boutique?

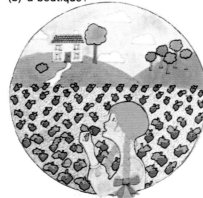

8. Which of these strange pets wouldn't give you the creeps?
(b) A vampire bat.
(d) A poisonous lizard.
(a) A tropical bird-eating spider.
(c) A bright green bullfrog.

9. What would your recipe for warding off bad luck be?
(d) Will-power and foresight.
(a) Two frog's legs on a bed of garlic.
(c) Your zodiac sign on a silver chain.
(b) A thread of silk from the robe of a Tibetan monk.

10. If you could live in any house you wanted, which would you prefer?
(c) A tiny stone cottage with roses round the door, nestling in green country-side.
(b) A magnificent mansion with miles and miles of desolate, craggy moorland all around.
(a) A super-modern white villa on top of a cliff, with a terrific view of the rocky coastline and the sea.
(d) An ancient castle, complete with towers, turrets and secret passages, hidden deep in the Highlands.

11. Which musical sound sets your heart beating faster, and makes you feel romantic?
(a) A brass band playing in a busy street.
(d) Mournful bagpipes carrying over the hills.
(b) A lilting lone flute echoing through the green woodlands.
(c) Beautiful, mellow violins, floating through your window, by the light of the moon.

2. Which sight gladdens your heart most?
a) An outstretched cat basking on the lawn.
b) Wild geese flying over the marshland.
c) Baby lambs frolicking in the wild flowers.
d) An eagle hovering over snowcapped mountains.

3. If you had lived in olden times, which of these gorgeous boys would you have chosen to go on a date with?
c) The poet-minstrel.
d) The brave young gladiator.
b) The knight on his fast white horse.
a) The handsome young court jester.

14. Which of the following hotels would you choose as being most promising for a fabulous holiday romance?
(b) A wayside lodge, with miles of beautiful garden stretching behind it.
(a) An enormous hotel with all mod cons and a disco, on the coast of Spain.
(d) A country hotel, where you can enjoy lovely home cooking and long walks in the countryside.
(c) A pretty little inn, on the outskirts of a seaside town.

15. Where would you prefer to acquire your beautiful golden suntan?
(a) In a deck-chair on the French Riviera.
(d) On a chair-lift over the Swiss Alps.
(c) On a yacht off the Greek Islands.
(b) On a pony through the forests of Bavaria.

Now count your score, mainly (a), (b), (c) or (d) and turn to the conclusions below.

CONCLUSIONS

Mostly (a)
You're a **Summer Girl**, living for the moment, enjoying the sunshine, sailing happily without a care in the world. Life for you should be perpetual summertime, with a holiday atmosphere and lazy, hazy heatwave days.

Virtues — Your main virtue is your naturally warm personality to match the summer months. With your charm and great sense of humour you have an infectious personality, so that others around you catch your zest for pleasure and enjoyment. You're extremely generous, both with your money and your friendship.

Faults — One of the unfortunate side-effects of your easy-going nature is that you tend to dismiss problems and ignore danger signals, so that you sometimes think before you act. Curb that impulsive nature a bit and you could find life a lot easier.

Relationships — You tend to fall in love often and quickly with good-looking boys. At the moment, you don't want to get involved with anyone — you're only interested in having a good time. Though you think you fall in love easily, you're usually completely in command of your feelings. Really, it takes time (and a very special person) for you to get into a really deep involvement. But, right now, the fun and good times are all you need because you're an incurable flirt! True love can wait till you've settled down a bit and allowed yourself to be a bit more serious!

The Future — Although you might sometimes *appear* to be lazy, you have hidden strength and boundless energy when you want to use it. You're not afraid of life, and once you put your mind to a career or course of action, you have the guts, confidence and vitality to achieve sucess!

Mostly (b)
You are an **Autumn Girl**, changeable and unpredictable, sometimes stormy, sometimes sweet and gentle. You can be secretive and difficult to understand yet at other times full of wit, conversation and enthusiasm!

Virtues — Your main virtue is your lively, questing mind. You want to get at the truth, to understand people and situations and to formulate your own ideas about the world around you. You're an interesting person to talk to, for you're aware and sensitive with a great deal of creative talent. You're emotionally honest with strong convictions and emotions. You're an original person with the courage to be different from the herd.

Faults — Patches of depression and moodiness are your main problem, coupled sometimes with an unrealistic view of yourself and the world. You expect a great deal out of life and tend to be disappointed when things don't work out right. Your inner life sometimes causes you to appear distracted and aloof and you make no effort to be nice to people you're not interested in. We're not suggesting you should put on an insincere act, but a bit of polite consideration wouldn't come amiss!

Relationships — You have the ability to become extremely emotionally involved and it's all-important that your friends should be on your wavelength. When you fall for a boy it's the real thing and you become totally involved (dare we say obsessed?) with that one person. Love is extremely serious to you, and your relationships might tend to be difficult and stormy at times, full of dramas and complications. But it's worth going through the bad times, because you get so much joy and pleasure from the good times!

The Future — Like your personality, the future is unpredictable because there are so many ways you could go, so many abilities and talents you could develop. So, by trusting your instincts and being an individual, you can look forward to a future full of rich experience, variety and interest.

Mostly (c)
You're a **Spring Girl**, romantic and dreamy, exciting and feminine, with all the good qualities anyone could wish for. You have a creative spirit, you appreciate beauty and you bring hope, encouragement and love into the world!

Virtues — Your main virtue is your kindness and affectionate nature. People seem to sense that they can trust you and confide in you, for you have endless sympathy and understanding. Although you appear to be shy and modest, you have a lot of inner strength and an instinctive faith in yourself.

Faults — Your only faults stem from your over-emotional character, which makes you easily led and extra-sensitive to criticism. On an emotional see-saw, you can cry one moment and laugh the next, and for your own self-preservation it would be wise to try to toughen up a tiny bit. You tend to be impatient for perfection, and you're bound to be disillusioned occasionally if you set yourself such high ideals.

Relationships — Love and affection are second nature to you and you fall in love easily and deeply without ever thinking whether you might get hurt. Other people might make do with friendship or surface romance and flirtation, but for you it has to be a grand emotion. In all your close relationships you're loyal, loving, and are prepared to give a lot. As well as being romantically loving, you care for those people you love, and make them feel secure and happy. You of all people know how powerful love is, and your life would be meaningless without it.

The Future — You look for beauty, peace, true love and affection and an atmosphere that radiates quiet, inner happiness. This, needless to say, is sometimes hard to find, but you won't give up and your spirit refuses to be dampened. So you have every chance of making your dreams a reality!

Mostly (d) — You're a **Winter Girl**, strong-willed, quick-witted and independent. You can use your head as well as your heart, and reflecting the power and influence of the winter season, you're a courageous person and a natural leader.

Virtues — You have high standards and ambitions and you want to make your mark on the world; but at the same time you're without vanity or conceit, and you have the determination and the practical ability to achieve your goals. Although you can be quite tough and calculating when you need to be, you have a great sense of justice and others know that you are reliable with a genuinely kind heart.

Faults — Impatience is one of your faults, together with a hot temper and a very obstinate streak. It would be worth your while at least to *listen* to others sometimes — even if you decide to reject their advice in the end! Although you give the impression of not needing people, this is far from the truth and perhaps you need friendship and reassurance more than you're prepared to admit.

Relationships — You're so cool and capable, people tend to be scared of you sometimes, and, being a very strong personality, you often dominate others without even realising you're doing it. Your taste in boys is high-powered, and a boy has to be a really clever, strong character to keep you interested. You look for equal partnerships of mutual love and respect, and although love is essential in your life you can't bear to be caged and you need space to be free and independent.

The Future — You're good at planning and organising and you like to have goals and objectives to work towards. You should make the most of your clear-sighted mind and studying ability. You're one of life's natural survivors and whatever you decide to do, we can't see you going far wrong!

CHRISTMAS FARE!

Christmas time nearly always means party time, so if you're having people round it would be even nicer if you could say that you'd made some of the food yourself. These recipes are really simple, but very tasty, so go ahead, try them!

TOMATO FIZZ

You need several large bottles or cans of tomato juice and bitter lemon for this recipe, depending on the number of people invited.

Simply pour the tomato juice onto ice cubes in tall glasses, and top up with bitter lemon.

MUSHROOM AND HAM DIP

2 oz. lean boiled ham; ¼ pt. fresh double cream; 1 carton yoghurt; 1 medium can condensed mushroom soup; cayenne pepper to garnish.

Chop the ham. Lightly whip cream and stir in the yoghurt and soup. Add the ham to this mixture. Now place the mixture in a serving dish, garnish with a sprinkling of cayenne pepper, and arrange small biscuits, bread and crisps around it.

SPICY WHIP

Makes a lovely ending to any party, especially when it's cold outside!

You'll need: 1½ pints milk; 2 oz. syrup; grated nutmeg.

Bring the milk almost to the boil, stir in the syrup, and pour the mixture into mugs. Sprinkle with a pinch of nutmeg.

WHOLEMEAL BREAD

You don't have to use yeast, so this bread recipe is much simpler and quicker to make than most.

Mix together — 4 oz. plain white flour; 4 oz. plain brown flour; 1 teaspoonful salt; 1 teaspoonful baking soda; 1 teaspoonful cream of tartar.

Rub in 2 oz. margarine, until the mixture is the consistency of breadcrumbs. Add 2 tablespoonfuls syrup and a little milk until the dough is stiff. Place in a greased loaf tin and bake in a moderate oven for 1-1½ hours.

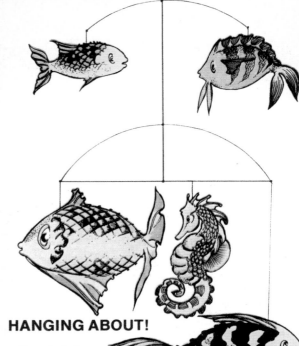

HANGING ABOUT!

Ever looked around your bedroom and thought what a lot of wasted space there was between the top of your head and the ceiling? Well, so have lots of other people — and they came up with mobiles! Mobiles are three-dimensional decorations (usually with some movement) that you can use to brighten up your bedroom, any room, in fact! They're usually suspended from the ceiling, so they don't take up space *and* they brighten your room.

It isn't always easy to find something that's cheap, easy *and* original to make your room more interesting and more your own, but mobiles fit the bill! You can use almost anything for the actual decoration once you have the wire for the framework. It can be any size or shape, too.

So, if you're sitting comfortably, this is how you begin . . . Wire is usually used for the framework so a couple of wire coathangers are ideal for this. Use them in a cross-shape, binding them together with thread — or have them hanging at different levels to give an interesting effect. Then you need some fine string or strong thread to use for hanging the shapes from the frame.

Leave the hook on the hanger so that you can Sellotape it to the ceiling above a window, or hang it from a picture-hanger on the wall. This means that you can move it around and have it in different positions in your bedroom, too.

All you need to do now is choose what you'd like as the subject of your mobile, and this depends a lot on where you're going to hang it. If it's in your own room, you might like to stick pictures of your favourite pop star — or boy! — on to some card (covering both sides). If so, cut the card into heart-shapes and attach the thread neatly to the top of the card then to the long bottom section of the hanger. To make them all hang at various levels, just use different lengths of thread. If you place the mobile near a window, air movement will make the pictures turn, so that you're always getting a new view of that gorgeous fella!

Basically, that's all there is to it!

GOLDEN OLDIES!

So you're lying slumped in a chair absolutely stuffed after ploughing your way through Christmas dinner. You're occasionally craning your neck a couple of inches to the right to gaze at all the lovely pressies you got from Santa, and you're making a really big effort to ignore your father who *always* gets a bit carried away at this time of the year and tries to get the whole family to do really energetic things, like pulling Christmas crackers!

Never mind, it could be worse, you know, you could have been celebrating Christmasses past and they would have taken a lot more out of you than just the effort of lifting the last spoonful of Christmas pud to your mouth!

In ye olden dayes things were a little different!

There were dozens of courses to the Christmas meal — goose, beef, swan, venison, peacocks with their beaks gilded, and their tails spread out, and just to finish things off, boar's head — garlanded with rosemary and bay and with an apple in its mouth!

There was a great deal of ceremony connected with bringing the boar's head into the feast. In the time of Elizabeth the First it was carried in by a young woman of high rank, on a gold or silver platter. Trumpets

were blown and a procession of minstrels and servants followed it. It was considered a great honour to be chosen for the task of carrying in the boar's head, but things could — and did — go wrong!

One young damsel who tripped daintily into the Queen's presence with the dish managed to get herself into really hot water. Her Majesty was entertaining some foreign guests, and the boar's head was carried in on a silver platter instead of a gold one! Horrors! The young lady had hoped to get the Queen's permission to marry but she withheld it for a year as a punishment!

Of course, many of the things you'd be eating then would be quite familiar to you — mari-

golds, primroses, cowslips — yes, we *do* mean the flowers! *And* pies made from carp's tongues, which are rather fiddly things to eat, but then you wouldn't have had to bother about getting them to stay on your fork because you wouldn't have been using one — that's why finger-bowls were so necessary!

And on the subject of fingers, one of the games played was Snapdragon. It consisted of snatching raisins from a bowl of burning brandy — *without* burning your hand(!) They still do this in France, on New Year's Eve, to this day!

So, be thankful that all *you* cope with are turkey and Christmas pud!

FLATTERY GETS YOU EVERY-WHERE!

"FLATTERY will get you nowhere" is one of those sayings like, "Life is just a bowl of cherries" — it's hardly ever true! Flattery will get you plenty of places. The question is, will it get you where you want to go — which is out on a date with the boy you fancy. Of course it will — if you know how to go about it . . .

You *can* overdo flattery, just like you can overdo eating, drinking and jumping up and down, but in small doses it can be very useful and, be honest, don't you love someone paying *you* a compliment?

Everyone likes to be told something nice about themselves and they will appreciate you for telling them, but it's no use rushing up to the fella you like and gushing, "You move like Mick Jagger, you look like Andy Gibb and I'm free on Friday night."

The first lesson to learn is BE SUBTLE.

If there's someone you want to get to know better, watch what he enjoys doing, the things he's good at. If it's football and you're standing on the sidelines shivering, don't rush up when the whistle blows, fling your arms round him and burble, "You were terrific!"

Just saunter up quietly, catch him on his own and tell him seriously, "You know, that pass you made across the goal about ten minutes into the second half, that reminded me very much of Kevin Keegan. You have the same ball control."

Smile gently and stroll off. You may not know who Kevin Keegan is. It doesn't matter.

Your victim will feel so tall he'll be able to touch the top of the goal post and you'll have learnt the second lesson about Good Flattery which is — SOUND CONVINCING.

If there's a boy you want to impress, learn about the things that matter to him so that you can appreciate when he's doing well at them. He may be a musician and you're probably tired of making endless cups of coffee while he's ploughing through, "Learn the Guitar in Ten Weeks."

So pick up a few useful words like "riff" or "middle-eight" and instead of walking in with ear-plugs, listen for a while and when he stops, pretend you're lost in thought for a second and then say, "I heard Peter Frampton play a riff like that at Wembley, but I think it sounds better when it's played gently."

If he says, "Actually that part was the middle-eight" then you'll have to go back to studying "Handy Hints for Guitarists' Girlfriends," but don't be discouraged, half the battle is over.

He knows you're trying to compliment him — and that counts for a lot.

MOST boys like to be compared favourably with their idols, whatever they want to shine at, but sometimes flattery is at its best when it's just a direct statement like, "I really like that shirt." You can bet he's taken trouble choosing it and he'll enjoy the fact that someone's noticed.

If you're dancing with someone you like, it does no harm at all to say, "Hey, where did you learn to move like that?" It's a dead cert he'll ask you for another dance, especially if you add, "I've watched a lot of guys here tonight and half of them just don't *feel* the music, do you know what I mean?"

He'll know what you mean all right. And it's highly unlikely he'll sit down for the rest of the disco. He'll be dancing — with you!

It's not difficult to flatter boys when it comes to things mechanical, either. To most girls the inside of a Kawasaki engine is about as easy to understand as "A"-level Chinese, and if you seem to spend most of your Sundays huddled in the garage while he tunes up his bike, there *are* a couple of alternatives.

You *could* study the Works Manual and either end up buying a bike of your own and dismantling it next to his, which won't go down too well (especially if you end up with a faster bike!) or you can accept the fact that what's inside the bike is strictly his territory and concentrate on the outside.

Helping him clean and polish it shouldn't be beyond you — and that's a form of flattery in itself. And when he finally slides out from under the exhaust, don't tell him he's covered in oil and you'll see him when he's washed. Grit your teeth, snuggle up close and say, "Why don't they make an after-shave that smells like engine oil? It's lovely."

Besides, imitation is supposed to be the sincerest form of flattery. So don't try to beat him, join him. Turn up in your oldest jeans and tightest T-shirt with a large spanner, making sure your hair and face look good and ask him how his tappets are.

Either he'll be so touched with your concern that he'll actually *tell* you, or more likely, he'll decide to do other things on Sunday afternoons. Like go out with you.

ONE thing you'll have to learn if you intend to become a tip-top flatterer, though, is to receive compliments graciously yourself. Because once you've said a few nice things to a boyfriend, it's fairly certain you'll get one or two flying your way.

It's easy to get embarrassed when someone's being nice but try being confident. If he says, "Your hair looks terrific," smile and say, "Thank you" rather than muttering, "It's absolutely filthy really, I was going to wash it tonight."

If you do, don't be surprised if he replies, "Oh, I was going to ask you out but I suppose you'll be staying in to wash your hair."

Yes, flattery is a two-way thing. Take it gently and try it out on one or two people you know well first. Tell them their hair or clothes are smashing and you'll be amazed how they blossom and light up.

Lots of people are too quick to criticise and too slow to flatter. Don't be like that.

A good flatterer is nice to have around. She's popular because she makes people feel good and if you get flattery down to a fine art you won't have to worry about what to say to friends — they'll be too busy telling you how terrific *you* are!

BACK TO BASICS

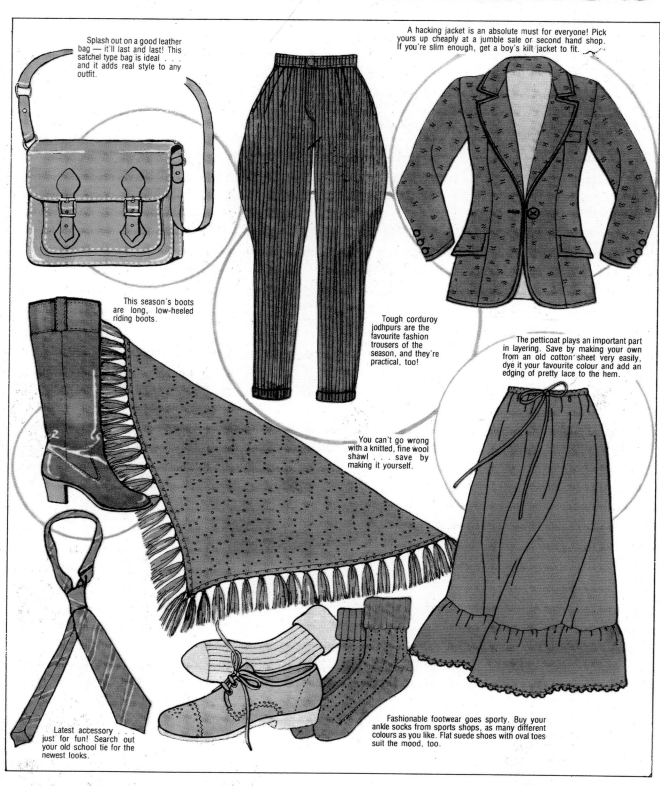

Splash out on a good leather bag — it'll last and last! This satchel type bag is ideal . . . and it adds real style to any outfit.

A hacking jacket is an absolute must for everyone! Pick yours up cheaply at a jumble sale or second hand shop. If you're slim enough, get a boy's kilt jacket to fit.

This season's boots are long, low-heeled riding boots.

Tough corduroy jodhpurs are the favourite fashion trousers of the season, and they're practical, too!

The petticoat plays an important part in layering. Save by making your own from an old cotton sheet very easily, dye it your favourite colour and add an edging of pretty lace to the hem.

You can't go wrong with a knitted, fine wool shawl . . . save by making it yourself.

Latest accessory . . . just for fun! Search out your old school tie for the newest looks.

Fashionable footwear goes sporty. Buy your ankle socks from sports shops, as many different colours as you like. Flat suede shoes with oval toes suit the mood, too.

It's back to basics for winter dressing . . . and here's how to look absolutely stunning on a low budget! The secret lies in sticking to basic colours, unusual mixing and matching, and choosing the right accessories! Start off with the basics, then follow our ideas and you'll have at least a dozen different outfits to see you through the winter — beautifully!

JACKIE FASHION

Steal an idea from the French . . . they're all mad about tartan! A plaid skirt in muted colours looks terrific. Knife pleats are in, too.

Don't splash out on an ultra-fashionable jumper which dates quickly. Instead go for something simple with style, in a colour which goes with everything.

A man's tweedy cap is the perfect accessory for your winter wardrobe.

Chunky cream fisherman's polo looks good, keeps you warm *and* mixes and matches.

Make sure your tights match everything . . . thick, woolly ones look terrific with your ankle socks.

Your pretty cotton summer dress becomes part of your winter wardrobe too! Give it a new lease of life by dyeing it a different colour.

Be prepared for the weather! Get yourself a super, chunky, wooden-handled umbrella, more expensive than usual — but definitely worth the extra.

Wear two belts together — unusual ideas give you special style.

Try A Fry-up!

Fancy a fry-up or see yourself in super stripes? Either way, our fantastic bag and beret pattern designed by knitting designer Alan Dart, is just the thing to brighten up a dull winter's day! So go on . . . we're egging you on to be rasher than ever!

WHAT YOU'LL NEED

NEEDLES: A pair of 4 mm (No. 8) needles.

WOOL: Stripes: 3 (25g) balls of Sirdar Superwash wool D.K. in Black (013), 1 ball each of Gorse (124), Emerald (034), and Cyclamen (005).

Fry-up: 3 (40g) balls of Sirdar Wash 'N' Wear Double Crêpe in Lemon (252), oddments of double knitting (or 4 ply used double) in beige, brown, pink, white, yellow and green.

PLUS: A 15 cm (6 in.) nylon zip.

TENSION: 22 sts and 28 rows to 10 cm (4 in.) square stocking stitch.

ABBREVIATIONS: K — knit, P — purl, sts — stitches, tog — together, inc and K — increase by knitting into front and back of next stitch, making 2 sts from 1.

WHAT TO DO

FRY-UP

BERET: Cast on 121 sts and work 8 rows K1, P1 rib.

Continue in stocking stitch (1 row knit, 1 row purl).

Work 2 rows.

Next row: (Inc and K, K 13, inc and K), repeat to last 1 st, K1 (137 sts).

Work 3 rows.

Next row: (Inc and K, K 15, inc and K), repeat to last 1 st, K 1 (153 sts)

Work 7 rows.

*1st row: (K2 tog, K15, K2 tog), repeat to last 1 st, K 1.

2nd row: Purl.

3rd row: Knit.

4th row: Purl.

Repeat these last 4 rows, decreasing the amount of sts in brackets by 2 every time round — e.g. next row: (K2 tog, K 13, K2 tog), to last 1 st, K 1.

Continue in this manner until 25 sts remain on the needle and a block of 4 rows has been completed.

Next row: (K3 tog) to last 1 st, K 1 (9 sts).

Next row: Purl.

Break off yarn, thread through sts on needle and pull up. Join seam.

BAG (2 pieces alike): Cast on 153 sts and work 4 rows stocking stitch. Repeat as for beret from * to end.

STRIPES

BERET: With black wool cast on 121 sts and work 8 rows K1, P1 rib. Continue as for 'fry-up' in 2 row stripes of yellow, black, pink, black, green and black.

BAG: As for 'fry-up' starting with 2 rows black and continuing in pattern to end.

FRIED FOOD MENU —

CHIPS, garter stitch (K every row) used throughout.

With beige wool cast on 6 sts and work 20 rows. Cast off.

SAUSAGE, stocking stitch.

With brown wool cast on 20 sts, and work 40 rows. Cast off.

BACON, garter stitch.

With pink wool, cast on 60 sts and work 8 rows. Work 4 rows beige, 2 pink, 2 beige, 2 pink, 6 beige. Cast off in brown.

EGG, stocking stitch.

With white wool cast on 56 sts and work 4 rows.

Next row: (K2 tog, K 3, K2 tog) to end.

Work 3 rows.

Change to yellow wool and work 2 rows.

Next row: (K2 tog, K 1, K2 tog) to end.

Work 3 rows.

Next row: (K3 tog) to end.

Next row: Purl.

Break off yarn, thread through sts on needle and pull up. Join seam.

Repeat for second egg.

PORTION OF PEAS

With green wool cast on 19 sts.

1st row: K 1, make bobble by knitting into front and back of next st twice (4 sts from 1), turn and P 4, turn and K 4, turn and P 4, turn and K 4 tog, (K 3, make bobble) to last 1 st, K 1.

2nd row: Purl.

3rd row: K2 tog, K to last 2 sts, K2 tog.

4th row: P2 tog, P to last 2 sts, P2 tog.

Repeat these last 4 rows 3 more times (3 sts left on needle).

Next row: K 1, make bobble, K 1.

Next row: P 3.

Next row: K3 tog, and cast off.

TO MAKE UP: Sew ends in and press all pieces lightly on the wrong side with a damp cloth. Sew bag pieces together leaving 15 cms open. Sew in zip. Cut a 12 metre length of wool, fold in half and half again (4 strands). Make a loop in open end and slip over a doorknob. Pull yarn taut and twist tightly. Bring ends together and cord will twist. Attach to ends of bag opening. Join long side of chips to make tubes. Gather short ends of sausage and sew along length leaving an opening. Stuff with wadding, kapok or old tights, and sew up. Attach egg to beret by sewing round yolk line, padding yolk lightly with wadding. Sew edges of egg to beret.

Sirdar Superwash DK wool costs 40p for a 25 gram ball and Wash 'N' Wear Double Crepe costs 40p for a 40 grm ball. both come in a large selection of assorted colours. available from most wool shops and many department stores throughout the country. If you have problems with stockists. write to Sirdar Ltd., P.O. Box 31, Alvethorpe, Wakefield WF2 9ND enclosing an s.a.e. for the address of your nearest stockists.

Bored with shoulder-length hair but don't really want to have it cut? Try out these super styles and you can look different every day — so start now for a completely new you!

BE RIGHT ON TOP!

YOU'LL need lots of hairgrips and special covered elastic hair bands which are on sale at most chemists and department stores. Ordinary rubber bands are rough and will break the hair shaft as they rub along the hair, so don't use them. Now you're ready for:

A Beauty Box Special

MODEL-GIRL CHIGNON

Pull all the hair up on the top of your head and secure it with a band, then tuck all the ends under and secure them with grips. This will make a tight little bun that looks really good and will stay for hours, if you pin it up properly.

SEVENTIES' PONYTAIL

Great . . . just pull the hair together to a point off centre and close to the front of your head and secure with a covered band. If your ponytail flops over and you'd rather have it straight, try back-combing the ends a little to make it stiff.

THE PINEAPPLE

Gather all your hair together and secure on top with a covered band. Leave the ends to bounce loose as shown. This is a bubbly style that looks great for parties . . . try a simple pair of earrings to finish off the look.

FIFTIES' PONYTAIL

This is really simple! Just draw all your hair into a band high up at the back of your head, then tie a really bright ribbon into a super bow for a really lively rock 'n' roll fifties' look!

BALLERINA CHIGNON

This is a little bun at the back of the neck. Just pull all the hair to the back into a ponytail held with a band, then turn the ends under and secure with grips to make a small, neat bun. Let a few wisps of hair escape to soften the hairline!

PRE-RAPHAELITE BUNCHES

Nice for shoulder-length or longer hair. All you do is wash your hair and plait it into lots of tiny plaits while it's still wet! Let it dry naturally, then undo the plaits and you'll find you've got lovely, crinkly hair. Make two bunches high on the sides of your head, secured with covered bands.

SWISS PLAITS

Part your hair in the middle and make a plait each side starting at ear level. Pull the plaits up across your head and secure them with grips. This style will show off your ears, so earrings will look really good.

TWENTIES' HEADPHONES

Try this one just for fun! Part your hair in the middle and plait each side, starting at ear level. Coil each plait carefully into a wheel, over your ears, and pin securely so the coils sit over your ears!

All these styles will look best if your hair's clean and shining, so make it a rule to wash regularly with a shampoo that's made for your hair-type . . . greasy, normal or dry, or use a mild, medicated shampoo if you have dandruff. Visit a good hairdresser every six weeks for a trim and don't be afraid to experiment with different styles. Your hair tells people a lot about you, so don't neglect it!

WHO WANTS THEM?

There are some boys we'd all give anything to go out with — like David Soul, Barry Gibb, etc., etc.! Everyone knows the most-wanted boys around and no-one in their right mind would want to avoid them. But — what about the boys you *do* want to avoid? The ones you'd pay your little brother 50p to take on a toad-hunting expedition; the ones you tell lies to about not being able to go out because you've got to visit your granny/ look after the hamster/finish off your macramé. In short, the ones you'd rather be seen *without!* These are the unwanted men — the ones for whom there's positively no reward for capturing! The trouble is, though, they're out to capture *you!* So, to help you avoid them, here's our fun list of unwanted men. Memorise them so you can recognise the bad lads at a glance!

STEVE SLOB

UNWANTED FOR SMUGGLING GERMS INTO THE COUNTRY

Appearance
5 ft. 5 ins., heavily built, thick dark hair with dandruff and spiders in it, black fingernails, and toadstools growing out of his ears.

Haunts
Filthy old caffs, slagheaps, rubbish tips and waste-paper baskets.

Crime
Germ Smuggling. Slob follows girls around. He never has a steady girlfriend but will sit down next to girls on buses and envelop them in his appalling pong as he chats them up, flashing his mossy green teeth at them. He's a great threat to the environment and girls have had to be rescued from his clutches by firemen.

WARNING: Slob's fumes can cause unconsciousness and make paint blister off buses. So if you see him . . . call the Fire Brigade.

WILLIE WEEDY

UNWANTED FOR WHEEDLING AND CLINGING

Appearance
5 ft. 5 ins., pale, thin, knock-kneed, wearing thick vests knitted by his mum and a weenie beanie crocheted by his Auntie Jeanie.

Haunts
In his mum's kitchen, or watching TV, curled up on her knee. That was OK once, but now he's sixteen!

Crime
Wheedling and Clinging. Weedy is spoilt, a definite Mummy's boy. So he expects his girlfriend to wait on him hand and foot, massage his brow when he's feeling weary, and embroider his initials on his teeny hankies. Whatever **he** wants to do is law. The girl is never consulted. After all, she's a mere female, and if his mum never taught him anything else, she sure taught him this — girls aren't fit to kiss the soles of his Hush Puppies. He'll wheedle and cling till he gets his way, so watch out!

WARNING: Weedy really needs a stiff blast of pesticide. It's the only thing that'll solve his problem. So if you see him, inform the Ministry of Agriculture, and they'll send a weed-killing aeroplane over.

JERRY JEALOUS

UNWANTED FOR EMOTIONAL BLACKMAIL

Appearance
5 ft. 10 ins., red hair, green darting eyes, usually carries a pair of binoculars, a telescope and a magnifying glass.

Haunts
Anywhere! Cafés, cl[..] cinemas, parties . . . so w[..] out!

Crime
Emotional Blackmail, Petty Jealousy. Jealous get[..] know a girl, and at first he ca[..] extremely attractive. Gradu[..] though, she finds herself b[..] cross-examined. "Where [..] you been?" "You're late." "[..] have you been with?" "Who is [..] bloke across the road o[..] you?" "What do you mean, [..] don't know him?" If she [..] to other boys at par[..] Jealous can turn nasty, sho[..] sly looks at her, looking dag[..] at everybody else, and gene[..] poisoning the atmosphere.

WARNING: Jealous can [..] extremely poisonous, so if [..] see him, jump into a paper [..] and call the Health Inspector

HARD HARRY

UNWANTED FOR BREAKING AND TAMPERING

Appearance
6 ft. 3 ins., burly build, broken nose, huge fists, a Pumping Iron T-shirt and a tattoo on each arm which says ROCK HARD.

Haunts
Gymnasiums, backstre[..] sleazy alleyways, outside t[..] aways, leaning up against [..] machines, etc.

Crime
Breaking and Tamperi[..] Basically Harry goes aro[..] proving how hard he is by br[..] ing windows, furniture, tr[..] walls, and bones. And he tam[..] with locks, slot-machines, [..] doors and anything else he [..] lay his big hairy mitts on. [..] approach to girls is crude, b[..] and more like a rugby ta[..] than anything else. His embra[..] crack girls' ribs, his kisses kn[..] their teeth out, and when [..] grabs them by the hand, the[..] a crackling noise.

WARNING: This guy's [..] monster. If you see him, [..] your local safari patrol who [..] shoot tranquillising darts a[..] him and remove him to the z[..]

How to disguise that you love him

So you love him . . . but does he love you? He talks to you, he says hello, but he hasn't actually asked you out yet. Is he going to? Does he feel about you the way you feel about him? You don't know, and you've got to cover up the fact that you think he's the greatest thing on two legs until *he* gets round to thinking that about *you*! So here are the reasons why you *shouldn't* let him know you love him and some tips for disguising the fact that you do . . .

OK. You've seen him once or twice and thought, "He's nice." Then you've noticed how good he looks. Then suddenly you find you're looking out for him and you're disappointed when he's not there. The whole evening seems pointless if he doesn't show up. You find you're thinking about him all the time — at the bus-stop, at school, watching television. That's love.

And falling in love is a bit like falling off a log. It doesn't really hurt until you've done it.

You might have been prancing along the tree trunk thinking, "This is fun" when suddenly, "Wallop!" Every bone in your body aches or more exactly your heart aches. And the trouble with aching hearts is that it's hard to hide the fact that you're in agony.

If the same thing happens to him and he asks you out in a couple of days, terrific. But it doesn't usually happen as easily as that.

More often than not, one person falls in love first and if it's you, then it's important to disguise the fact that you're crazy about him — for a number of reasons.

The first is that girls are naturally more romantic than boys.

The second reason is linked to the first. How many boys do you know who listen to the words of love songs? Mostly they like heavy rock.

Well, so do girls, of course, but girls will still spend far more time listening to slow dreamy records and, unlike boys, almost **expect** to fall in love every time they meet someone new.

So, although he may like you, he won't necessarily go home and dream about you — the first time!

And, another reason to disguise that you love him, of course, is that you might, just might, be making a mistake. After a few more meetings you may feel he's not that terrific after all.

Putting on a disguise gives you — and him — time to find out if it really is love or just a five-minute wonder.

SO now that you've decided to hide your love from him, how do you go about it? There are a few things which *will* give you away, so you've got to watch out for them . . .

Blushing

This is a dead give-away! If you're inclined to blush whenever he speaks to you, you've got two alternatives.

Either wear a light tan foundation when you know he's going to be around or, if you feel a blush coming on just say, "I've spent all day in the garden, don't you think I've caught the sun?" But do remember that blushing makes just about everyone look prettier — he might even be flattered!

Eyes

Another problem area because they bare your soul to the world!

Most people are afraid to look someone they really like in the eyes. They want to, but they're afraid of giving too much away if they do!

So try, if you can, to look straight into his eyes when he's talking to you. Firstly, he'll look at you, which means you'll have sweet dreams and secondly, it's a lot easier to have a normal conversation once your knees have stopped turning to jelly!

Excitement

Talking of jellied knees, you'll find it very difficult to behave normally when he's around.

Even if no-one tells you, it's a fair bet that you'll know the minute he walks through the door and you'll want to turn round. **Don't.** Count to ten and take a deep breath. It **does** work.

Awkwardness

You'll find it hard to manage simple things if he's near. Holding a pen can become a severe case of the shakes. Walk out of the door and you're bound to trip up!

Just try to do everything twice as slowly and force your mind to concentrate on what you're doing. You'll feel far less self-conscious if you concentrate on something else — besides him!

Shut up!

In other words, don't, if you can possibly help it, tell anyone else about your feelings, especially not another girl.

Word **does** get around, however good a friend is at keeping a secret. And even if she just raises her eyebrows and looks at you when he appears, it will be enough to send you into a flat spin and him straight out of the door.

Try not to giggle, too. There **are** times when a good giggle is a great idea but keep it to yourselves when there are boys around. Especially **the** boy!!

Be sociable

Talk to other boys within your crowd, but don't keep glancing over to see if he's listening. If he likes you, he will be!

Talk slowly and calmly and don't butt into conversations he's having unless you've **really** got something to say. Think before you speak, and don't rush your words!

And remember it'll all be worthwhile when he finally says, "I've wanted to ask you out for ages but I wasn't sure if you liked me." When that happens, don't give yourself away at the last minute by falling into a dead faint. Just smile and say, "Oh really?"

Russian

Continental Sports

Nadia Comaneci

THE vast "Pool" was alive with colour and excitement, as the huge crowd filed their way into their seats to the cheerful sounds of the band of the Grenadier Guards.

Then, as silence and expectation fell over the hall, the Guards performed the Soviet National Anthem, the lights fell, and spotlights picked out the Russian gymnasts, led by flag bearers, marching smartly into the arena.

There followed a dazzling display of dynamic modern gymnastics. The crowd held their breath as tiny 15-year-old Elena Davidova somersaulted *on* to the beam to start her exercise; they laughed at the antics of World Champion tumblers Yuri Zikumov and Alexander Russolin; they were enchanted by World Champion Galina Shugurova, who used ropes, hoops, balls and ribbons to create a beautiful pattern of rhythmic movement.

They were amazed by the sheer skill of the leading Soviet girl gymnast — Nelli Kim — who, whether on the vault, asymmetric bars, the beam or the floor, was in a class all of her own!

AFTER this amazing display, in which 50 Soviet gymnasts took part, I was lucky enough to go backstage and ask Nelli Kim just what it was like to reach the very top in World Gymnastics.

"It's marvellous," she said, smiling radiantly. "Really a dream come true. But don't imagine that it has all happened overnight.

"I've been working day and night at gymnastics for eleven years and it was only at the Montreal Olympics in 1976 that I really got international recognition!"

Nelli, of course, won the Olympic gold medals in the individual floor exercise and the vault, and the silver medal in the overall competition. She also managed to score two "perfect" ten out of ten marks, once for her vault and once for her floor exercise!

Backstage in her dressing room, while Nelli continued to take off the stage make-up which she wears for displays, I asked her what it was like to be "perfect" in gymnastics. After all, that's something

that very few of us ever achieve in any field!

Nelli laughed and then said seriously, "I may have scored ten out of ten, but there can never really be perfection in this sport, because you *always* feel you can do better. It is very annoying, but it is true!

"There are always new movements, new difficulties, so you can never learn enough. For instance, Olga (Korbut) was the first girl to do a back somersault on the beam, and now Russian girls are doing forward beam somersaults!"

THE Soviet team are always pushing the frontiers of gymnastics forward and everyone's really looking forward to the 1980 Moscow Olympics. But surely none more so than Nelli.

"I cannot wait for the Olympics to begin," she told me enthusiastically. "I've been working on my programme for two and a half years already, and it will take another year to perfect. Sometimes when I have been working terribly hard, the Olympics seem a very long way away!"

So when you watch the Olympics on TV and gasp at Nelli's ability, remember

that she'll have been practising th particular programme for three and a h years!

When I asked Nelli about the comp tition expected from the Rumanians, and particular Nadia Comaneci, she answer confidently:

"I don't think they will be as mu of a problem as during the Montre Olympics.

"After all," she went on, "you have keep cheerful and I'm always optimist But at the same time, don't think I underestimating the competitio because that would be fatal . . ."

Nelli is obviously dedicated to sport and not ashamed of being competiti or admitting she's determined to to win. But when she isn't performi Nelli likes doing the same kinds things as most of us.

"I love listening to records. M favourites are western stars like C Richard, as well as our Soviet groups.

"I also enjoy making my own cloth I think the London shops are amazi so many beautiful fashions which ha given me lots of ideas for when I home!

"Yes, London is lovely, I just wi we had more time to see the rest the country.

"But that is one of the penalties of be a gymnast," Nelli admitted. "We trav the world — we're touring the Unit States next — but we get very little fr time.

"We are always either practising performing. Still, to be honest, I love and wouldn't have it any other way!"

NELLI then had to leave to speak her coach, so I had a word with year-old Irena Derjugika — the Wor Overall Champion of Modern Rhythm Gymnastics. This incorporates balle dance, skips and jumps. You don't ne conventional apparatus, but instead u hoops, flowing ribbons, clubs and balls.

There are accepted patterns, certa moves, skips and jumps which mu feature in the gymnast's programme, b there's also great scope for improvisati and a wide choice of accompanying musi

Earlier I had seen Irena twirling a17-fo long ribbon effortlessly around herse tracing beautiful patterns, and weaving and out of the loops it formed with the mo graceful movement I've ever seen!

To The Top!

Irena Derjugika

Nelli Kim *British gymnast Denise Jones*

Now she was happy to stop and speak for a little while and tell me about her career so far, in perfect English!

"I started by training for the ballet," she said, "but my mother was a famous gymnast. She's now a coach in Kiev, in Russia, and so I decided to try to follow her.

"My father also won an Olympic Gold Medal at Melbourne in 1956 for the Modern Pentathlon, so you could say sport was in the family!

"Of course," Irena went on, "when people come to see our displays very few of them realise just how many years of hard work have gone into making it appear effortless!

"Gymnastics is a hard life, and you have to be devoted to it. Also it's sad, because by the age of, say, 22, you're considered to be old and past it!"

That was hard to imagine, looking at Irena's perfectly enviable figure, lovely hair and deep blue eyes, so I wasn't surprised when she said, "I'm hoping to become an actress when my career as a gymnast is over. And, luckily, I've already been offered a couple of parts in Soviet films!"

MOST of the top Soviet gymnasts turn to coaching when their careers as performers are over. Ludmila Tourischeva and Olga Korbut, for instance, are now both coaching the Soviet hopefuls for the 1980 Olympics!

And as the Russian gymnasts left Olympia behind for another year, and returned to their West End hotel, I'm sure they'd encouraged lots of girls to start thinking seriously about taking up gymnastics!

If you were one of them, or just think that you'd like to know more about

this fascinating sport (where you can start training for instance), then write to —
Mr Tony Murdock,
Development Officer,
British Amateur Gymnastics Association,
23a High Street,
Slough, Berks SL1 1DY,
enclosing an S.A.E.

And get in training for the 1984 Olympics! After all, we can't let the Russians have it *all* their own way!

Party Posers

GIVE your brain some exercise with these Oh! level teasers. Or liven up your party by splitting guests into two teams grappling with them while you work out what to give the winners!

1. What do the following words have in common? Sighing, deft, first, stun, canopy, calmness.

2. Express 100 by using the same figure six times.

3. An L.P. has a total diameter of 12 inches. There's an outer margin of an inch and the diameter of the unused centre is four inches. There are 90 grooves to the inch. How far does the stylus travel when the disc is played?

4. DOORJNEWSUT. Can you rearrange these letters to spell just one word? Not a proper name or anything foreign or unusual.

5. A painter needs three days to paint a room. How long would it take him, working at the same rate, to paint a room twice as long, twice as wide and twice as high?

6. Can you make eight 8s equal 1000?

7. Even the most ardent women's-libber would never claim that boys *always* lie and girls *always* tell the truth, but that's the ridiculous assumption we want you to make for this test of reasoning power.

At dusk, you are rowing towards the shore on which you see, dimly, three figures wearing trousers. You shout to them, "Are you boys or girls?" One of them answers but the words are blown away by the wind. The second person says, "She says she's a girl. She is a girl and so am I." The third person shouts: "They're boys but I'm a girl." What is the true sex of each?

ANSWERS:

1. They all contain three consecutive letters in alphabetical order, like sigh-.
2. 99 99/99.
3. Three inches. The grooves per inch has nothing to do with it, as it's the record which turns round the needle. We know the radius of the disc is six inches so leaving out the unused margin (1 in.) and the radius of the unused centre (2 in.) you can see that the stylus moves three inches (six inches minus three inches) towards the centre of the disc when it's being played.
4. Just one word. Well, that's what we asked for, isn't it?
5. Twelve days. Work it out with a little sketch and you'll see the room is four times as big.
6. 888 + 88 + 8 + 8 + 8.
7. If the first person was a boy, he'd have lied and answered, "I'm a girl." If a girl, she'd have said that, right? In either case, the words blown away by the wind were "I'm a girl." So the second speaker told the truth about what the first person said, therefore must be a girl. Since the first two are girls, the third person is obviously a boy. Lying rat!

Everyone who's ever lived has had parent trouble — it can happen at any age but you probably notice it first around the age of twelve. It's a hard time for you because you've got all the problems of your rapidly changing body and mixed-up emotions to cope with, and it's a tough time for your parents because they're learning to cope with the almost entirely new person you're turning into. So it's not too surprising if your life at home sometimes resembles a battlefield rather than "home sweet home"!

Well, here's how to cope with most of the problems you'll come across and how to make this difficult stage both you *and* your parents are going through right now a lot more bearable!

DO YOU HAVE PROBLEM PARENTS?

YOU'VE got your whole life ahead of you — and you just can't wait to live it! You think about all the discos you'll be going to, the places you'll see, the friends you'll have, the boys you'll meet. You're beginning to want to stay out a little later, to try all the latest clothes and make-up — in short, do all sorts of things that didn't interest you at all before . . .

You'd be one in a million if you could actually go on and do *all* of these things, though, as and when you want, because most of us have parents whose idea of what's good for us, and what definitely *isn't*, is the exact opposite of ours!

So what happens? Well, you probably argue all the time, which makes your life and theirs a complete misery. Because they won't let you stay out as late as you'd like, because they might not approve of your friends, your make-up, your boyfriend, clothes, almost everything you care about most, in fact . . .

I HATE THEM!

THIS is a terrible thing to say, I know, but it's true that sometimes I actually hate my mum and dad. And I really mean *hate*. All we ever do is argue. Mum nags me to death about the mess my room's in, the way I leave my clothes lying about, even about the way I *walk*, for goodness' sake, and a million and one other things.

"Dad makes these awful scenes if I ask to stay out a little bit late one night, complains about my make-up and clothes, my friends . . . And, of course, I'm much too young for boyfriends. You name it, we argue about it. They're making my whole life a misery and I don't think I can stand it any longer." — Jill, 13.

To put it mildly, Jill's having a very tough time at home right now. Her parents don't seem to want her to have any fun out of life at all. The way she sees it, they're going to say no to anything she asks. They treat her like a child and refuse to face the fact that she's growing up.

Her parents are going through a pretty tough time too, though. All of a sudden, she's moody, she's wearing make-up, wants to choose her own clothes and even have boyfriends. It seems like only yesterday she was the sweet little girl they'd always known and loved. Now, suddenly, she's almost like a stranger. They can't understand her. She doesn't tell them things the way she used to, and she's taken to locking herself in her room. And all that, you must admit, is an awful lot to get used to!

If you're in a pretty similar situation to Jill, there's an awful lot *you* can do to improve your relationship with your parents. You'll have to do quite a bit of positive thinking. And you'll probably have to change your *attitude* — which in turn will change theirs — and make your life a whole lot easier in the process.

How Do You Behave At Home?

Do you throw tantrums to get your own way, or sulk for days on end in your room, or just slouch around looking miserable when you can't get to go out with that

boy, stay out a little later one night, or get that dress you really, really want?

If so . . . try to stop all that and act responsibly from now on. It's no use throwing tantrums if you can't get your own way — that sort of behaviour's really childish anyway, and you're not a child any more . . . are you? The simple fact is, they won't allow you a lot of freedom if you don't let them see you can cope with it. If you throw tantrums, they're bound to ignore your demands and be unable to take you seriously. So keep your cool.

Is your room a complete and utter pigsty? Do you chuck your clothes any old place once you've finished with them? And is it your mum who's got the charming job of cleaning up after you?

If that's the case, then you're certainly not the grown-up, sophisticated person you're trying to make yourself out to [be]. Clean up your own room yourse[lf], you shouldn't even need to be asked t[o do] this, you should know it's your job [and] nobody else's. Even better, you c[ould] also help your mum out around the ho[use,] make the tea sometimes, go for [the] shopping. Do things for your parents [and] they'll be only too happy to return [the] compliment. You'll soon notice [the] difference in their attitude to you the[n.]

Do your parents object to make-up?

If it is make-up they object to, remem[ber] that nothing's more guaranteed to [give] parents heart attacks than the sig[ht of] their previously well-scrubbed, ultra cle[an-] faced daughter emerging from her bedro[om] flashing bright blue eye shadow like it[s] going out of fashion, plastered with [lots] and generally covered in blusher [and] lipstick!

So go easy on the make-up, to begin with anyway — give them a chance to get used to the idea. Read up on as many beauty articles as you can (turn to pages 17-21 for a start!) and get a good idea of how to apply it properly. It's often quite difficult at first, when you're not used to make-up, to get the proper balance.

And the same goes for clothes. Don't go all out to persuade Mum to buy you that incredibly sexy, plunging satin lurex dress you fancy. Instead, go for something subtle. And to show how sensible you are, save up for one or two things you really want and buy them yourself. Both your mum and dad are bound to be impressed with that!

Do your parents object to boyfriends?

If it's boyfriends that are the trouble, you'll have to figure out why your parents don't want you to have any.

If they think you're too young, for instance, you'll have to show them that you're *not* a child any longer, by acting as maturely as you can. They can't tell you you're too young forever, remember, and maybe you can speed things along a little by getting your parents to respect you and your wishes *now*, by talking the matter over as coolly and calmly as you can, explaining how you feel. Then, wait until the right moment to bring him home on an ever so casual basis, of course (like his dropping by to borrow a school book!), and then take it from there.

On the other hand, if they think he's totally unsuitable, there's nothing else for it but to arrange for him to meet them so that you can all discuss the problem together. If he's serious enough about you (and deserves you), he ought to prove them wrong! But whatever the outcome, it's best not to deceive your parents about boys — they're bound to find out what you're up to eventually, and if they discover you've been going behind their backs, it's going to take them an awful long time to trust you ever again.

SO YOU WANT TO LEAVE HOME?

SOMETIMES, things can get so bad between you and your parents that the worst comes to the worst and you feel there's nothing else for it but to make the ultimate break for freedom and leave home . . .

It's sad, but it does happen that the situation arises where living together in the same house becomes totally unbearable. So what do you do? Well, leaving home is a pretty drastic solution and running away from a problem very rarely solves anything.

So you've got to be positive about it all and examine *why* things have broken down to such an extent.

Do you expect far too much from your parents, much more than they can possibly give? If you're really feeling mixed up and confused about what you want, it's possible that it could be *because* of the fact that you're growing up that you want to leave home and start afresh. Bide your time and when the growing-up process starts to settle down, and when your emotions have adjusted, you'll find yourself much calmer and more confident and better able to get on with your parents and your present environment.

Remember here, too, that your *body* is going through enormous changes to do with growing up, changes which not only disturb your chemical balance, but psychological changes which can play havoc with your feelings and emotions. So it's normal to

THEY DON'T CARE ABOUT ME!

BUT what if you feel your parents actually don't like you, never mind love you? Sue, who's 16 now, remembers the time when she thought her mum and dad actually *hated* her.

"Things reached a head when I was 14 and Mum was pregnant. When I first found out I was about to have a little brother or sister I was really shocked, not pleased at all," Sue told us. "I thought it was a bit much. We were a happy enough family already and I thought Mum was mad to have another baby at her age!" (Sue's mum was the grand old age of 36 at the time — not exactly a great granny!)

"Well, Mum had a little girl and I could see she and Dad were over the moon about it. But I certainly wasn't. Before, we could always talk to each other and got on really great. Now, it was the baby this, the baby that — no time for me, and I felt really rotten. Honestly, I could have grown horns and no-one would have noticed!"

Sue felt ignored, and worst of all, unloved. Her mum and dad couldn't see past the new baby, or so she thought. So she started staying out later and later, not telling her parents where she was going or who she was with.

"Actually, I wasn't doing anything much — I just used to go round to my friend's, but Mum started narking at me, saying I was to be in earlier and help with the baby. We fought an awful lot at the time — we were always arguing. But what's really awful is the fact that I actually enjoyed making them so miserable and worried about me . . ."

Sue realises now that she acted a bit selfishly at the time, and that most of her resentment was sparked off by a kind of subconscious jealousy and a feeling of being left out in the cold by her parents' new relationship with the baby. It wasn't that they didn't love *her* any more — just that a new baby is a big event in anyone's life, and her parents were behaving completely naturally.

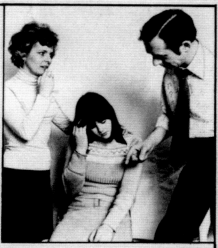

DO you feel a little bit rejected — unloved — like Sue? Well, before you take the same drastic measures she did, try to understand *why* your parents seem to be ignoring you.

It could be they've got money troubles — which most people have nowadays! It could be they've got a lot of worries on their minds about one thing or another — it's up to you to see if you can help them out, even if it's just helping Mum out around the house, doing the garden for your dad — *anything* to show them that you're around and there, if and when they need you. And they'll know you're a responsible person, one they can be really proud of.

The same goes if you're the eldest in the family and feel a little left out — and forgotten at times. It's probably just the case that your mum and dad feel they can trust you to do and cope with a lot more than the younger ones — which is a compliment to you, really!

If you've got any kind of grudge against your parents' attitude towards you it's best to speak up about it. Don't bottle things up — this just leads to even more resentment and, eventually, a hurtful wall of silence.

Remember, always try to air your grievances — don't try to hide them or shut your parents out of your life. It's very rarely hate that causes coldness between you and your parents — just a kind of breakdown in communication, and a failure to understand what makes each other tick. So always try to talk over your problems with them first, or they may not realise there are any!

feel on top of the world one minute and then down in the dumps enough to want to leave home the next.

But if it really is your parents that are causing all your problems, you must find someone to talk things over with first, before you do anything drastic. If it's your mum who seems to be making your life a complete misery, then talk things over with your dad first of all, and vice versa. Or a friend or her mum, or even your brother or sister — and find out how they cope.

Finally, act responsibly. Don't shout your head off or lock yourself in your room if you can't get your own way about things.

Remember, too, that if your parents seem really heavy-handed sometimes, it's probably because they're really worried about you . . . that you'll be easily led, get in with a bad crowd, start to take drugs, maybe even get pregnant. They don't mean to be rotten to you, they just want to protect you till you show them that you can look after yourself.

*So if you're going through a bad patch with your parents right now, just try your hardest not to argue or let things get on top of you too much, and be as patient and understanding as you possibly can. And try to **talk** to your parents, too, and let them know how you really feel about things.*

After all, if you really think about it, not only would they feel lost without you, you'd probably feel lost without them, too!

It IS possible to be fifteen years old and a superstar — and here are two fifteen-year-old girls who've proved it! Tatum O'Neal and Jodie Foster are both making big names for themselves, they're both film stars and they're both American. So what do they think of their success? And how far do they resemble each other when it comes to personality? We decided to talk to each of them and find out . . .

"My Name's Tatum~NOT Tantrum!"

SOMETIMES, I think newspaper men confuse my name with Tantrum, the stories they print about me!" 15-year-old American film star, Tatum O'Neal, said.

"They make out that I spend my entire life going to parties in low-necked dresses or to discos with a boyfriend on each arm. They say I'm too forward, pushy, a brat, or real nasty!"

Tatum O'Neal is, of course, the daughter of famous actor Ryan O'Neal and an Oscar-winning actress in her own right. In fact, she's a star, the sixth biggest box-office draw in the world.

But life hasn't been a total fairy story for the green-eyed, very attractive Tatum.

"My parents were divorced when I was three," she told me, "and I was brought up by my mother (actress Joanna Moore) on a ranch near Los Angeles. Then my dad won custody of me.

"But he couldn't look after me all the time, so he sent me away to boarding school, which I hated — and I ran away."

Luckily for Tatum, though, round about that time Ryan O'Neal was offered the starring part in the film "Paper Moon" and realised that the part of the little girl was ideally suited for his daughter, Tatum.

"I didn't want to do it at first," Tatum admitted. "I didn't think I could handle it.

"But then I realised I'd be with Dad all the time, and wouldn't have to go back to school — so, of course, I said yes!"

Apart from being able to dodge school for a while, Tatum also managed to upstage her father and win an Oscar for her part in the film — and all at the tender age of nine!

"I love making films," she said, her eyes sparkling, "and, obviously, it's going to be my career. On the bad side, though, there are lots of problems about being an actress at my age.

"For instance, while other kids at school get to do fun things like going to a baseball game, I have to go to work."

STILL, there's one thing Tatum doesn't miss much — and that's school! "As a student, I'm not the best," she admitted ruefully. "And although I have a tutor when I'm filming, I'm still a little behind when I go back to school."

But there's another reason why Tatum doesn't like school much.

Tatum in "International Velvet."

"Because I'm in movies, the other kids don't like it, they're a bit envious I guess, so that makes things awkward.

"Anyway," Tatum went on, sounding just a little bit hurt, "that's why I constantly bug my dad to keep me working, and why I don't bother too much about lessons!"

Not that Tatum would want her life any other way, though.

"Acting in films has given me so much. Things that the average teenager just never gets to experience," she says.

"Take the film 'International Velvet' for instance. That was really fantastic — learning to ride with the best coach in the world — William Steinkraus, the American Olympic Medallist — and with people like Richard Mead (British Gold Medallist in the Three Day Event) on hand to advise me!"

WHEN she isn't acting, Tatum lives at home with her father in a beach house at Malibu, California.

"We look after ourselves, and I'm quite good at cooking," Tatum explained. "A lady comes in to do the cleaning, but apart from that we're very self-sufficient."

She also tends to move round socially with her father, too. Not many girls would fancy going out with their dads all the time, but then Ryan O'Neal isn't exactly an ordinary dad!

"We go to parties together quite often," Tatum said proudly. "And, of course, then I like to dress fashionably — and wear make-up and generally look as good as I can.

"So when people who don't know me see me at parties they think, 'That girl's so forward for her age!'

"In fact, normally I hang around in jeans and T-shirts, don't wear any make-up and look my age!"

It must be said though — Tatum *is* far more mature, poised and graceful than most girls of her age.

And, of course, she's already going out wi boys and thinking seriously about romance.

I NEVER used to be interested in guys Tatum said, laughing. "I was a real tor boy — my biggest pleasure in life wa scrapping with my brothers.

"But I grew up sort of suddenly when I wa twelve, and I became much more seriou Now, though, I think I'm at the age to be ab to give and receive love, and to have a prop boyfriend."

Tatum doesn't have any one particular typ of boy in mind as her ideal, but she's rea sure of one thing.

"I wouldn't *ever* want to go out with a ma like my dad! Of course, he's the neatest gu in the world with me," she hurriedly e plained, "but he runs around with too man girls!"

Most girls would probably find it hard get used to their father going out with succession of glamorous women.

But, Tatum says, "I'm very close to m father, and he lets me meet all his girlfriend so I can tell him just what I think of them.

"Actually, I get along with most of them OI One thing Tatum wouldn't like, though, wou be to see her father get married again.

"I should hate that," she said honestly "We have a nice thing going at home, so wh bring someone else in?

"Besides," she added, joking, "I don't thir there's anyone in the world in their right min who would take us both on."

So, for the time being anyway, Tatum more than happy living with her dad, playin Frisbee on the beach at Malibu, riding he horse and travelling the world making films.

As for the future, she just shrugs he shoulders and says — "I'll think about tha when I'm grown up!"

TWO GIRLS!

"I'm Quite A Good Girl, Really"

KNOCKED at the door of the flat Jodie Foster and her mother had rented while Jodie was ~ming "Candleshoe" in England. I waited a ~ment and then Jodie's clear blue eyes ~ered through the letter-box.

"Kick it," she told me, "it's stuck."

Feeling a bit like a burglar, I heaved the door ~d it opened.

Jodie was standing there grinning. "I'm really ~rry," she explained. "It's just been painted."

She ran her fingers through her straight ~nde hair and led me into the sunny living-~m.

"I stayed up late watching the midnight ~vie," Jodie rubbed her eyes, and flopped ~ to a sofa, "and I've just got up."

Jodie had hastily pulled on jeans and a T-shirt ~en she heard my knock at the door, but ~w she was wide awake and rushed round the ~t, which was stacked with boxes and parcels, ~owing me all the things she'd bought while ~'d been in England.

"This is great, isn't it?" She plonked a tweed ~p on her head and peered down her nose, "it ~kes me look like a street kid."

Her real name is Elisa, but it's easy to see ~y her mother decided, "she looked more like ~odie". It certainly seems to fit her tomboyish ~sy-going attitude to life.

And yet, at 15, Jodie is a very big star. ~Her co-star in "Candleshoe," David Niven, ~led her, "the most brilliant, natural actress ~ave ever seen work" — and Jodie thinks he's ~solutely terrific as well!

But what makes Jodie so unusual is that every ~e she does something, she does it right.

"It isn't hard work for me," she told me, ~cking a peppermint. "The only hard work is ~iting around between shots.

"I worry more about school plays and things ~n movies. That's why I'd never go on stage. ~et so nervous.

"I love going to the theatre, but I don't want

to be part of it. Films are what I love. I'd like to be an all-round film-maker, maybe a director later."

AND it's quite likely that Jodie will end up as a director because she's been a part of the film and television business since the age of three when she did her first TV commercial in Los Angeles, her home.

Now Jodie travels the world making movies. Her mother is always with her and she also has a tutor on hand to keep her school-work up to date.

"School's OK," Jodie says, "because school's where you meet all your friends and school's where you have your lunch and where you lose weight because you don't eat the lunches!

"And just when you're getting bored, a film comes up and off you go. I remember one time when I was filming 'Taxi Driver'. I went back to school after filming and there were still traces of the make-up I'd had to wear. The other kids really teased me about that!

"Really, though, I don't see why boys go for make-up. It just looks stupid. I suppose it's OK as a cover-up job.

"Maybe I should use it since I've got a big thing about my nose.

"I used to have a perfect nose until I sprained it. Now it goes like this." She drew a hook with her finger.

It doesn't, of course, but it's typical of Jodie that she's very critical of herself. She's equally critical of her screen performances.

She watches her films, often taking friends to see them. "But I keep thinking how I would have done it differently," she says. "I criticise myself all the time."

JODIE has quite a deep voice with a warm Californian accent. Watching her curled up on the sofa, it's hard to believe that she's not just the girl next door. She lives the sort of life most girls just dream about, but she doesn't think it's glamorous.

"Sometimes it's fun and sometimes it's boring, but it's no big deal," Jodie told me.

"We don't live in an enormous film star mansion. In fact, I've always lived in the same house since I was a kid. Maybe we have more money now, but it doesn't seem that different."

Jodie loves watching other actors and actresses like Paul Newman and Shirley Maclaine, but her real hero is rock singer Peter Frampton. When she found out that he was staying at the same hotel in Paris as she was recently, she wanted to sit on the floor by the lift all night, just to say hello, except that her mum decided she needed some sleep!

IN "Candleshoe", Jodie plays a very confi- dent young American orphan, who is believed to be the long-lost heiress of the Candleshoe fortune. In real life, though, Jodie is a very funny girl. "She makes me laugh," as David Niven said.

She leaves all the business side of things to her mother and, unlike Casey in "Candle- shoe ", she's in no hurry to fly off on her own and be independent.

"I'd like to think of myself as a kid for a long time," she said. "Until I'm eighteen, my mother has to travel with me by law but we get on terrifically and I don't want to grow up too fast.

"I'm not being conceited," she laughed, "but I don't think I do things that need heavy discipline. When I'm away, about all I do when I'm not working is sit and watch TV. I guess I'm quite a good girl, really."

And although she managed a cheeky grin as she said it, she's right. And certainly, as an actress, she's a very "good girl" indeed!

What's The Worst Christma

We all look forward to Christmas — the holly and the ivy, all that kissing under the mistletoe — but admit it, the thing we all really enjoy most is opening all those lovely presents! But what about those beautifully-gift-wrapped boxes that have something absolutely awful inside? What about the presents we'd rather we *hadn't* been given? We asked some of you and lots of your favourite stars about the Christmas presents they wish they *hadn't* found in their stockings!

Jan Williamson, Newcastle.

A friend once gave me a fantastic, very expensive, eye-make up kit that I'd hinted about for ages — and one hour after being given it, and with streaming red eyes, I had to admit I was allergic to it!

Alan Breneton, Edinburgh.

I'd wanted a new Punk album for ages, but what with buying Christmas presents for everyone else, I couldn't afford anything for myself. So when my auntie told me she was getting me something I'd really like for Christmas, and handed me an unmistakable album-shaped package, I was really pleased — but Abba's not really my idea of Punk rock!

RITA RAY of Darts

It's certainly the most ridiculous present I've had as well! When the band first started to succeed, a well-wisher sent us a Christmas present — a shaving kit for every member of the group — not knowing, I suppose, that one of us was female. They must have thought one of the boys had a really high voice! I don't use it, but I didn't throw it away either. I've got it still . . . as a souvenir.

ELTON JOHN

Last Christmas BLUE decided to give me two silly presents. One was a complete gift pack of Brut — everything you can imagine in that line — talc, after shave, pre-shave, soap, lotion — you name it, it was in that pack. They know full well that I don't even like Brut! Also, they bought me a felt mat which — when you unroll — is covered in kiddies' games — ludo, snakes and ladders and the like! I'm sure plenty of kids would've been delighted with it, but it wasn't really me!

ANNA of Abba

Somebody sent me a slimming machine — one of the ones that vibrate and have belts that you put round yourself — for my bottom. It was sent anonymously and I expect it was meant for a joke, but I was very hurt and offended at first because I didn't think I needed it.

Gill Bains, Barnstaple, Devon.

It was when I was twelve, and I knew I was due to get a late present about a week after Christmas. Of course, I started to think about it a lot, and what it might be, and I was really looking forward to it — and it turned out to be a Noddy jigsaw puzzle!

Glenis Beardsley, Yelland, Devon.

A shocking pink cat suit given to me by an aunt who thought, wrongly, that it was really ''trendy''! And the worst thing was, any time this aunt was due to visit, I had to wear the horrible outfit!

Susan Little, Darlington, Yorks.

A relation in Singapore sent me a beautiful, silk, hand-embroidered tunic top. The only thing was, it was two sizes too small — and I had to give it to my younger sister!

MARTIN SHAW (The Professionals)

A melted Coca-Cola bottle. One of those that's been heated under a blow lamp and then, while it's soft, distorted and pulled out into funny shapes. I thought that was really silly. It was my best friend who gave it to me, too. I suppose it was meant as a joke. We've known each other for about twenty-five years, and practically grew up together, so he'd know exactly how desperately I needed a bent Coca-Cola bottle!

DENIS WATERMAN

When I was young, the first Christmas I was given socks and underpants was when I realised I wasn't a little boy any more, and it meant I wouldn't get sports books, toys, and so on in the future! Those socks meant I was classified as an adult from then on, and I didn't like it!

ELKIE BROOKS

I don't think I've had one, unless it was bein broke. That was the worst Christmas remember, when I was still with Vinega Joe before starting my solo career. We wei so hard up we had to share one chicke between all of us — me, the band, the roa crew — for our Christmas dinner. We couldn even afford to follow it up with Christma pudding, let alone go out and buy a turkey!

LEWIS COLLINS (The Professionals)

Every year I get handkerchiefs, and I'v never, ever, used one. I've got dozens unopened packets of them in my drawers. Th other thing I dislike is when someone gives yo money, that's always a disappointment. It making the effort of going out and buying some thing and wrapping it that matters, really. I g too far, myself, I'm a bit of a softie and I bu dozens of things, but it's because the happies times of my life when I was growing up were a Christmas and I love it. That being so, of course I'm usually delighted with whatever I get — even at the time, those hankies!

Present You've Ever Had?

ILLY IDOL (Generation X)

Every year I get the same useless present from my auntie in Canada — a pair of woolly ar muffs!! I wouldn't be seen dead in them! The rst year it was a bit of a laugh, but now it's ot to the stage when I don't even bother to pen up the parcel because I know exactly hat's inside!

OB DAVIES (Mud)

About four or five years ago my parents ought me a really horrible dressing-gown. It as a mauve and black silky thing and when I pened the parcel all I could find to say was Ugh!' I think they were rather upset by my esponse!

AVID NICHOLSON (Blue)

Several years ago, my older brother Matt ought me two equally stupid presents. One as a kit for making a Chinese Junk, and when opened the box the kit consisted of about five r six large pieces which could be put gether within about one minute! The other resent was a tool kit with everything being ade of either plastic or rubber. Something think Matt must have overlooked — the ct that I was 16 at the time!

KATE BUSH

The worst of all was a shower set somebody gave me. It had curtains, rails, pipes, the whole bit, and as far as I was concerned, it was useless. You see, I really love lying in the bath for ages and I've practically never used a shower in my entire life! I don't know where it is now, stuck in a drawer and forgotten, I expect — I'll certainly never fit it up.

BOB GELDOF (Boomtown Rats)

About three years ago I received something far worse than a horrible Christmas present — I received no presents at all! It was a pretty miserable day for me.

MIDGE URE (Rich Kids)

Somebody once sent me a huge crate filled with chocolate fudge — and I can't bear the stuff!

PHIL LYNOTT (Thin Lizzy)

The worst Christmas present I've ever had is being ill — and I've had that twice. The first time was when I was ten or eleven and got pneumonia, which meant I had to spend the whole holidays in bed when I wanted to be out with my friends. Then, a couple of years ago, I contracted hepatitis; and this time I was stuck in bed for about four weeks. I hope that never happens again.

NOEL EDMONDS

Three Christmasses ago an uncle sent me a record token! I know it sounds ungrateful, but honestly the last person who needs a record token is a disc jockey! But I felt I had to use it, so I went out and bought an album, but I can't for the life of me remember now which one it was.

OUR FAVOURITE

We could all think of hundreds of gorgeous good guys to choose from if we had to, we know, but how about feasting your beady little eyes on this bunch of beautiful bad guys for a change? We chose some of our favourites, and hope you'll agree that most of them would make you fall for the baddies every time — given the chance!! The worse the better . . . if you see what we mean!

Kermit — We've classed him as a Bad Guy because he keeps playing hard to get with poor Miss Piggy!

Jean Jaques Burnel — We'd like to get a stranglehold on him!

Clint Eastwood — The Good, the Bad and the — Oh, he's wonderful!

Ronnie Barker — He may be bad, but, like porridge, he can be soft and slushy, too!

Vincent Price — Fear at any Price!

Mick Jagger — We'd take the mick an

Darth Vadar — Dark, mysterious ar Force is with him!

BAD GUYS OK!

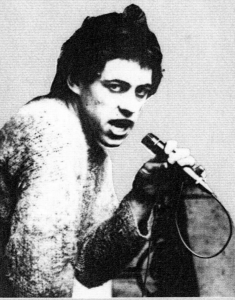

Animal — He's really wild!

Davison — When he played Tristan in "Creatures Great and Small," we wouldn't have minded giving him the treatment, anytime!

Bob Geldof — How's about rat!

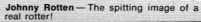

Tom — He's not really bad, 'cos we know he wouldn't do anything nasty to Jerry even if he did manage to catch him!

John Travolta — He's not really bad, either — in fact he's good enough to look at in our photo finish on page 93, too!

Johnny Rotten — The spitting image of a real rotter!

Nastase — We don't care how nasty he is, we love him anyway!

Jimmy Connors — He's not quite as nasty as Ilie Nastase, but he's still a smashing bad guy!

THE JUNGLE GAME

How good are your relationships with those around you? Are you beloved by everyone, from your granny to the newspaper boy? Or is the sight of your face enough to scatter everyone to the wind, screaming for mercy?

Well, very few of us fall into those two extreme categories but to discover just how nice a person you are to have around, make your way through the human jungle, with this special game we've devised. You'll have fun and you'll also learn quite a bit about yourself.

Playing the game is also a test of how honest you are. If you give a false answer, the other players have a right to challenge you. And if, horrors of horrors, it's proved that you've been dishonest, the rules of the game decree that you'll have to go right back to the beginning!

The luck of the dice permitting, the person who wins the game is the one who has the best relationship with friends, parents, boyfriends and the whole world in general. Woe betide anyone who can't get away from Rotten relationships though. All we can say for you is that you must be extremely honest!

TO PLAY

You need a dice and different coloured counters, one for each player. (Tiddlywinks, buttons or any small object will do). The first person to throw a six starts the game, and from then on you take it in turns to throw the dice seeing how far you get each time. Follow the Yes and No answers to wherever they lead.

Start at Rotten relationships and (hopefully) you'll be able to battle your way through the jungle up to the treehouse where all is sweetness, joy and Good relationships!

FINISH — Sweetness and joy. Good relationships.

64

Have you ... or thoug ... anything about a ... today?

No

All in all, do you think you're a popular person?

49   50

YES   No

Have you made any new enemies in the past couple of months?

48   47

YES   No

Are you very envious of any of your friends?

33   34

No   YES

Do you often snap at your best friend?

Hav ... pulled ... face at a ... today?

32   31

No   YES   No

Have you kicked the dog (or your kid brother) this week?

17   18   1

YES   No

Have you been rude to/upset/argued with your mum this week?

Has anyo ... told you ... nasty you ...

16   15   1

YES   No   YES

START — Rotten relationships.   1   2

GIRLS AT THE TOP!

Gaye Advert wasn't taken very seriously when she first came on the scene as the bass player with the Adverts. But now she's proved to everyone that she plays an equally important part in one of today's best New Wave bands!

1978 has certainly been the best year the music business has seen for a long, long time. Not only have we been treated to more super new groups than ever before, but at last girls have finally made a really firm stand in the charts. And if you think we're exaggerating, take a look at the faces below . . . and remember, they're just a few!

Olivia Newton-John has been making a new name for herself — this time as an actress. She must be the envy of every girl because she stars in the film version of "Grease" with none other than dishy John Travolta! Olivia's appeared in films before, but this is the biggest to date. She looks all set to leap into stardom!

Suzi Quatro made a big comeback in 1978 with her hit single "If You Can't Give Me Love." Gone were the leather cat-suits and in their place were silk shirts and a much softer approach. But don't be fooled by it — Suzi's special brand of music hasn't lost one bit of its bounce. In fact, if anything, it's better!

And Suzi's turned to acting as well, with none other than The Fonz himself! She's appeared in several "Happy Days" episodes playing the part of Leather Tuscadero, The Fonz's girl-friend's sister!

Rita Ray is the only girl in that group of lovable lunatics, Darts. We often wonder how she manages to survive! She says she really enjoys her life, though, and that she wouldn't swop it for anything.

1978 must have been the year of the film star, because **Anna** and **Frida** of **Abba** graced the silver screen too, along with Benny and Bjorn in "Abba — The Movie." How many of us dreamed that this Scandinavian quartet who won the Eurovision Song Contest all those years ago would be the huge success they are — and deserve to be!

Lovely **Debbie Harry** is much more than just a beautiful face — she has a great figure, a super voice and she can really dance! Can you blame your boyfriend/brother/father for forgetting everything else when Blondie are on television?

Debbie has brought style and glamour back into the music business but she's quick to point out that it's not all fun and games.

"I sometimes wonder if I could cope with the strain of touring if I were on my own," she says. "I'm lucky that Chris, my boyfriend, is in the group,too,because it's a tremendous help. And I wouldn't want to change what I do for anything in the world!"

Kris Kristofferson isn't the only singing member of his family — his wife, beautiful **Rita Coolidge**, is an established singer herself, with hit singles like "Words".

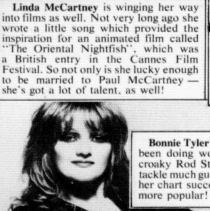

Linda McCartney is winging her way into films as well. Not very long ago she wrote a little song which provided the inspiration for an animated film called "The Oriental Nightfish", which was a British entry in the Cannes Film Festival. So not only is she lucky enough to be married to Paul McCartney — she's got a lot of talent, as well!

Kate Bush entered the pop world with her very first single, "Wuthering Heights", which flew straight to number one, and since Kate wrote the song herself, it was twice as big an acheivement.

"But I don't want to concentrate on singing entirely," Kate says. "I want to learn more about the art of mime so that I can include it in my stage act!"

So there you are. Eleven lovely ladies who are a very important part of the music business. 1978 has shown that girls expect to be taken seriously when it comes to making hits, and let's hope that 1979 goes the same way, too!

Bonnie Tyler's new image has certainly been doing wonders for her. With her croaky Rod Stewart-type voice she can tackle much gutsier songs, and judging by her chart success they're certainly a lot more popular!

CLEANING AND CARING FOR YOUR ANTIQUE CLOTHES

ONE of the nicest things about old clothes is that the fabrics they're made of *are* so natural — but this can lead to some problems.

Obviously, if you dig up an old garment that's been lying around for years, the first thing you're going to want to do is get it properly cleaned up and looking good. Old garments, though, need a lot of special care and attention — it's not a case of just throwing it into the washing machine and forgetting all about it!

Take care washing your finds — use warm, but not hot, soapy water, using a mild brand of soap flakes — a lot of these old clothes don't have any labels on them, and it's sometimes difficult to tell what fabric they're actually made of.

After you've rinsed the garment thoroughly but carefully in cold water, don't wring or twist or remove excess water — it could damage delicate fabrics. Instead, if the garment is made of heavy material, get rid of any excess water by sandwiching it between two towels laid flat on the floor. To finish drying, hang the garment on a wooden or plastic hanger. For lighter fabrics, drying on a hanger will be fine — you can miss out the first step here.

Finally — ironing and pressing. Always iron old clothes on the *wrong* side, using a low setting, and a pressing cloth.

If you are really in doubt about very delicate clothes, don't attempt any repairs until you've asked your local historical society or museum for their professional opinion — you'll probably find they'll be only too happy to help you!

SHRUG IT OFF!

A shrug is about the most useful thing you could possibly have this winter. It's delicate, fluffy and flattering, neater than a shawl and really easy to wear. It ties at the front so it stays on . . . doesn't keep slipping off your shoulders.

This is a really simple pattern designed for Jackie by Emu wools, using just four balls of Emu Filigree wool which you can buy from most wool shops, price about 54p a ball. This means that you'll be able to knit it up for £2.16. It's in one size only and will fit all shapes and sizes. Emu Filigree comes in loads of delicious colours. The one we chose is Moontide, then there's a gorgeous beigey colour called Silver Beige, Scarlet, Quicksilver, Cranberry, Lavender, Dusky Pink, White, Bluebell, Black, Copper, Turquoise, Mink and Sunset.

You'll need a pair of size 2 needles and a pair of size 6/0 needles–the really thick ones. Make sure you don't make the mistake of using size 6 needles which are much thinner. Remember, for the best results you should use the recommended wool.

Here's what to do:

Amount of wool required – 4 balls of Emu Filigree.

Materials — *Aero Knitting Needles* sizes 2 and 6/0.

Abbreviations — *K – knit; p – purl; st(s) – stitch(es); rep – repeat; k.1B – knit into stitch below next stitch on left hand needle; m.1 – make one by picking up the bar that lies between stitch just worked and next stitch on left hand needle and knitting into the back of it; sl – slip; psso – pass slipped stitch over; tog – together.*

Using size 2 needles, cast on 49 sts.

1st row (right side) — K 1, *p 1, k 1, rep from * to end.

2nd row — P 1, *k 1, p 1, rep from * to end.
Rep these 2 rows once.
Change to size 6/0 needles and pattern.

1st row — K 2, *k.1B. (see abbreviations), k 1, rep from * to last st., k 1.

2nd row — K 1, *k.1B., k 1, rep from * to end.
Rep these 2 rows 4 times more, then the 1st row once.
Change to size 2 needles.

Next row — Purl.

Next row — K 3, *m.1 (see abbreviations), k 6 rep from * to last 4 sts, m.1., k 4. (57 sts).

Next row — Purl.
Change to size 6/0 needles. Work 1st and 2nd rows of pattern 6 times, then 1st row once. Change to size 2 needles.

Next row — Purl.

Next row — K 6, *m 1, k 5, rep from * to last 6 sts, m 1, k 6. (67 sts).

Next row — Purl.
Change to size 6/0 needles. Work 1st and 2nd rows of pattern 6 times, then the 1st row once. Change to size 2 needles.

Next row — Purl.

Next row — K 6, *m 1, k 5, rep from * to last 6 sts, m 1, k 6. (79 sts).

Next row — Purl.
Change to size 6/0 needles. Work 1st and 2nd rows of pattern 8 times.
Cast off very loosely.

TIE ENDS

With right side of work facing and using size 2 needles, pick up and k 25 sts evenly along one short edge.

Next row — K 3, p to last 3 sts, k 3.

Next row — K 10, sl 1, k 1, psso, k 1, k 2 tog, k 10.

Next row — K 3, p to last 3 sts, k 3.

Next row — K 9, sl 1, k 1, psso, k 1, k 2 tog, k 9.

Next row — K 3, p to last 3 sts, k 3.

Next row — K 8, sl 1, k 1, psso, k 1, k 2 tog, k 8.
Continue to dec in this way until 9 sts remain, ending with a wrong side row.

Next row — K 3, sl 1, k 2 tog, psso, k 3 – 7 sts remain.
Change to size 6/0 needles. Work 1st and 2nd rows of pattern 16 times.
Cast off very loosely.
Work other edge in the same way.

21 Ways To Make Him Notice You

YOU'VE got your little eye on this fanciable fella, but as far as he's concerned, you just don't exist! About time the poor lad knew what he was missing, so do him a favour and get yourself noticed. How? Well, work your way through this little lot . . .

THE SUBTLE APPROACH FIRST . . .

1. Get wise to his favourite haunts and just be there, ever so casually.

2. At the club don't strive to win games or push yourself forward (lots of boys are scared of pushy girls). Lose games with a good-natured smile, stick around and help clear up the debris afterwards. He'll soon cotton on.

3. A nice sincere smile and a friendly "hello" without angling for more talk will relax him, make him think he must get to know you.

4. Don't cling to a girl-friend for courage, it'll put him off. Being on your own with a slightly lost look (but not hidden at the back of the crowd) encourages him to get things started.

5. Find a nice, unmanageable, preferably large dog and take it for walks where you'll find your other dumb friend and leave the rest to nature!

6. At a crowded social do, wear something that makes you stand out. A plain, clear colour is often better than patterns from the eye-catching point of view. Or an all-white trouser-suit. Or a mini when the rest have gone below-the-knee (especially if you have good legs!).

7. Perfume. Lots of girls don't bother. Make yours always the same and he will recognise you before he sees you. But make sure it's a subtle one, nothing overpowering!

THE DIRECT INVITATION, BUT NICELY . . .

8. Ask him the time (but hide your watch first).

9. Request change for the phone, the bus, the fruit machine.

10. Ask him the way somewhere. If you're suitably dense he may even take you there himself!

11. Carry a large (empty) parcel everywhere. Ask him to hold it while you get your purse out of your bag . . .

12. . . . and if necessary, leave the parcel behind, beside him. Of course, you'll have your address on it in large block capitals.

sandra blake 38 park st

13. In the coffee bar ask him to pass you the sugar, the salt, the vinegar, tomato sauce, mustard, more sugar and the menu. As you've only ordered an orange-ade, that should get him interested!

14. On the bus or train, ask him the best stop to get off for the swimming baths (or whatever you like).

IF ALL ELSE FAILS . . .

15. Look the other way and walk right into him.

16. Drop the ice-cream you're licking all over his sleeve. Then you have to clean it off, don't you!

17. Offer him a chip, crisp or sweet.

18. Ask if he'll sponsor you for a charity walk. Make sure you get his address, to collect what he owes, later.

19. Pretend you think he's a friend of someone you know and chatter away nonstop before you discover he isn't.

20. "Faint" in front of him.

21. Ask him for a date!

WHAT? You've honestly worked your way through and he still hasn't noticed you? Are you sure he's still breathing? Maybe you should try your fatal charms on another bloke. Good luck!

HOW DO YOU PICTURE YOURSELF?

A JACKIE QUIZ

HOW much do you know about your inner self? You probably imagine you know all about yourself and are aware of all your particular personality traits — but there may be lots more for you to discover! The true secrets of your personality lie hidden in our psycho-picture, which may look just like a pretty picture to you, but in fact, it's full of deep meanings and hidden significance!

To unlock the secrets of the picture — and the secrets of your personality — do our fun quiz and find out all about your true self!

1. Do you think the artist who painted this picture is —
(b) a young, handsome, successful artist,
(c) married with three kids,
(d) starving in a Parisian garret,
(a) an idealistic art student with a lot of talent but no success?

2. Do you think this picture was inspired by —
(d) an ancient Greek legend,
(b) a traditional European fairy story,
(a) an obscure Russian folk story,
(c) an old Irish nursery rhyme?

3. What is the river called?
(a) The River of Boundlessness.
(d) River-Bird Springs.
(c) Little-Snodmarsh Waterway.
(b) The Great Northern Boundary Canal.

4. Are the boy and girl —
(a) orphans on a voyage of discovery,
(c) a couple in the throes of a super holiday romance,
(d) desperately in love and eloping secretly,
(b) travelling to seek fame and fortune in the big city?

5. Are they going to —
(c) cross the bridge to visit the cottage,
(a) cross the bridge and head for the mountains,
(b) take the lowland road,
(d) take a boat and sail down the river?

6. Who lives in the cottage?
(c) A farm worker.
(d) A dear little old lady.
(a) No-one — it's a wayfarer's cottage open to all who pass by.
(b) A millionaire who uses it for fishing at weekends.

7. Where do you think the boy and girl have just come from?
(a) They've just escaped from the dark, brooding castle of an evil witch.
(b) They've just left their little country village because nothing ever happened there.
(c) They've just come from their hotel, where they're on holiday with their parents.
(d) They've just come from taking food to a poor, lonely old woodcutter.

8. What are the birds flying overhead?
(b) Kestrels.
(c) Swallows.
(d) Skylarks.
(a) Hawks.

9. What are the mountains like?
(d) They're full of mountain goats and rare wild flowers.
(c) They're dotted with holiday villas and ski slopes.
(a) They're volcanic and pitted with caves.
(b) They're lush with vegetation and olive groves.

10. What do the clouds in the sky mean?
(a) Evil.
(d) Doubt and uncertainty.
(c) Pain.
(b) A terrible, dramatic, electric storm brewing.

11. How would you sum up the general mood and atmosphere of the picture?
(d) Beautiful and dreamlike.
(b) An amusing, fairly normal image of childhood.
(a) Rather strange and mysterious.
(c) Very nice and pretty.

12. What do you think that dragon's doing in the middle of this peaceful rural scene?
(c) It's not a real dragon, it's only a stone-carving!
(a) It's symbolic of all the hardships and problems facing the young couple.
(b) The artist put the dragon into the wrong picture by mistake.
(d) The dragon is one of the central characters in the story of the boy and girl.

13. Is there anything which isn't in the picture which you'd like to see in it?
(b) A few witches and broomsticks, a couple of gnomes and an electric kettle in case the poor old dragon runs out of steam.
(a) A really dark, dense mysterious forest on the foothills of the mountains for added dramatic atmosphere.
(c) A big red double-decker bus going over the bridge 'cos the boy and girl are getting awfully tired of walking.
(d) A beautiful fairytale castle, swarms of rare butterflies and exotic birds of paradise, a galloping white horse and a golden harp.

Now count your score, mainly (a), (b), (c) or (d) and turn to the conclusions.

IF YOUR ANSWERS WERE:

Mostly (a) — You have a creative mind, and are fascinated by unusual, complicated and mind-boggling thoughts and ideas! You enjoy working things out for yourself, and the harder the puzzle the more of a challenge it is for you. You have a great deal of nervous energy and your mind is very alive, constantly ticking over and aware. Sometimes you tend to take this a bit too far, though, reading far too much into situations and crediting people with motives and feelings which are often non-existent. The point is that, rather than accepting things at face value, you always look for a reason. No wonder your relationships tend to be difficult and more complicated than they need to be!

You look for friends on your own special wavelength, people you can talk to and confide in, but your emotions tend to chop and change where people are concerned. The danger is that you go overboard on friendships, building the other person up in your mind, and then you tend to be disillusioned when they fail to live up to your expectations of them.

However, you tend to favour close friendships and once you have found a deep and trusting relationship, you're an interesting, lively companion. You're a bit moody at times, though, and you tend to be a bit over-emotional. You're a real character, an individual, and if you are mixed up sometimes, this is just part and parcel of being rather a special, interesting person!

Mostly (b) — You're quick witted and lively, often hot tempered and impatient, quite aggressive but able to look after yourself. Although you're friendly and sociable, and at ease with all kinds of people, you never lose sight of yourself or your own feelings and opinions.

Sometimes you take this quality to extremes and become self-willed and obstinate, refusing to take criticism or advice, but at other times it simply means that you're self-confident, self-reliant and capable. You usually know what you're doing and it's within your powers to be calculating when you have to be. You're ambitious, you cope well with responsibility and you find challenges exciting. You need an active life, you enjoy meeting people, and if you ever feel shy you're good at hiding it and controlling it. Money and power are attractive to you and you're more inclined to go for a sophisticated lifestyle than to be content with the simple life.

You want to travel far and pack a lot of experience into your life. You're attracted to people who are successful, and even if the boy next door is a very nice guy, you'll turn your back on him and go for the more impressive stranger. You have a great deal of energy — and you'll need all of it to embark on your journey up the dizzy ladder of success!

Mostly (c) — The thing that really comes across about your character is your sense of humour and your sheer bubbling enjoyment of life. You're like champagne — fizzy, extrovert, quite zany and even a little bit wicked sometimes! You're a boaster and a bit of a show-off, though, and you'll grab the limelight and sail through life without much thought for other people's feelings. But if you blunder into awkward situations and crash into catastrophies, there's usually someone on hand to bail you out.

Your fantastic but zany and uncontrolled personality is the sort which makes others protective towards you. You're like a refresher course and a stimulant to those around you! You get on well with people, not always going in for deep friendships, but you have a spontaneous warmth which attracts people.

Perhaps your biggest fault is that you refuse

to face problems because you can alw convince yourself they don't exist! It's always easy to get you to be emotional, you tend to dismiss emotion, and although may feel things very deeply, you're o loth to share your real heart-felt feeli with others. But on the bonus side, you h a naturally cheerful and optimistic approac life, bags of confidence and enough ene for ten people! So be grateful for th mercies!

Mostly (d) — You're a warm, genuine per with warm, genuine feelings for others. live on your emotions and your heart r your head. Your impulsive feelings always win over logic and you trust your instincts. You have true feminine intuit which enables you to float through life, gi in to the whim of the moment, acting instinct and getting deeply involved people.

All this helps you to get a lot of satisfac from life, but it also sometimes causes and heartache when things go wro But, however many times you are let de emotionally by people, you will carry trusting them, because that's your nat Hardness and cynicism doesn't come ea to you, and you try to live out your roma day-dreams in real life. So whatever happe your life is always emotionally rich, during good patches your happiness is equalled.

You also have a rich imagination and a q self-confident philosophy of life. You'll disappointed and depressed sometimes, to make up for the bad times you are capa of experiencing real joy. You're inclined to sentimental and although you don't harp the past, you enjoy past memories, but also have a sense of hope and excitem about the future.

PHOTO FINISH!

Here we are, at the end of another Jackie annual! But we can't say goodbye without a special thank-you to all the lovely people who've brought us a lot of happiness over the past few months. They've all got that extra something which makes them very special!

THE BEE GEES
It's lovely to see The Bee Gees back on Robin, Maurice and Barry were around i 60's, but they're even more lovely now. they look fantastic in their Sergeant P outfits? Then, of course, there was all great music for "Saturday Night Fever terrific, talented trio . . .

LAURA
The Jackie face of 1978, Laura Letham is bang up to the minute with fashion, and her own gentle Punk looks. She's one of our very favourite models, so keep your eyes open for her in 1979!

DAVID SOUL
Soul-searching time again. This page just wouldn't be complete without David. Just one smile and we all go ga-ga. Wonder what it is about that sexy smile, blond hair and long legs? Sigh . . .

PAUL MICHAEL GLASER
Unglaze those glasered eyes! It's lovely P.M. himself, pastrami-on-rye lover extraordinaire! If we ate that stuff he got through as Starsky, we'd all be like balloons. Still, he needs lots of energy — to keep running from all his fans!

MISS PIGGY
A firm favourite, but what can you say about a pig with class . . . (We couldn't get hold of Kermit for a photograph. He was last seen hot-webbing it through Outer Mongolia. Rumour has it Miss Piggy finally got that kissie, kissie, and Kermit hasn't looked back since . . .)

THE PROFESSIONALS
What a team — they should have won the World for looks! It's Martin Shaw and Lewis Colli of "The Professionals" of course, who the most exciting TV partnership for ye Bet they've got hearts of gold under th grim exteriors!

MARK HAMILL
None of us will ever forget "Star Wars," nor will we forget the lovely Mark Hamill who played Luke Skywalker. He's out of this world — a real heavenly body, and long may he shine among the stars.

THE FONZ
Hey-y-y! It's thumbs up to Henry "The Fonz" Winkler, who's shown us how it was in the 50's when everything was so Daddy Cool. Thanks for all those "happy days," Fonzie!

DEBBIE HARRY
Grrr . . . The lovely Debbie Harry of Blondie shot on to the scene early in 1978 with "Denis." Boys swooned, grandfathers gaped, and girls, well, let's face it . . . weren't we all a teeny, weeny bit jealous?

JOHN TRAVOLTA
Reports started coming in at the beginning of last year about the new Fred Astaire. "Oh, yeah?" we all said — until we saw John Travolta in action for ourselves, in "Saturday Night Fever." And, well, what can you say? Except that he was incredible. Mr Superstar himself . . .

SANDY
. . . and this little fella just trotted along to stardom, as Annie's dog in the musical. He's become loved by thousands, and no wonder, he's so cute. A shaggy dog story, if ever there was one!

ANDREA McARDLE
Andrea McArdle hit Britain in May 1978 as the star of the musical "Annie." She's a great actress, a great singer, and she won lots of hearts on stage. Keep your eyes and ears open for Andrea. She's got a big future ahead of her.

KATE BUSH
1978 was Kate Bush's year, when she made us all Cathys looking for our own Heathcliffes. She's brought a new dimension to the pop world with her lovely voice and looks and now she's reached the "Heights" let's hope she'll stay there.

PRINCE ANDREW
Last year a certain boy grew up and started to get himself noticed by girls all over the world. Yes, Prince Andrew, and isn't he gorgeous? Until he finds his own special princess, we'd just like him to know that we're all available!

JOHN LLOYD
If you're wondering who the deuce this is, then shame on you, and score love all! It's John Lloyd, and he's the dishiest thing around in tennis shorts. Roll on next summer, for another glimpse of those golden thighs!

BOOMTOWN RATS
One of the nicest packs around — of rats, that is. The Boomtown Rats have given us so much — from their great music, to Johnny Fingers, who's certainly "struck a chord" in those crazy pyjamas!

NICHOLAS BALL
As 'Azell, 'e really 'ad us all 'anging on 'is every word!

F GARRETT
great favourite of ours, is Leif Garrett. He pt into our lives on a skateboard, and cked us out with his singing. Long may his els keep turning!

Jackie PIN-UP
ROBERT POWELL

Pic 1 "Just sit down while I put the kettle on," Paul said. "There's some newspapers on the coffee table, if you want to read them."

What a choice — reading about world affairs or watching Paul Young make you a cup of coffee!

Pic 2 Yes — this is what we looked at over our cornflakes!

Pic 3 After breakfast, Paul went for a quick work out in his mini-gym.

"It's what keeps me fit," Paul explained. "I need to be really

breakfast at PAUL's

An invitation to breakfast with Paul Young isn't something to turn down without a second thought . . . we didn't even need ½ a second to say 'Yes.'

strong and healthy in order to go on tour — and survive!"

Pic 4 Another cup of coffee. I need to recover from my exercise before I do anything else.

"The pictures on the wall? Oh, they're all my heroes — and heroines. Isn't Marilyn Monroe beautiful?"

P.S. If you're really eagle-eyed you'll be able to spot the Gold Disc lurking in this photo.

Pic 5 On the way to work.

Oh well, all good things have to come to an end!

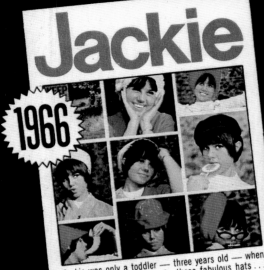

1966

Jackie was only a toddler — three years old — when you had the chance to make these fabulous hats . . . (what, *sarcasm* from *our* Ed?)

1967

I want a pair of wellies and a potty to wear on my head just like hers!

1968

Peace, love and . . . time John Lenno . . . were on the cove . . .

1971

The ethereal look — or how to look a million dollars in your mum's old net curtain.

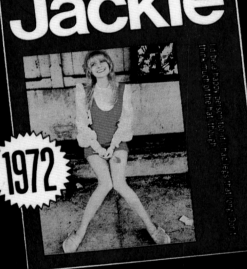

1972

1975

David Essex is o . . .

EYES RIGHT!
How To Make
Great Big
Beautiful Eyes

Find Out About
Your Feelings From
Our Fantastic Qui

STAR WARS
EXCLUSIVE! MAKING
HIS MARK!
Mark Hamill tells all

SPECIAL
SUPER SIZE
DAVID SOUL
PIN-UP
Part One This Wee

1978

David Soul was a pop star when this was on the streets . . . and green was the ultimate in up-to-the-minute beauty . . .

WHAT
SECRETS
ARE YOU
GIVING
AWAY?
Find out on
page 30 . . .

WE
TALK TO
BLONDI
See page

DELICIOUS
DAVID ESSEX
PIN-UP

1980

What — David Essex again? And fashion was bordering on the fringe . . .

YOUR
JACKIE
POP
ALENDAR!
rt One This Wee

LOW
TO 1981
Our Spe
Feature
You Ho

ARY NU
AST CO
Picture Spe

And Gary Numa